Arithmetic
Skills
Workbook

Arithmetic Skills Workbook

Calman Goozner

Dedicated to serving

AMSCO

our nation's youth

When ordering this book, please specify
either **R 147 W** or ARITHMETIC SKILLS WORKBOOK

AMSCO SCHOOL PUBLICATIONS, INC.
315 Hudson Street   New York, N.Y. 10013

ISBN 0-87720-236-2

PRINTED IN THE UNITED STATES OF AMERICA

Preface

ARITHMETIC SKILLS WORKBOOK offers a complete one-year course of instruction designed to develop the student's ability to perform arithmetic computations. For the student who has experienced difficulty in learning arithmetic, this book should prove especially helpful.

The first half of the book (Units 1 to 65) covers the fundamentals of arithmetic, including percents and word problems. The last half (Units 66 to 111) deals with the applications of these fundamentals to such topics as personal finances, retail buying and selling, automobile ownership, checking accounts, graphs, and the use of arithmetic techniques to solve simple algebraic equations. Units 78 and 79 give a basic description of the metric system and its uses. The text deals with the most common metric units and their English equivalents—meters and yards, liters and gallons, kilograms and pounds, etc. A more detailed table is given in the Appendix for the student who wishes a fuller treatment of the metric system.

Throughout ARITHMETIC SKILLS WORK-BOOK, the author teaches by example, wherever possible, rather than by exposition. Thus, the Examples in each unit form a vital part of the text proper. Also, a Sample Solution at the beginning of each set of exercises shows the student how he is supposed to proceed.

Visual techniques such as arrows showing how decimal points are moved or how a number is manipulated, as well as hand-written solutions, are frequently used to facilitate learning.

The author has had much experience with students who have difficulty with such techniques as long division. In the author's experience, most errors in long division stem from the student's confusion about writing zeros in the answer. Thus, Units 15 to 18 each deal with a different situation in which a zero must be written in the quotient.

Recognizing the difficulty many students face in solving verbal problems, the author has developed original aids to problem solving. For example, the "IS/OF" fraction is used in solving fractional part problems, percentage problems, and unit-price problems. The author's familiarity with these and other sources of student difficulties should make ARITHMETIC SKILLS WORKBOOK uniquely helpful.

The student's understanding of each topic is immediately reinforced through the use of exercises and application problems. Each of the 111 units in the book has exercises and often problems as well. The exercises can be done as classwork, while the application problems can be assigned as homework. There are, in addition, 23 review tests that can be used to test the student's understanding and ability.

Since the book is designed to permit self-study, the more competent students can proceed on their own, with a minimum of supervision, thus freeing the teacher to work with students who need help.

The author is grateful to Mr. Richard Rimpici for his valuable assistance and suggestions.

Calman Goozner

Contents

CONTENTS

Part I. Numbers and Numerals

Unit 1. Understanding Whole Numbers

Words to know

A **whole number** is a number we use for counting.

All whole numbers are formed from the **digits** 1, 2, 3, 4, 5, 6, 7, 8, 9, 0. For example, the number **57** contains the digits **5** and **7**.

The right-hand digit of a whole number is called the **ones digit**. In the number **57**, the ones digit is **7**.

The digit to the left of the ones digit is called the **tens digit**. In the number **57**, the tens digit is **5**. In the number **608**, the tens digit is **0**.

Numbers that consist of the digit 1 followed by one or more zeros are called **powers of ten**. Examples are 10, 100, 1,000, and 10,000.

All over the world, scientists, businessmen, and students solve arithmetic problems by using numbers. We will first study **whole numbers**.

We use ten symbols, called **digits**, to represent whole numbers:

With only these ten symbols, we can express any number at all, small or large. We can start from the smallest whole number, 0, which means "nothing" and we can count all the way up to the number of people in the world or to the number of miles to the most distant visible star.

When you count, "1, 2, 3, 4, 5, 6, 7, 8, 9, 10," the number 10 is different from the first nine numbers. To make the 10, you take the digits 1 and 0 and combine them to form a *different kind of number*. The numbers from 1 to 9 are known as **ones digits**, because they represent values of one. The number 8 means "8 ones" and the number 9 means "9 ones." The number 10, however, means "1 ten." Similarly, the number 20 means "2 tens" and the number 80 means "8 tens." In any number, the digit to the left of the ones digit is known as the **tens digit**.

In everyday life, you know that 10 pennies make a dime and that 10 dimes make a dollar. Similarly, ten 1's make 10, ten 10's make 100, and ten 100's make 1,000. Thus, as whole numbers get larger, they are expressed in **powers of ten**.

Now, you will learn the names and the values of whole numbers. In reading the value of a number, you must note the *position* of each digit in the number.

The number 10 means:

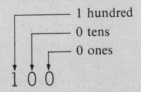
- 1 ten
- 0 ones

The number 100 means:

- 1 hundred
- 0 tens
- 0 ones

The number 1,000 means:

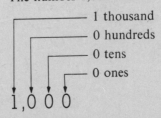
- 1 thousand
- 0 hundreds
- 0 tens
- 0 ones

The number 10,000 means:

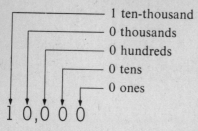

The number 100,000 means:

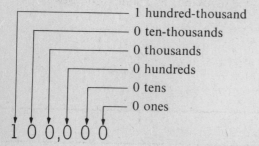

The number 1,000,000 means:

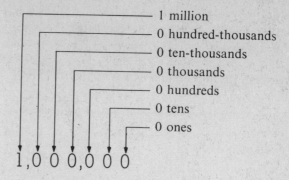

In the preceding six numbers, note that the digit 1 changes in value from "ten" to "one million," depending on its *position*.

Table I gives the values of all whole numbers from one to one billion. Also, it tells how many digits are required to write any given number.

Table I: *Whole Numbers*

Value of Largest Digit	How Many Digits	Possible Numbers
one	1 digit	1 to 9
ten	2 digits	10 to 99
hundred	3 digits	100 to 999
thousand	4 digits	1,000 to 9,999
ten-thousand	5 digits	10,000 to 99,999
hundred-thousand	6 digits	100,000 to 999,999
million	7 digits	1,000,000 to 9,999,999
ten-million	8 digits	10,000,000 to 99,999,999
hundred-million	9 digits	100,000,000 to 999,999,999
billion	10 digits	1,000,000,000

When you see a number such as 347, Table I tells you that a number of 3 digits is in the hundreds. You read 347 as "three hundred forty-seven." The value of this number is found by adding the values of each digit:

3 hundreds + 4 tens + 7 ones

Using the symbol " = " to mean "equals,"

3 hundreds	=	300
4 tens	=	40
7 ones	=	7
total value	=	347

The number 2,465 is read as "two thousand, four hundred sixty-five," and the value is:

2 thousands + 4 hundreds + 6 tens + 5 ones
2,000 + 400 + 60 + 5 = 2,465

It is difficult to read a number such as:

$$5321642$$

To make the reading of a large number easier, you must first "punctuate" the number with commas.

To punctuate a number, *place a comma between every three digits of the number, moving from right to left.* Thus:

$$5,321,642$$

What you have done is to separate the number into three groups: the *hundreds* group, the *thousands* group, and the *millions* group. (The hundreds group actually consists of hundreds, tens, and ones.)

Remember: You separate a number from right to left, but you read a number from left to right.

Let's look at the number again:

$$5,321,642$$

The right-hand group of digits means *hundreds*, *tens*, and *ones*. The three digits to the left of the right-hand group mean *thousands*. Since the number has another digit to the left of the thousands, the highest value of the number is in the *millions*. (Table I shows us that when a number has 7 digits, the value of the largest digit is in the millions.)

How many millions?   5,321,642 ———— 5 millions

How many thousands?   5,321,642 ———— 321 thousands

How many hundreds, tens, and ones?   5,321,642 ———— 6 hundreds, 4 tens, 2 ones

You read the number as "five million, three hundred twenty-one thousand, six hundred forty-two."

EXERCISES

In 1 to 15, read each number and write it as a word statement.

Sample solution

245   *two hundred forty-five*

1. 53 _____
2. 71 _____
3. 95 _____
4. 17 _____
5. 68 _____
6. 123 _____
7. 467 _____
8. 351 _____
9. 915 _____
10. 673 _____
11. 8,015 _____
12. 29,040 _____
13. 261,451 _____
14. 5,653,000 _____
15. 23,520,825 _____

In 16 to 25, write the value of each digit in the given number.

Sample solution

317 = ___*3*___ hundreds, ___*1*___ tens, ___*7*___ ones

16. 14 = _____ tens, _____ ones
17. 37 = _____ tens, _____ ones
18. 89 = _____ tens, _____ ones
19. 335 = _____ hundreds, _____ tens, _____ ones
20. 510 = _____ hundreds, _____ tens, _____ ones
21. 809 = _____ hundreds, _____ tens, _____ ones
22. 1,043 = _____ thousands, _____ hundreds, _____ tens, _____ ones

23. 26,413 = _____ ten-thousands, _____ thousands, _____ hundreds, _____ tens, _____ ones

24. 237,000 = _____ hundred-thousands, _____ ten-thousands, _____ thousands, _____ hundreds, _____ tens, _____ ones

25. 15,865,437 = _____ ten-millions, _____ millions, _____ hundred-thousands, _____ ten-thousands, _____ thousands, _____ hundreds, _____ tens, _____ ones

In 26 to 35, write each word statement as a number.

Sample solution

eighty-four ___*84*___

26. twenty-five _____

27. ninety-six _____

28. three hundred five _____

29. eight hundred seventy-three _____

30. four thousand, nineteen _____

31. seven thousand, three hundred twenty-seven _____

32. thirteen thousand, five _____

33. eighty-six thousand, four hundred _____

34. three hundred thousand, four hundred fifty-seven _____

35. nineteen million, four hundred twenty-three thousand, six hundred fifteen _____

APPLICATION PROBLEMS

In 1 to 5, write a word statement for the number in each given fact.

Sample Solution

John bought a car for $3,423.

___*three thousand, four hundred twenty-three dollars*___

1. Frank's total income last year was $8,523.

_____

2. The Wilson family paid $24,095 for their new home.

_____

3. The new school was completed at a cost of $375,485.

_____

4. The population of Castleton is 13,473,000.

_____

5. A government study reveals that 15,963,400 people are employed as office workers.

_____

Unit 2. Rounding Off Numbers

Words to know

A number is **rounded off** when its actual value is changed to an approximate value. The population of New York City in 1970 was 7,895,563. We say that the population of New York City in 1970 was 8,000,000, rounded off to the nearest million.

In the above example, the number 7,895,563 is **rounded off** to 8,000,000. We round off numbers when we do not need the exact value that the number represents.

Suppose that 53,968 people go to a baseball game. In the morning newspapers, the attendance figure is reported as 54,000. This value is obtained by rounding off the actual attendance to the nearest thousand.

Before rounding off any number, you must decide on the value you want to round off to. By "value," we mean the value of the digit in the rounded-off number that comes just before the 0's. In the rounded-off number 8,000,000, the digit 8 has a value of *millions*. In the rounded-off number 54,000, the digit 4 has a value of *thousands*.

Table I in the preceding unit gives such values from *one* all the way up to *one billion*.

After deciding on the value to be rounded off to, do the following steps:

Step 1: Place parentheses around all digits to the right of this value.

Step 2: A. If the left-hand digit inside the parentheses is 5 or more, add 1 to the part outside the parentheses.

Step 2: B. If the left-hand digit inside the parentheses is less than 5, do not add 1.

Step 3: Substitute 0's for the digits inside the parentheses.

EXAMPLE 1. Round off 7,465 to the nearest *ten*.

Solution:

Step 1: Place parentheses around the digit to the right of the *tens* value.

$$7,46(5)$$

Step 2: Because the digit inside the parentheses is 5, add 1 to the *tens* digit.

$$\begin{array}{r} 7,46(5) \\ +1 \\ \hline 7,47(5) \end{array}$$

Step 3: Substitute a 0 for the digit inside the parentheses.

$$7,47(0)$$

Answer: 7,470

EXAMPLE 2. Round off 7,465 to the nearest *hundred*.

Solution:

Step 1: Place parentheses around the digits to the right of the *hundreds* place.

$$7,4(65)$$

Steps 2 and 3: Because the left-hand digit inside the parentheses is 6, which is 5 or more, add 1 to the *hundreds* digit. Then substitute 0's for the digits inside the parentheses.

$$\begin{array}{r} 7,4(65) \\ +1 \\ \hline 7,5(00) \end{array}$$

Answer: 7,500

EXAMPLE 3. Round off 7,465 to the nearest *thousand*.

Solution:

Step 1: Place parentheses around the digits to the right of the *thousands* place.

$$7,(465)$$

Steps 2 and 3: Because the left-hand digit inside the parentheses is 4, which is less than 5, *do not* add 1. (You can think of "do not add 1" as "add zero.") Substitute 0's for all the digits in the parentheses.

$$\begin{array}{r} 7,(465) \\ +0 \\ \hline 7,(000) \end{array}$$

Answer: 7,000

After a little practice, you should be able to perform steps 2 and 3 *mentally*.

EXERCISES

In 1 to 8, round off each number to the nearest *ten*.

Sample solution

4(7) _50_

1. 68 _____   2. 84 _____   3. 135 _____   4. 324 _____

5. 5,048 _____   6. 8,964 _____

7. 11,475 _____   8. 18,388 _____

In 9 to 16, round off each number to the nearest *hundred*.

Sample solution

4(38) _400_

9. 362 _____   10. 538 _____   11. 895 _____

12. 2,809 _____   13. 5,243 _____

14. 8,556 _____   15. 15,045 _____

16. 21,099 _____

In 17 to 24, round off each number to the nearest *thousand*.

Sample solution

8,(762) _9,000_

17. 9,462 _____   18. 6,548 _____

19. 3,817 _____   20. 4,072 _____

21. 21,628 _____   22. 41,314 _____

23. 35,089 _____   24. 61,529 _____

In 25 to 32, round off each number to the nearest *ten-thousand*.

Sample solution

1(5,681) _20,000_

25. 23,510 _____   26. 15,010 _____

27. 94,215 _____   28. 195,628 _____

29. 507,128 _____   30. 704,852 _____

31. 5,246,117 _____   32. 8,375,000 _____

In 33 to 40, round off each number to the nearest *hundred-thousand*.

Sample solution

1(21,502) *100,000*

33. 158,708 _____

34. 605,235 _____

35. 820,718 _____

36. 2,073,210 _____

37. 5,621,187 _____

38. 37,162,115 _____

39. 65,973,508 _____

40. 80,053,287 _____

In 41 to 48, round off each number to the nearest *million*.

Sample solution

4(528,116) *5,000,000*

41. 3,417,128 _____

42. 5,617,249 _____

43. 1,500,000 _____

44. 8,310,000 _____

45. 20,583,117 _____

46. 25,021,320 _____

47. 61,621,187 _____

48. 10,421,356 _____

APPLICATION PROBLEMS

1. Round off the numbers in the following sentence to the nearest *thousand*: In a certain week, the United States produced 163,478 cars, 143,627 trucks, and 53,067 buses.

cars: _____

trucks: _____

buses: _____

2. Round off, to the nearest *hundred-thousand*, the following numbers that show the 1970 populations of ten American cities. As a sample solution, the population of New York has been rounded off.

New York: 7,8(95,563)   *7,900,000*   .

Chicago: 3,369,359 _____

Los Angeles: 2,816,061 _____

Philadelphia: 1,950,098 _____

Detroit: 1,512,893 _____

Houston: 1,232,802 _____

Baltimore: 905,759 _____

Dallas: 844,401 _____

Washington: 756,510 _____

Cleveland: 750,879 _____

Review of Part I (Units 1 and 2)

In 1 to 5, read each number and write it as a word statement.

1. 5,125 _____

2. 14,085 _____

3. 321,560 _____

4. 5,321,565 _____

5. 28,671,305 _____

In 6 to 10, write the value of each digit in the given number.

6. 453: _____ hundreds, _____ tens, _____ ones

7. 905: _____ hundreds, _____ tens, _____ ones

8. 3,438: _____ thousands, _____ hundreds, _____ tens, _____ ones

9. 28,068: _____ ten-thousands, _____ thousands, _____ hundreds, _____ tens, _____ ones

10. 507,234: _____ hundred-thousands, _____ ten-thousands, _____ thousands, _____ hundreds, _____ tens, _____ ones

11. Round off each number to the nearest *ten*.

   a. 364 _____   *b.* 495 _____   *c.* 638 _____

12. Round off each number to the nearest *hundred*.

   a. 2,658 _____   *b.* 3,085 _____

   c. 5,963 _____

13. Round off each number to the nearest *thousand*.

   a. 12,485 _____   *b.* 15,862 _____

   c. 20,573 _____

14. Round off each number to the nearest *ten-thousand*.

   a. 243,670 _____   *b.* 567,210 _____

   c. 705,340 _____

15. Round off each number to the nearest *hundred-thousand*.

   a. 3,625,138 _____

   b. 4,965,362 _____

   c. 6,852,000 _____

16. Round off each number to the nearest *million*.

   a. 25,326,120 _____

   b. 32,725,000 _____

   c. 40,860,000 _____

Part II. Adding Whole Numbers

Unit 3. Addition of Numbers

Words to know

When the values of two or more numbers are combined to form a larger number, the process is called **addition**.

The larger number that results from addition is called the **sum** or the **total**.

The numbers that are added are called **addends**.

When you perform **addition**, you combine two or more numbers to get one larger number called the **sum**, or **total**. The sum of an addition problem must always be larger than any one of the numbers you are adding. Addition is indicated by writing the symbol " + " with the numbers to be added. To indicate that the number 17 and the number 11 are to be added, write $17 + 11$ or

$$
\begin{array}{r}
17 \\
+11 \\
\hline
\end{array}
$$

In setting up the numbers to be added, known as **addends**, you must always be sure to line up your digits correctly: ones digit under ones digit, tens digit under tens digit, etc. A column of ones digits is called the *ones column*, a column of tens digits is called the *tens column*, etc.

EXAMPLE 1. Find the sum of 25 and 7.

Solution: The 5 in the number 25 means 5 ones. The 7 in the number 7 means 7 ones. Therefore, *the 7 must line up directly under the 5.*

$$
\begin{array}{r}
25 \\
+7 \\
\hline
\end{array}
$$

Now, you add the 7 and the 5 (7 ones and 5 ones) and get 12 (1 ten and 2 ones). You write the 2 under the ones column and carry the " 1 " to the tens column. (The " 1 " means " 1 ten.") Add the 1 to the 2 and write the sum, 3, under the tens column (1 ten + 2 tens = 3 tens).

$$
\begin{array}{r}
\overset{1}{2}5 \\
+7 \\
\hline
32 \\
\end{array}
$$

Answer: $25 + 7 = 32$

EXAMPLE 2. Add: $395 + 37$

Solution: Again, line up your digits correctly: ones under ones and tens under tens. Add: 7 plus 5 equals 12. Write down the 2 under the ones column and carry the " 1 " to the tens column. Add: 1 plus 3 plus 9 equals 13. Write the 3 under the tens column and carry the " 1 " to the hundreds column (this " 1 " means " 1 hundred "). Add: 1 plus 3 equals 4. Write the 4 under the hundreds column.

$$
\begin{array}{r}
\overset{1}{3}9\overset{\cdot}{5} \\
+37 \\
\hline
\end{array}
$$

$$
\begin{array}{r}
395 \\
+37 \\
\hline
\overset{11}{} \\
432 \\
\end{array}
$$

Answer: $395 + 37 = 432$

EXAMPLE 3. Add: $5,327 + 462 + 578$

Solution: Line up your digits correctly: ones under ones, tens under tens, and hundreds under hundreds. Add: $8 + 2 + 7 = 17$. Write the 7 under the ones column and carry the " 1 " to the tens column. Add: $1 + 7 + 6 + 2 = 16$. Write the 6 under the tens column and carry to " 1 " to the hundreds column. Add: $1 + 5 + 4 + 3 = 13$. Write the 3 under the hundreds column and carry the " 1 " to the thousands column. Add: $1 + 5 = 6$. Write the 6 under the thousands column.

$$
\begin{array}{r}
5,327 \\
462 \\
578 \\
\hline
\end{array}
$$

$$
\begin{array}{r}
5,327 \\
462 \\
578 \\
\hline
\overset{1\ 11}{} \\
6,367 \\
\end{array}
$$

Check: To check an addition problem, add the columns again, but start adding from the top down to the answer.

$$
\begin{array}{r}
\overset{1\ 11}{5,327} \\
462 \\
578 \\
\hline
6,367 \\
\end{array}
$$
add down

Answer:
$5,327 + 462 + 578 = 6,367$

EXERCISES

In 1 to 10, add and check.

1. 234
    +25
    _____

2. 327
    +68
    _____

3. 437
    +98
    _____

4. 368
    +56
    _____

5. 629
    +82
    _____

6. 4,628
    +407
    _____

7. 6,724
    +368
    _____

8. 3,247
    +845
    _____

9. 8,207
    +636
    _____

10. 5,237
    +568
    _____

In 11 to 18, find the sum and check each answer.

11. $324+85+7$

12. $168+67+4$

13. $763+46+9$

14. $572+73+8$

15. $678+59+6$

16. $368+38+3$

17. $273+89$

18. $972+65+7$

In 19 to 26, add and check.

19. 3,428
    734
    235
    58
    _____

20. 5,742
    837
    768
    53
    _____

21. 7,209
    568
    47
    59
    _____

22. 8,796
    467
    85
    93
    _____

23. 6,748   24. 5,680   25. 2,471   26. 6,592
      264   974   687   749
       19   63   86   53
        8   7   3   5
    _____   _____   _____   _____

In 27 to 38, find the sum and check each answer.

27. $3,827+463+75+82$

28. $5,649+329+67+8$

29. $3,558+379+56+7$

30. $6,857+574+38+6$

31. $2,463+595+63+3$

32. $5,361+768+56+9$

33. $4,736+429+38+5$

34. $6,729+647+58+3$

35. $3,427+2,685+347+22$

36. $5,692+478+363+42+8$

37. $5,238+3,595+765+528+49$

38. $7,562+8,473+597+98+8$

In 39 to 42, add and check.

39. 23,478   40. 235,407   41. 478,629   42. 629,319
    47,593   346,972   962,523   492,748
    39,267   53,863   593,093   68,492
     9,432   17,093   468   9,716
       827   841   793   345
       963   493   658   729
    _____   _____   _____   _____

APPLICATION PROBLEMS

Sample solution

Last week the Council Rock football team gained 84 yards rushing and 121 yards passing. What was the total yardage gained?

```
  84 yd. rushing
+ 121 yd. passing
  205 Total yd.
```

1. A company deposited checks in the following amounts: $235, $76, $865, $245. Find the total amount deposited.

2. How much will a set of living room furniture cost if the couch costs $348, a club chair costs $73, a coffee table costs $68, and an end table costs $54?

3. A grocery store had the following daily sales: Monday, $937; Tuesday, $875; Wednesday, $1,125; Thursday, $1,020; Friday, $1,248; Saturday, $1,368. Find the total sales for the week.

4. A school has the following enrollment: 1,627 freshmen; 1,327 sophomores; 1,148 juniors; 953 seniors. What is the total enrollment?

5. The local library has 4,389 books of fiction, 3,235 nonfiction books, 358 reference books, and 175 magazines. What is the total number of books and magazines?

Unit 4. Addition When the Number of Digits in the Addends Varies

It is often necessary to add a group of numbers that are expressed in dollars and cents. It is not uncommon for amounts of money to vary widely, from a few cents to thousands of dollars.

To avoid mistakes, you should arrange the column by using the highest number first, then the next largest, and so on, down to the smallest number. When adding amounts of money, be sure to line up the digits correctly, cents under cents, and dollars under dollars. The decimal points must always line up, one under the other, in a straight line.

Suppose you must add the following amounts:

$23.50 $1,625.50 $8.45
$.43 $11,698.50 $153.65

Start your column with the largest number, $11,698.50. Write the number down and then *cross it out* of the original list.

$23.50 $1,625.50 $8.45
$.43 ~~$11,698.50~~ $153.65

$11,698.50

Select the next largest number, $1,625.50. Write it down, aligning the digits correctly, and cross it out of the list. (It is not necessary to repeat the dollar sign.)

$23.50 ~~$1,625.50~~ $8.45
$.43 ~~$11,698.50~~ $153.65

$11,698.50
  1,625.50

Select the next largest number, $153.65. Write it down and cross it out of the list.

$23.50 ~~$1,625.50~~ $8.45
$.43 ~~$11,698.50~~ ~~$153.65~~

$11,698.50
  1,625.50
    153.65

Follow this procedure until all the numbers are brought down in the descending order of their values, and all of the numbers have been crossed out of the original list. Complete the addition, bringing down the dollar sign. The completed addition should look like this:

~~$23.50~~ ~~$1,625.50~~ ~~$8.45~~
~~$.43~~ ~~$11,698.50~~ ~~$153.65~~

$11,698.50
  1,625.50
    153.65
     23.50
      8.45
       .43
────────────
$13,510.03

The technique of forming a column of numbers in the *descending order of their values* (largest value first) is not limited to the addition of dollars and cents. It is used whenever a group of numbers of varying values must be added. By "varying values," we mean that the number of digits in the addends varies.

EXAMPLE. In the addition problem shown, the answer is wrong. Find the correct sum by forming a column of numbers in the descending order of their values.

```
   4827
    123
      4
     82
+ 50000
─────────
X232570
```
wrong

Solution: Whoever added the numbers forgot to line up his digits correctly. Here is how the column of numbers should be formed:

```
~~4827~~        50,000
~~123~~          4,827
~~4~~              123
~~82~~              82
~~50000~~       +     4
              ─────────
               55,036
```

Answer: The correct sum is 55,036.

EXERCISES

In 1 to 14, add the numbers by arranging them in the descending order of their values.

Sample solution

~~28 + 5 + 235~~

```
 235
  28
   5
─────
 268
```

268

1. $47 + 423 + 8$

2. $2 + 576 + 68$

3. $19 + 486 + 68 + 2,519$

4. $357 + 8 + 5,694 + 62$

5. $42 + 634 + 7 + 6,927 + 23$

6.	7.	8.
248	6,409	36
47	4	18,437
15,620	254	7
8	8,623	422
6,537	34	3,294
12	+14,638	+52
+634		

9. $\$5,246.50 + \$9.80 + \$368.25 + \$84.00 + \$16,472.00$
$+ \$234.75 + \$575.10$

10. $\$.38 + \$122.75 + \$.08 + \$92.37 + \$1,196.27 + \$7.96$
$+ \$276.48$

11. $\$3.29 + \$.06 + \$2,415.08 + \$.47 + \$89.27 + \$6.80$
$+ \$342.37$

12. $73 + 14,193 + 754 + 8 + 9,634 + 521 + 758 + 38$

13. $19,627 + 72 + 235,537 + 6 + 9,427 + 135,364 + 47,638$

14. $94 + 32,763 + 18 + 897 + 7,458 + 347,905 + 8$

APPLICATION PROBLEMS

Sample solution

Dave McGraw made a bank deposit of the following items: $.84 in pennies, $6.35 in nickels, $2.00 in dimes, a check for $16.79, and a check for $3.58. How much did he deposit?

$16.79
6.35
3.58
2.00
.84
———
$29.56

$29.56

---

1. A salesman traveled the following distances: 235 miles, 9 miles, 47 miles, 97 miles, and 125 miles. How many miles did he travel altogether?

2. What is the total seating capacity of the local stadium if there are 893 box seats, 8,329 reserved seats, 19,365 general admission seats, 3,478 bleacher seats, and 8 press seats?

3. Dave Watts made the following purchases: An overcoat for $135, a suit for $78, a tie for $3, a sports jacket for $38, and three pairs of socks for $4. How much did he spend?

4. Jim bought a car for $2,378. He also bought the following extras: air conditioning, $375; car speaker, $23; undercoating, $9; power brakes, $68; power steering, $135. Find the total cost.

5. The Jackson family bought a house for $19,378 and made the following improvements: central air conditioning, $1,865; gas barbecue, $95; fence, $378; patio, $325. What was the total cost of the house including the improvements?

Unit 5. Horizontal Addition

There are many times when it is convenient to be able to add a group of numbers that is arranged horizontally. This arrangement may slow down the addition of the numbers unless you practice and develop the skill of adding horizontally.

A good way to develop this skill is to use a *rhythmic pattern of adding*. In other words, you should add in a steady beat with the eye "bouncing" from one number to the next in regular rhythm.

For example, add the following numbers, going from left to right:

$$\overrightarrow{8+5+7+6+5+9+2+4}$$

Say: 13 20 26 31 40 42 46

The sum is 46.

You should also be able to add from right to left:

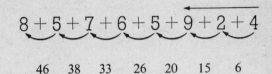

46 38 33 26 20 15 6

The sum is 46.

EXERCISES

In 1 to 6, add horizontally.

1. $5 + 7 + 4 + 8 + 5 + 2 =$ _____

2. $9 + 6 + 5 + 3 + 7 + 4 + 8 =$ _____

3. $8 + 5 + 7 + 9 + 3 + 6 + 8 + 2 =$ _____

4. $6 + 9 + 8 + 5 + 3 + 7 + 9 + 5 =$ _____

5. $13 + 23 + 42 + 15 =$ _____

6. $25 + 32 + 47 + 56 =$ _____

In 7 and 8, add horizontally and vertically, as shown in the sample solution.

Sample solution

$$
\begin{aligned}
15 + \ \ 23 + \ \ 87 &= 125 \\
18 + \ \ 52 + \ \ 35 &= 105 \\
35 + \ \ 63 + \ \ 52 &= 150 \\
\hline
68 + 138 + 174 &= 380
\end{aligned}
$$

7.
$$
\begin{aligned}
47 + \ \ 68 + \ \ 74 &= \\
65 + \ \ 46 + \ \ 59 &= \\
78 + \ \ 96 + \ \ 54 &= \ \ \_\_\_\_ \\
\hline
\ \ \ + \ \ \ \ \ + \ \ \ \ \ &=
\end{aligned}
$$

8.
$$
\begin{aligned}
34 + \ \ 59 + \ \ 72 &= \\
67 + \ \ 85 + \ \ 98 &= \\
37 + \ \ 48 + \ \ 54 &= \\
23 + \ \ 64 + \ \ 82 &= \ \ \_\_\_\_ \\
\hline
\ \ \ + \ \ \ \ \ + \ \ \ \ \ &=
\end{aligned}
$$

APPLICATION PROBLEMS

In these problems, do *not* form columns of numbers. Find the answers by adding horizontally.

1. A salesman earned the following commissions:

$13, $57, $14, $43, $89.

Find the total commission he earned.

2. A bookstore sold the following numbers of books last week:

MON	TUE	WED	THU	FRI	SAT
58	37	89	68	148	215

What was the total number of books sold?

3. Last year, Mr. Wilson bought the following numbers of gallons of fuel oil:

NOV	DEC	JAN	FEB	MAR
160	210	240	170	180

Find the total number of gallons.

4. John delivered the following numbers of newspapers last week:

Monday, 76; Tuesday, 78; Wednesday, 82;

Thursday, 69; Friday, 73; Sunday, 87.

How many newspapers did he deliver last week?

5. A secretary mailed the following numbers of letters each day:

230, 350, 280, 360, 250

How many letters did she send out?

Review of Part II (Units 3 to 5)

In 1 to 10, add and check.

1. 8,368	2. 4,763	3. 7,248	4. 3,873	5. 6,973
9,654	2,572	5,734	9,638	4,865

6.	638	7.	374	8.	863	9.	528	10.	338
	521		463		535		862		569
	368		985		415		978		342
	865		742		768		484		894

In 11 to 16, add by arranging the numbers in the descending order of their values.

11. $95+1,230+5+12,562+678$

12. $28+8+235,325+615+18,690$

13. $5,385+7+895+35,615+38$

14. $735+215,563+25+65,426+7,325$

15. $\$156+\$2+\$1,500+\$37+\$99$

16. $\$.15+\$72.50+\$1.62+\$223.75+\$.98$

In 17 to 20, add horizontally and vertically.

17.
$$324+ \quad 563+ \quad 235=$$
$$473+ \quad 248+ \quad 563=$$
$$254+ \quad 537+ \quad 364=$$
$$637+ \quad 432+ \quad 764=$$
$$\underline{}$$
$$+ \quad\quad + \quad\quad =$$

18.
$$243+ \quad 416+ \quad 425=$$
$$354+ \quad 625+ \quad 867=$$
$$678+ \quad 345+ \quad 568=$$
$$278+ \quad 465+ \quad 753=$$
$$\underline{}$$
$$+ \quad\quad + \quad\quad =$$

19.
$$563+ \quad 428+ \quad 754=$$
$$425+ \quad 634+ \quad 325=$$
$$653+ \quad 719+ \quad 466=$$
$$327+ \quad 532+ \quad 845=$$
$$\underline{}$$
$$+ \quad\quad + \quad\quad =$$

20.
$$235+ \quad 464+ \quad 532=$$
$$528+ \quad 427+ \quad 852=$$
$$735+ \quad 563+ \quad 895=$$
$$215+ \quad 472+ \quad 368=$$
$$\underline{}$$
$$+ \quad\quad + \quad\quad =$$

Part III. Subtracting Whole Numbers

Unit 6. Subtraction of Numbers

Words to know

When the value of a smaller number is "taken away" from the value of a larger number, the process is called **subtraction**.

The number that results from subtraction is called the **difference** or the **remainder**.

The larger number is called the **minuend**.

The smaller number, the number that is subtracted, is called the **subtrahend**.

Subtraction is the opposite of addition. In subtraction, you take away a smaller number (the **subtrahend**) from a larger number (the **minuend**). Your answer is called the **difference** or the **remainder**. The difference is *always smaller* than the larger number of the problem. (Only two numbers are involved in a subtraction problem.) Subtraction is indicated by writing the symbol "—" in front of the number to be subtracted. To indicate that 16 is to be subtracted from 48, write 48 − 16 or

$$\begin{array}{r} 48 \\ -16 \\ \hline \end{array}$$

Setting up a subtraction problem is similar to setting up an addition problem. As in addition, be sure to line up the digits correctly: ones under ones, tens under tens, and so on. Since, in subtraction, you must take the smaller number from the larger number, *always place the larger number above the smaller one.*

EXAMPLE 1. Subtract: 47 − 23

Solution: Set up the problem with the larger number on top and the digits correctly aligned. Take away 3 from 7, getting 4; write the 4 under the ones column. Take away 2 from 4, getting 2; write the 2 under the tens column.

$$\begin{array}{r} 47 \\ -23 \\ \hline 24 \end{array}$$

Answer: 47 − 23 = 24

EXAMPLE 2. Subtract 223 from 547.

Solution: Write the minuend on top and correctly line up the subtrahend under it. Subtract: 7 − 3 = 4. Write the 4 under the ones column. Subtract: 4 − 2 = 2. Write the 2 under the tens column. Subtract: 5 − 2 = 3. Write the 3 under the hundreds column.

$$\begin{array}{r} 547 \\ -223 \\ \hline 324 \end{array}$$

Answer: 547 − 223 = 324

You may check your answer in any subtraction problem by *adding* your answer to the number above it. This sum should equal the top number of the problem.

Let us check the preceding example:

$$\begin{array}{r} 547 \\ -223 \\ \hline 324 \end{array}$$ ← minuend
← subtrahend
← remainder

Add the answer (the remainder) to the number above it (the subtrahend): In the ones column, 4 + 3 = 7. In the tens column, 2 + 2 = 4. In the hundreds column, 3 + 2 = 5. Thus, 324 + 223 = 547. Since the remainder plus the subtrahend equals the original minuend of the problem, you know that the arithmetic is correct.

Remember: Remainder + Subtrahend = Minuend

EXERCISES

In 1 to 20, subtract the smaller number from the larger number. Check.

1.	2.	3.	4.	5.	6.
39 −7	28 −5	26 −4	57 −4	48 −32	67 −15

7.	8.	9.	10.	11.	12.
49 −26	27 −13	576 −32	769 −47	687 −327	6,574 −43

13.	14.	15.	16.
7,645 −5,224	4,857 −1,204	8,793 −3,670	15,627 −2,403

17.	18.	19.	20.
47,874 −25,521	84,691 −23,270	60,507 −20,105	65,000 −42,000

In 21 to 37, subtract as indicated.

21. $47 - 32$ 22. $85 - 34$ 23. $68 - 26$ 24. $98 - 43$

25. $258 - 27$ 26. $476 - 52$ 27. $398 - 23$ 28. $479 - 53$

29. $5,684 - 341$ 30. $9,879 - 637$

31. $7,687 - 235$ 32. $47,683 - 5,151$

33. $85,298 - 32,073$ 34. $658,976 - 235,432$

35. 798,000 − 522,000   **36.** 869,621 − 327,200

37. 758,372 − 205,020

In 38 to 43, subtract:

38. 23 from 47   **39.** 52 from 95   **40.** 24 from 87

41. 47 from 279   **42.** 262 from 797   **43.** 364 from 2,987

In 44 to 49, find the difference between:

44. 47 and 89   **45.** 23 and 75   **46.** 42 and 98

47. 287 and 232   **48.** 768 and 523   **49.** 896,785 and 71,352

APPLICATION PROBLEMS

Sample solution

During the 1968 presidential election in California, Mr. Nixon received 3,467,700 votes (rounded off to the nearest hundred) and Mr. Humphrey received 3,244,300 votes. By how many votes did Nixon beat Humphrey?

$$
\begin{array}{r}
3,467,700 \\
-3,244,300 \\
\hline
223,400
\end{array}
$$

1. Last year Mr. Gonzales earned $8,324, and this year he will earn $9,765. How much more will he earn this year than last year?

2. The DeLucca family bought a house for $16,253. Five years later they sold it for $27,576. How much profit did they make on the sale of the house?

3. Joseph bought a car for $2,875. The price of the car was $352 more this year than it was last year. What was the price of the car last year?

_____

4. Victor rented a car that had an odometer (mileage indicator) reading of 42,357. At the end of the year, the reading was 77,898. What was the mileage added by Victor?

_____

5. Last year's school enrollment was 2,325. This year, the enrollment is 2,879. How many more students are enrolled this year?

Unit 7. Subtraction Problems With Borrowing

Words to know

In subtraction, we *must* subtract a smaller number from a larger number. However, the *digits* in the smaller number may be greater than those in the larger number. For example, let us try to subtract 99 from 321. We know that 99 is smaller than 321, but how do we subtract 9 from 1 in the ones column?

$$\begin{array}{r} 321 \\ -99 \\ \hline ? \end{array}$$

In this unit, we will learn the technique known as **borrowing** that enables us to perform such subtractions.

In doing subtraction problems, you may find that you have a larger digit to take from a smaller digit. In such a case, you will have to *borrow* from the digit to the left of the one you are working with.

EXAMPLE 1. Subtract 9 from 72.

Solution: Line up the digits correctly. Then, as with all adding and subtracting, begin with the ones column. You cannot take away 9 from 2, so you borrow 1 from the 7, *the digit to the left* (in the tens column). You change the 7 to a 6, since $7 - 1 = 6$. Then you place the 1 you borrowed in front of the 2, the digit you borrowed it for, changing the 2 to 12. Now you can subtract 9 from 12, and your answer is 3. Write the 3 in the ones column and then bring down the 6 in the tens column. Your final answer is 63.

$$\begin{array}{r} 72 \\ -9 \\ \hline \end{array}$$

$$\begin{array}{r} 6 \\ \cancel{7}^{1}2 \\ -9 \\ \hline 63 \end{array}$$

Answer: $72 - 9 = 63$

EXAMPLE 2. Subtract 258 from 535.

Solution: Line up the digits correctly. Then, as with all adding and subtracting, begin with the ones column. You cannot take away 8 from 5, so you borrow 1 from the 3, *the digit to the left* (in the tens column). You change the 3 to a 2, since $3 - 1 = 2$. Then you place the 1 you borrowed in front of the 5, the digit you borrowed it for, changing the 5 to 15. Now you can subtract 8 from 15, and your answer is 7.

In the tens column, you cannot take away 5 from 2. Therefore, you borrow 1 from the 5, *the digit to the left* (in the hundreds column). You change the 5 to a 4 since $5 - 1 = 4$. Then you place the 1 you borrowed in front of the 2, the digit you borrowed it for, changing the 2 to 12. Subtract 5 from 12; your answer is 7.

$$\begin{array}{r} 535 \\ -258 \\ \hline \end{array}$$

$$\begin{array}{r} 2 \\ 5\cancel{3}^{1}5 \\ -258 \\ \hline 7 \end{array}$$

$$\begin{array}{r} 4\,2 \\ \cancel{5}\cancel{3}^{1}5 \\ -258 \\ \hline 77 \end{array}$$

In the hundreds column, you subtract 2 from 4, and your answer is 2.

$$\begin{array}{r} 4'2 \\ \cancel{5}\cancel{3}5 \\ -258 \\ \hline 277 \end{array}$$

EXAMPLE 3. Subtract: 321 − 99

Solution:
In the ones column: 11 − 9 = 2
In the tens column: 11 − 9 = 2
In the hundreds column: 2 − 0 = 2

Answer: 321 − 99 = 222

$$\begin{array}{r} 2'1 \\ \cancel{3}\cancel{2}1 \\ -99 \\ \hline 222 \end{array}$$

Check: Does the remainder plus the subtrahend equal the minuend? 277 + 258 = 535 ✓

Answer: 535 − 258 = 277

$$\begin{array}{r} 277 \\ +258 \\ \hline 535 \end{array}$$

EXAMPLE 4. Subtract: 851 − 276

Solution:
In the ones column: 11 − 6 = 5
In the tens column: 14 − 7 = 7
In the hundreds column: 7 − 2 = 5

Answer: 851 − 276 = 575

$$\begin{array}{r} 7'4 \\ \cancel{8}\cancel{5}1 \\ -276 \\ \hline 575 \end{array}$$

EXERCISES

In 1 to 47, subtract.

1. $\begin{array}{r} 73 \\ -54 \\ \hline \end{array}$	2. $\begin{array}{r} 85 \\ -38 \\ \hline \end{array}$	3. $\begin{array}{r} 93 \\ -65 \\ \hline \end{array}$	4. $\begin{array}{r} 72 \\ -67 \\ \hline \end{array}$	5. $\begin{array}{r} 47 \\ -29 \\ \hline \end{array}$
6. $\begin{array}{r} 56 \\ -37 \\ \hline \end{array}$	7. $\begin{array}{r} 254 \\ -38 \\ \hline \end{array}$	8. $\begin{array}{r} 457 \\ -63 \\ \hline \end{array}$	9. $\begin{array}{r} 539 \\ -54 \\ \hline \end{array}$	10. $\begin{array}{r} 626 \\ -72 \\ \hline \end{array}$
11. $\begin{array}{r} 138 \\ -63 \\ \hline \end{array}$	12. $\begin{array}{r} 247 \\ -82 \\ \hline \end{array}$	13. $\begin{array}{r} 352 \\ -47 \\ \hline \end{array}$	14. $\begin{array}{r} 139 \\ -57 \\ \hline \end{array}$	15. $\begin{array}{r} 265 \\ -28 \\ \hline \end{array}$
16. $\begin{array}{r} 432 \\ -265 \\ \hline \end{array}$	17. $\begin{array}{r} 621 \\ -284 \\ \hline \end{array}$	18. $\begin{array}{r} 426 \\ -189 \\ \hline \end{array}$	19. $\begin{array}{r} 754 \\ -376 \\ \hline \end{array}$	20. $\begin{array}{r} 833 \\ -356 \\ \hline \end{array}$
21. $\begin{array}{r} 3,232 \\ -758 \\ \hline \end{array}$	22. $\begin{array}{r} 1,257 \\ -389 \\ \hline \end{array}$	23. $\begin{array}{r} 1,452 \\ -785 \\ \hline \end{array}$	24. $\begin{array}{r} 3,625 \\ -746 \\ \hline \end{array}$	25. $\begin{array}{r} 4,351 \\ -983 \\ \hline \end{array}$
26. $\begin{array}{r} 5,354 \\ -2,698 \\ \hline \end{array}$	27. $\begin{array}{r} 4,236 \\ -3,548 \\ \hline \end{array}$	28. $\begin{array}{r} 6,426 \\ -5,659 \\ \hline \end{array}$	29. $\begin{array}{r} 8,435 \\ -3,878 \\ \hline \end{array}$	
30. $\begin{array}{r} 7,263 \\ -6,796 \\ \hline \end{array}$	31. $\begin{array}{r} 25,431 \\ -8,273 \\ \hline \end{array}$	32. $\begin{array}{r} 34,522 \\ -6,784 \\ \hline \end{array}$	33. $\begin{array}{r} 27,534 \\ -6,847 \\ \hline \end{array}$	

34. 17,235
    −6,568

35. 23,425
    −13,837

36. 45,357
    −38,748

37. 37,432
    −28,855

38. 86,436
    −76,859

39. 832,738
    −625,465

40. 758,374
    −373,548

41. 472,648
    −337,582

42. 372,634
    −245,378

43. 342,637
    −153,849

44. 453,455
    −374,457

45. 23,453,235
    −18,765,859

46. 17,346,324
    −16,589,536

47. 27,453,634
    −18,674,857

APPLICATION PROBLEMS

Sample solution

In 1968, the net yearly income of an average farm in Hawaii was $19,321. In 1970, the net income was $18,766. By how much had the net income decreased?

$$\begin{array}{r} 8\,2\,1 \\ 1\,9,3\,2\,1 \\ -\,1\,8,7\,6\,6 \\ \hline 5\,5\,5 \end{array}$$

1. James invested $1,867 in stocks. Three years later he sold the stocks for $2,846. How much profit did he make?

2. A retail store sold $24,479 worth of merchandise last month. This month the sales were $25,238. How much more merchandise did the store sell this month than last month?

3. In the last local election, 75,678 voters went to the polls out of 123,452 registered voters. How many registered voters did not vote?

4. In the last 5 years, the population of a city increased from 876,589 to 1,342,467. Find the increase in population.

5. The Greens bought a house for $24,325. If they made a down payment of $4,638, how much more remains to be paid?

Unit 8. Borrowing From Zero

Sometimes the digit you want to borrow from will be a 0. In such a case, you must move to the left until you reach a digit that is not 0.

EXAMPLE 1. Subtract 258 from 705.

Solution: Set up the problem correctly. You want to borrow a 1 for the 5 so that you can change the 5 to 15. Since you cannot borrow from the 0, the digit to the left of the 5, you must move over one more digit to the left. You then borrow 1 from the 70. Since 70 − 1 = 69, change the 70 to 69 and place the 1 you borrowed in front of the 5. Now subtract:

$$
\begin{array}{r}
705 \\
-258 \\
\end{array}
$$

Ones column: 15 − 8 = 7
Tens column: 9 − 5 = 4
Hundreds column: 6 − 2 = 4

$$
\begin{array}{r}
\overset{69,}{7\boxed{0}5} \\
-258 \\
\hline
447
\end{array}
$$

Check: Remainder + Subtrahend = Minuend
      447   +   258   =   705 ✓

Answer: 705 − 258 = 447

When there are two or more zeros to be borrowed from, follow the same procedure.

EXAMPLE 2. Subtract: 6,005 − 258

Solution: Set up the problem correctly. As before, you must borrow a 1 for the 5. But this time you must borrow from the 600. Since 600 − 1 = 599, change the 600 to 599 and place the 1 in front of the 5, changing it to 15. Subtract as before.

$$
\begin{array}{r}
\overset{599,}{\boxed{6,00}5} \\
-258 \\
\end{array}
$$

Ones column: 15 − 8 = 7
Tens column: 9 − 5 = 4
Hundreds column: 9 − 2 = 7
Thousands column: 5 − 0 = 5

$$
\begin{array}{r}
6,005 \\
-258 \\
\hline
5,747
\end{array}
$$

Answer: 6,005 − 258 = 5,747

EXAMPLE 3. Subtract: 80,000 − 9,873

Solution:

$$
\begin{array}{r}
\overset{79\,99,}{\boxed{80,00}0} \\
-9,873 \\
\hline
70,127
\end{array}
$$

Answer: 80,000 − 9,873 = 70,127

EXERCISES

In 1 to 38, subtract. When you must borrow from zero, draw a box as shown in the sample solutions.

Sample solutions

$$
\begin{array}{r}
\overset{29,}{\boxed{30}7} \\
-169 \\
\hline
138
\end{array}
\qquad
\begin{array}{r}
\overset{599,}{\boxed{6,00}3} \\
-3,517 \\
\hline
2,486
\end{array}
$$

1.
$$
\begin{array}{r}
50 \\
-37 \\
\end{array}
$$

2.
$$
\begin{array}{r}
60 \\
-43 \\
\end{array}
$$

3.
$$
\begin{array}{r}
460 \\
-26 \\
\end{array}
$$

4.
$$
\begin{array}{r}
703 \\
-56 \\
\end{array}
$$

5.
$$
\begin{array}{r}
800 \\
-534 \\
\end{array}
$$

6. 604
    −278

7. 903
    −565

8. 600
    −347

9. 803
    −638

10. 605
    −329

11. 5,037
    −743

12. 7,048
    −963

13. 3,056
    −362

14. 5,038
    −2,983

15. 3,004
    −738

16. 2,006
    −1,737

17. 5,000
    −2,267

18. 1,007
    −479

19. 3,005
    −1,837

20. 8,003
    −7,565

21. 10,005
    −7,328

22. 20,000
    −14,273

23. 60,005
    −59,376

24. 80,006
    −8,628

25. 40,001
    −16,383

26. 50,000
    −9,378

27. 10,004
    −9,248

28. 20,003
    −19,256

29. 30,000
    −14,735

30. 50,503
    −8,736

31. 80,305
    −12,658

32. 10,500
    −9,753

33. 30,206
    −7,479

34. 204,043
    −75,652

35. 410,400
    −83,764

36. 806,004
    −528,737

37. 800,306
    −245,729

38. 704,000
    −376,248

APPLICATION PROBLEMS

Sample solution

In Pennsylvania, there were 2,401 highway deaths in 1969 and 2,255 highway deaths in 1970. How many fewer deaths were there in 1970 than in 1969?

$$\begin{array}{r} 39 \\ 2,\boxed{40}1 \\ -2,255 \\ \hline 146 \end{array}$$

1. A real estate salesman sold a home for $20,500, which included his commission of $1,675. What was the cost of the home without the commission?

2. John won $5,000 in a state lottery and paid $1,250 in taxes. How much money did he win, after taxes?

3. Peter earns $10,000 a year and pays a total of $2,560 in taxes. How much does he earn in a year, after taxes?

4. Mary bought a color television set for $500. If she made a down payment of $125, how much does she still owe the store?

5. A stadium seats 40,500 people. If the attendance at a concert is 33,763, how many seats are unoccupied?

Review of Part III (Units 6 to 8)

In 1 to 10, subtract.

1.	$\begin{array}{r} 8,645 \\ -6,531 \\ \hline \end{array}$	**2.**	$\begin{array}{r} 6,594 \\ -3,261 \\ \hline \end{array}$	**3.**	$\begin{array}{r} 7,879 \\ -5,245 \\ \hline \end{array}$	**4.**	$\begin{array}{r} 6,968 \\ -5,345 \\ \hline \end{array}$

5.	$\begin{array}{r} 5,769 \\ -5,237 \\ \hline \end{array}$	**6.**	$\begin{array}{r} 35,874 \\ -13,543 \\ \hline \end{array}$	**7.**	$\begin{array}{r} 87,968 \\ -25,745 \\ \hline \end{array}$	**8.**	$\begin{array}{r} 69,786 \\ -35,332 \\ \hline \end{array}$

9.	$\begin{array}{r} 98,679 \\ -53,255 \\ \hline \end{array}$	**10.**	$\begin{array}{r} 69,587 \\ -34,243 \\ \hline \end{array}$

In 11 to 16, subtract.

11. $375 - 253$ **12.** $286 - 52$ **13.** $5,658 - 435$

14. $15,875 - 4,522$ **15.** $28,698 - 3,265$ **16.** $19,869 - 7,425$

In 17 to 22, find the difference between:

17. 8,658 and 3,435   **18.** 2,435 and 9,687

19. 3,234 and 7,867   **20.** 86,798 and 5,263

21. 65,659 and 23,537   **22.** 34,243 and 79,878

In 23 to 42, subtract.

23. $\begin{array}{r} 542 \\ -364 \\ \hline \end{array}$	**24.** $\begin{array}{r} 735 \\ -387 \\ \hline \end{array}$	**25.** $\begin{array}{r} 341 \\ -263 \\ \hline \end{array}$	**26.** $\begin{array}{r} 457 \\ -369 \\ \hline \end{array}$
27. $\begin{array}{r} 635 \\ -468 \\ \hline \end{array}$	**28.** $\begin{array}{r} 8,345 \\ -4,268 \\ \hline \end{array}$	**29.** $\begin{array}{r} 7,264 \\ -3,457 \\ \hline \end{array}$	**30.** $\begin{array}{r} 5,465 \\ -3,367 \\ \hline \end{array}$
31. $\begin{array}{r} 9,535 \\ -6,828 \\ \hline \end{array}$	**32.** $\begin{array}{r} 7,524 \\ -6,846 \\ \hline \end{array}$	**33.** $\begin{array}{r} 704 \\ -426 \\ \hline \end{array}$	**34.** $\begin{array}{r} 800 \\ -624 \\ \hline \end{array}$
35. $\begin{array}{r} 503 \\ -437 \\ \hline \end{array}$	**36.** $\begin{array}{r} 5,032 \\ -2,745 \\ \hline \end{array}$	**37.** $\begin{array}{r} 6,003 \\ -4,768 \\ \hline \end{array}$	**38.** $\begin{array}{r} 25,600 \\ -12,365 \\ \hline \end{array}$
39. $\begin{array}{r} 30,403 \\ -17,578 \\ \hline \end{array}$	**40.** $\begin{array}{r} 60,000 \\ -27,235 \\ \hline \end{array}$	**41.** $\begin{array}{r} 20,500 \\ -8,743 \\ \hline \end{array}$	**42.** $\begin{array}{r} 30,050 \\ -23,763 \\ \hline \end{array}$

Part IV. Multiplying Whole Numbers

Unit 9. Multiplication of Numbers

Words to know

When the number 6 is repeated five times, the five 6's add up to 30. We say that 6 is **multiplied** by 5, or $6 \times 5 = 30$. The symbol $\times$ indicates **multiplication**.

In multiplication, the number being multiplied is the **multiplicand**. The number doing the multiplying is the **multiplier**.

The answer to a multiplication problem is the **product**.

Multiplication is a short-cut method of doing addition. When you multiply numbers, you really add groups of numbers. Multiplying 5×5, which is read "5 times 5," is the same as adding five 5's:

$$5 \times 5 = 25 \qquad 5 + 5 + 5 + 5 + 5 = 25$$

Multiplication problems are set up like this:

$$534 \longleftarrow \text{multiplicand}$$
$$\times 3 \longleftarrow \text{multiplier}$$

Notice that the ones digits are aligned, as in addition and subtraction. Also, the bottom number is the **multiplier** and the top number is the **multiplicand**. In solving a problem in multiplication, always multiply from right to left, starting with the ones digit in the multiplicand. The answer to a multiplication problem is called the **product**.

EXAMPLE. Multiply: 534×3

Solution: Set up the problem correctly; then multiply from right to left.

First, 3 times 4 equals 12. Write the 2 under the ones column and carry the 1 to the next digit, the 3.

$$\overset{1}{\underset{2}{\begin{array}{r} 534 \\ \times\ 3 \\ \hline \end{array}}}$$

Then, 3 times 3 equals 9, plus the 1 you carried, equals 10. Write the 0 under the tens column and carry the 1 to the 5, the next digit.

$$\overset{11}{\underset{02}{\begin{array}{r} 534 \\ \times\ 3 \\ \hline \end{array}}}$$

Finally, 3 times 5 equals 15, plus the 1 you carried equals 16. Write the 6 under the hundreds column and write the 1 to the left.

$$\overset{11}{\underset{1{,}602}{\begin{array}{r} 534 \\ \times\ 3 \\ \hline \end{array}}}$$

Answer: $534 \times 3 = 1{,}602$

EXERCISES

In 1 to 54, multiply.

1.
$$\begin{array}{r} 43 \\ \times 2 \\ \hline \end{array}$$

2.
$$\begin{array}{r} 24 \\ \times 3 \\ \hline \end{array}$$

3.
$$\begin{array}{r} 31 \\ \times 4 \\ \hline \end{array}$$

4.
$$\begin{array}{r} 53 \\ \times 5 \\ \hline \end{array}$$

5.
$$\begin{array}{r} 34 \\ \times 4 \\ \hline \end{array}$$

6.
$$\begin{array}{r} 25 \\ \times 3 \\ \hline \end{array}$$

7. 42
×2

8. 24
×5

9. 33
×4

10. 26
×3

11. 35
×6

12. 46
×5

13. 27
×4

14. 38
×3

15. 46
×7

16. 52
×8

17. 63
×9

18. 84
×6

19. 95
×5

20. 76
×7

21. 46
×8

22. 27
×9

23. 46
×6

24. 78
×8

25. 97
×5

26. 69
×7

27. 56
×8

28. 48
×9

29. 57
×6

30. 79
×9

31. 69
×7

32. 59
×9

33. 367
×5

34. 496
×4

35. 786
×3

36. 988
×2

37. 568
×8

38. 784
×6

39. 987
×9

40. 756
×7

41. 875
×6

42. 987
×8

43. 3,428
×5

44. 2,768
×4

45. 5,697
×3

46. 6,798
×2

47. 9,874
×9

48. 5,987
×7

49. 23,542
×6

50. 35,645
×7

51. 65,678
×8

52. 76,568
×9

53. 87,986
×7

54. 67,879
×9

APPLICATION PROBLEMS

Sample solution

Henry flew from New York to Miami in exactly 4 hours. If his plane averaged 295 miles per hour, how many miles did the flight cover?

$$
\begin{array}{r}
32 \\
295 \\
\times 4 \\
\hline
1,180
\end{array}
$$

1. A farmer planted 37 rows of peach trees, with 8 trees in each row. How many trees did he plant?

2. A truck holds 678 crates of oranges. How many crates will 7 trucks hold?

3. According to last year's records, a mail order house sends out an average of 968 packages each day. Calculate how many packages will be sent out during a typical 6-day week. (Since your answer will be approximate, round off your product to the nearest *ten*.)

4. A retailer bought 586 blouses at $6 each. How much did he pay for all the blouses?

5. A theater sold 759 tickets at $5 each. How much money was received from the sale of these tickets?

Unit 10. Multiplication With Two or More Digits in the Multiplier

Words to know

When the multiplier has two or more digits, a problem in multiplication will have two or more **partial answers**. These partial answers must be added to obtain the product.

In a multiplication problem, the multiplier may have two or more digits. When this happens, you must multiply the top number by every digit of the multiplier, doing the multiplications separately. Each different multiplication results in a **partial answer**. If the multiplier has two digits, there will be *two* partial answers; if the multiplier has three digits, there will be *three* partial answers; and so on. When all the partial answers are added, the product is obtained.

Here are the steps for multiplying by a number that has two or more digits:

Step 1: Set up the problem correctly by lining up the ones digit of the multiplier with the ones digit of the multiplicand.

Step 2: Using the ones digit as the multiplier, multiply from right to left (exactly as you did in the preceding unit).

Step 3: Using the tens digit as the multiplier, multiply from right to left. Place the right-hand digit of this partial answer directly under the digit you are multiplying with. Repeat this step as often as necessary, depending on the number of digits in the multiplier.

Step 4: Add the partial answers to obtain the product.

EXAMPLE 1. Multiply: 235×23

Solution: Since the multiplier, 23, has two digits, you must multiply the top number two times: first, by the ones digit, 3; then, by the tens digit, 2.

Step 1: Set up the problem correctly.

Step 2: Using the digit 3 as the multiplier, multiply from right to left:

$$\begin{array}{r} 235 \\ \times\, 23 \\ \hline \end{array}$$

$3 \times 5 = 15$. Write the 5 *directly under the 3*, the digit you are multiplying with. Carry the 1 to the next digit, the 3.

$$\begin{array}{r} \overset{1\,1}{235} \\ \times\, 23 \\ \hline 705 \end{array} \longleftarrow \text{partial answer}$$

$3 \times 3 = 9$, plus the 1 you carried, equals 10. Write the 0 and carry the 1 to the next digit, the 2.

$3 \times 2 = 6$, plus the 1 you carried, equals 7. Write the 7. The number 705 is the partial answer.

Step 3: Multiply with the next digit, the 2. Write the first digit of this partial answer *directly under the 2*, the digit you are multiplying with:

$$\begin{array}{r} \overset{1}{\cancel{1}} \\ 235 \\ \times\, 23 \\ \hline 705 \\ 470 \end{array} \longleftarrow \text{partial answers}$$

$2 \times 5 = 10$. Write the 0 directly under the 2 and carry the 1 to the next digit, the 3.

$2 \times 3 = 6$, plus the 1 you carried, equals 7. Write the 7.

$2 \times 2 = 4$. Write the 4. The number 470 is the partial answer.

Step 4: Draw a line under the partial answers and add the two numbers

$$\begin{array}{r} 235 \\ \times\, 23 \\ \hline 705 \\ 4\,70 \\ \hline 5,405 \end{array}$$

to get the final answer, the product. Be sure to keep the partial answers correctly aligned.

Answer: $235 \times 23 = 5,405$

In the following example, note how the above procedure is applied to a 3-digit multiplier.

EXAMPLE 2. Multiply: 432×325

Solution:

$$\begin{array}{r} \overset{1\,1}{432} \\ \times\, 325 \\ \hline 2\,160 \\ 8\,64 \\ 129\,6 \\ \hline 140,400 \end{array}$$

Answer: $432 \times 325 = 140,400$

Remember: Always multiply with every digit in the multiplier. Place the first digit of each partial answer (the right-hand digit) directly under the digit you are multiplying with.

EXERCISES

In 1 to 31, multiply.

1. $$\begin{array}{r} 43 \\ \times\, 24 \\ \hline \end{array}$$

2. $$\begin{array}{r} 35 \\ \times\, 32 \\ \hline \end{array}$$

3. $$\begin{array}{r} 63 \\ \times\, 53 \\ \hline \end{array}$$

4. $$\begin{array}{r} 56 \\ \times\, 47 \\ \hline \end{array}$$

5.   85
    × 68

6.   95
    × 49

7.   87
    × 68

8.   76
    × 58

9.   75
    × 64

10.   87
    × 95

11.   59
    × 34

12.   89
    × 38

13.   84
    × 25

14.   43
    × 98

15.   81
    × 94

16.   68
    × 79

17.   423
    × 86

18.   674
    × 78

19.   937
    × 46

20.   634
    × 95

21.   847
    × 69

22.   486
    × 58

23.   2,468
    × 325

24.   8,657
    × 456

25.   7,564
    × 675

26.   9,687
    × 763

27.   7,478
    × 397

28.   23,435
    × 422

29. 34,675
   × 568

30. 57,189
   × 817

31. 86,497
   × 589

APPLICATION PROBLEMS

Sample solution

If a year has 365 days and a day has 24 hours, how many hours are there in a year?

$$
\begin{array}{r}
365 \\
\times 24 \\
\hline
1460 \\
730 \\
\hline
8,760
\end{array}
$$

1. June can type an average of 49 words per minute. How many words can she type in 45 minutes?

2. If sound travels at a speed of 1,188 feet per second, how far will sound travel in 65 seconds?

3. If light travels at a speed of 186,324 miles per second, how far does light travel in 96 seconds?

4. How many envelopes are contained in 689 boxes if each box holds 144 envelopes?

5. A crate contains 58 apples. How many apples will there be in 267 crates?

Unit 11. Multiplication With 0's in the Multiplicand

Many people make mistakes with 0's when multiplying. To avoid mistakes, remember that *any number multiplied by 0 equals 0.*

If you earned no money on Wednesday (0 dollars), no money on Thursday, and no money on Friday, how much money did you earn?

By addition: $0 + 0 + 0 = 0$.

By multiplication: $0 \times 3 = 0$.

EXAMPLE 1. Multiply: 403×3

Solution: Set up the problem correctly and multiply from right to left.

$3 \times 3 = 9$. Write the 9.

$3 \times 0 = 0$. Write the 0.

$3 \times 4 = 12$. Write the 12.

$$
\begin{array}{r}
403 \\
\times 3 \\
\hline
1,209
\end{array}
$$

Answer: $403 \times 3 = 1,209$

When the multiplier has two digits, follow the procedure in the preceding unit.

EXAMPLE 2. Multiply: 403×24

Solution:

$4 \times 3 = 12$. Write the 2 directly under the 4 and carry the 1.

$4 \times 0 = 0$, plus the 1 you carried, equals 1. Write the 1.

$4 \times 4 = 16$. Write the 16.

$$\begin{array}{r} \overset{1}{4}03 \\ \times 24 \\ \hline 1612 \end{array}$$

The partial answer is 1612.

$2 \times 3 = 6$. Write the 6 directly under the 2.

$2 \times 0 = 0$. Write the 0.

$2 \times 4 = 8$. Write the 8.

The partial answer is 806. Add the two partial answers to get the product.

$$\begin{array}{r} \overset{1}{4}03 \\ \times 24 \\ \hline 1\ 612 \\ 8\ 06 \\ \hline 9,672 \end{array}$$

Answer: $403 \times 24 = 9{,}672$

Remember: Any number multiplied by zero equals zero.

EXERCISES

In 1 to 27, multiply.

1.
$$\begin{array}{r} 30 \\ \times 4 \\ \hline \end{array}$$

2.
$$\begin{array}{r} 50 \\ \times 7 \\ \hline \end{array}$$

3.
$$\begin{array}{r} 80 \\ \times 5 \\ \hline \end{array}$$

4.
$$\begin{array}{r} 60 \\ \times 8 \\ \hline \end{array}$$

5.
$$\begin{array}{r} 70 \\ \times 6 \\ \hline \end{array}$$

6.
$$\begin{array}{r} 40 \\ \times 9 \\ \hline \end{array}$$

7.
$$\begin{array}{r} 90 \\ \times 7 \\ \hline \end{array}$$

8.
$$\begin{array}{r} 80 \\ \times 8 \\ \hline \end{array}$$

9.
$$\begin{array}{r} 307 \\ \times 24 \\ \hline \end{array}$$

10.
$$\begin{array}{r} 509 \\ \times 36 \\ \hline \end{array}$$

11.
$$\begin{array}{r} 807 \\ \times 48 \\ \hline \end{array}$$

12.
$$\begin{array}{r} 906 \\ \times 75 \\ \hline \end{array}$$

13.
$$\begin{array}{r} 706 \\ \times 98 \\ \hline \end{array}$$

14.
$$\begin{array}{r} 609 \\ \times 76 \\ \hline \end{array}$$

15.
$$\begin{array}{r} 805 \\ \times 69 \\ \hline \end{array}$$

16.
$$\begin{array}{r} 5{,}040 \\ \times 48 \\ \hline \end{array}$$

17.
$$\begin{array}{r} 7{,}500 \\ \times 64 \\ \hline \end{array}$$

18.
$$\begin{array}{r} 8{,}004 \\ \times 98 \\ \hline \end{array}$$

19.
$$\begin{array}{r} 6{,}050 \\ \times 77 \\ \hline \end{array}$$

20.
$$\begin{array}{r} 8{,}008 \\ \times 65 \\ \hline \end{array}$$

21. 27,057
    ×54

22. 30,205
    ×68

23. 50,074
    ×76

24. 76,005
    ×48

25. 205,300
    ×346

26. 460,206
    ×478

27. 760,089
    ×738

APPLICATION PROBLEMS

Sample solution

Dave's weekly take-home pay is $108. How much does he earn in a year? (Dave is paid for 52 weeks during the year.)

$$
\begin{array}{r}
108 \\
\times 52 \\
\hline
216 \\
540 \\
\hline
\$5,616
\end{array}
$$

1. If a truck costs $5,080, how much will 15 trucks cost?

2. A retailer bought 65 radios at $105 each. What is the total cost of the radios?

3. A construction firm is building 325 homes that will sell for $28,500 each. What will be the amount realized from the sale of the homes?

4. A department store bought 1,050 display cases at $37 each. Find the cost of the display cases.

5. A motel is installing 1,500 yards of carpeting at a cost of $4 a yard. Find the cost of the carpeting.

Unit 12. Multiplication With 0's in the Multiplier

When there are 0's in the multiplier, you can simplify the multiplication by using this rule:

Rule: When you come to a 0 in the multiplier, *do not multiply by 0*. Instead, bring down the 0 *in a straight line* as a place holder.

EXAMPLE 1. Multiply: 354 × 304

Solution: Set up the problem correctly and multiply with the right-hand digit, the 4.

4 × 4 = 16. Write the 6 directly under the 4 and carry the 1.

$$\begin{array}{r} 2\,1 \\ 354 \\ \times 304 \\ \hline 1416 \end{array}$$

4 × 5 = 20, plus the 1 you carried, equals 21. Write the 1 and carry the 2.

4 × 3 = 12, plus the 2 you carried, equals 14. Write the 14.

The partial answer is 1,416.

Since the next digit is 0, *do not multiply with it*. Instead, bring down the 0 *in a straight line* as a place holder.

$$\begin{array}{r} 2\,1 \\ 354 \\ \times 304 \\ \hline 1416 \\ 0 \end{array}$$

Now, multiply with the next digit, the 3.

3 × 4 = 12. Write the 2 directly under the 3 and carry the 1.

3 × 5 = 15, plus the 1 you carried, equals 16. Write the 6 and carry the 1.

3 × 3 = 9, plus the 1 you carried, equals 10. Write the 10.

The partial answer is 10,620.

$$\begin{array}{r} 1\,1 \\ 354 \\ \times 304 \\ \hline 1\,416 \\ 106\,20 \\ \hline 107{,}616 \end{array}$$

Add the two partial answers to get the product.

Answer: 354 × 304 = 107,616

Here are other examples of how the rule is used when there are 0's in the multiplier:

$$\begin{array}{r} 5 \\ 37 \\ \times 80 \\ \hline 2{,}960 \end{array} \qquad \begin{array}{r} 60 \\ \times 70 \\ \hline 4{,}200 \end{array} \qquad \begin{array}{r} 3\,6\,1 \\ 1{,}492 \\ \times 700 \\ \hline 1{,}044{,}400 \end{array}$$

EXERCISES

In 1 to 28, multiply.

1. 34 × 30
2. 47 × 50
3. 60 × 40
4. 76 × 80
5. 68 × 40
6. 90 × 90

7. 50 × 70
8. 49 × 80
9. 70 × 60
10. 234 × 307
11. 453 × 608
12. 765 × 460

13. 876 × 680
14. 605 × 306
15. 937 × 700
16. 8,075 × 350

17.   7,650   18.   4,075   19.   6,300   20.   5,000
     × 800   × 708   × 900   × 407

21.   28,000   22.   46,364   23.   53,647   24.   74,030
     × 570   × 806   × 508   × 450

25.   43,762   26.   76,628   27.   59,070   28.   78,365
    × 5,002   × 6,070   × 5,600   × 7,006

APPLICATION PROBLEMS

Sample solution

Mr. Jacobs works a 40-hour week for 50 weeks out of the year.
How many hours will he work in 20 years?

$$\begin{array}{r} 40 \text{ hr.} \\ \times\ 50 \text{ wk.} \\ \hline 2,000 \text{ hr. per yr.} \\ \times\ 20 \text{ yr.} \\ \hline 40,000 \text{ hr.} \end{array}$$

1. A taxi company ordered 20 taxis at $3,090 each. What is the total cost of the taxis?

2. Mr. Brown has a *30-payment life* insurance policy. This means that he must pay yearly premiums for 30 years. If his premiums are $263 a year, how much will he pay in premiums?

3. The Wilsons own a home that has a 30-year mortgage. The *monthly* payments to the bank are $215. How much will they pay to the bank in the 30 years?

4. If a package contains 500 sheets of writing paper, how many sheets will 144 packages contain?

5. Envelopes are packed 300 to a box. How many envelopes are there in 175 boxes?

Review of Part IV (Units 9 to 12)

In 1 to 24, multiply.

1. 5,685
    ×7

2. 6,765
    ×8

3. 5,658
    ×6

4. 8,735
    ×5

5. 9,756
    ×3

6. 5,798
    ×9

7. 5,453
    ×35

8. 7,465
    ×67

9. 9,547
    ×76

10. 7,658
    ×565

11. 9,674
    ×684

12. 4,367
    ×586

13. 7,608
    ×358

14. 8,500
    ×564

15. 6,080
    ×647

16. 23,500
    ×549

17. 25,006
    ×476

18. 40,500
    ×645

19. 5,650
    ×270

20. 7,057
    ×500

21. 6,050
    ×807

22. 4,657
    ×570

23. 47,659
    ×8,700

24. 53,968
    ×8,006

Part V. Dividing Whole Numbers

Unit 13. Division of Numbers

Words to know

When a pack of 52 playing cards is dealt to 4 players, each hand consists of 13 cards. We say that the pack has been **divided** among the 4 players.

When any number is broken down into smaller groups of numbers, the process is called **division**.

In division, the number being divided is the **dividend**. The number doing the division is the **divisor**.

The answer to a division problem is the **quotient**.

$$13 \longleftarrow \text{quotient}$$
$$\text{divisor} \longrightarrow 4\overline{)52} \longleftarrow \text{dividend}$$

The symbol $\overline{)}$ is called the **division box**.

Division is the opposite of multiplication. When you perform division, you find out how many times a smaller number (the **divisor**) is contained in a larger number (the **dividend**). For example, "How many 5's are there in 30?" Recalling that $5 \times 6 = 30$ and that division is the opposite of multiplication, we answer, "There are six 5's in 30." In other words, "30 divided by 5 equals 6." The answer, 6, is the **quotient**.

In symbols, we can indicate division problems in several ways. Using the symbol $\div$, which means "divided by," we can write the division problem like this:

$$30 \div 5$$

As you will learn (Unit 22), we can also write the division problem as a *fraction*:

$$\frac{30}{5}$$

However, the most common way of indicating a division problem is to use the **division box**:

$$5\overline{)30}$$

Let us solve a division problem by means of the division box.

EXAMPLE 1. Divide: $2\overline{)256}$

Solution: This problem asks, "How many 2's are there in 256?" Calculators can give us the answer in a fraction of a second, but the human mind cannot work so fast. In order to break down the dividend, 256, into a smaller number, you must perform a series of *separate division problems*. To get started, it is useful to draw a vertical line according to the following rule:

Rule: In the dividend, moving from left to right, move as many digits as is necessary to make a *new dividend* that is as large as, or larger than, the divisor. Then draw a vertical line.

In our example, draw a vertical line after the 2, the first digit in the dividend, because it is as large as the divisor. The division problem now looks like this:

$$2\overline{)2|56}$$

Consider the digit to the left of the line to be a *new dividend*. Instead of asking, "How many 2's

41

are there in 256?" you ask, "How many 2's are there in 2?" The answer is 1, so you place the 1 *directly above the digit you are using*, the 2.

$$\begin{array}{r} 1 \\ 2\overline{\smash{\big)}2\,5\,6} \end{array}$$

new dividend ———

The next step is to multiply this answer, 1, by the divisor, 2. The product is 2, and you place it under the 2 of the dividend.

$$\begin{array}{r} 1 \\ 2\overline{\smash{\big)}2\,5\,6} \\ 2 \end{array}$$

Next, subtract the bottom number from the top number, which results in 0. (It is not necessary to write the 0.) The next step is to bring down the next digit of the dividend, the 5, in a straight line. We call the 5 a *new dividend*, because you will now divide the 2 into the 5.

$$\begin{array}{r} 1 \\ 2\overline{\smash{\big)}2\,5\,6} \\ 2 \\ \hline 5 \end{array}$$

5 ←——— new dividend

Now you have a new problem: "How many times does 2 go into 5?" The answer is 2. You place the 2 *directly above the 5 in the division box.*

$$\begin{array}{r} 1\,2 \\ 2\overline{\smash{\big)}2\,5\,6} \\ 2 \\ \hline 5 \end{array}$$

Next, you multiply this answer, 2, by the divisor, which is also 2. The product is 4, and you place it under the 5. Subtract the 4 from the 5, and the result is 1.

$$\begin{array}{r} 1\,2 \\ 2\overline{\smash{\big)}2\,5\,6} \\ 2 \\ \hline 5 \\ 4 \\ \hline 1 \end{array}$$

The next step is to bring down the next digit, the 6, and place it next to the 1. This forms a *new dividend* of 16.

You again have a new problem: "How many times does 2 go into 16?" The answer is 8, and you place the 8 *directly above the 6 in the division box.*

$$\begin{array}{r} 1\,2\,8 \\ 2\overline{\smash{\big)}2\,5\,6} \\ 2 \\ \hline 5 \\ 4 \\ \hline 1\,6 \\ 1\,6 \\ \hline \end{array}$$

Multiply the 8 by the divisor, 2, giving you 16. Write the 16 under the new dividend, the 16, and subtract. This time there is no remainder.

Answer: $2\overline{\smash{\big)}256} = 128$

We say that, "There are 128 2's in 256." In other words, when 2 is divided into 256, the quotient is 128. According to our calculations, the number 256 contains 128 2's. We can check this by multiplying the answer of our problem (the quotient) by the divisor. This product should equal the dividend:

$$\begin{array}{r} 1\,2\,8 \\ \times\ \ 2 \\ \hline 2\,5\,6\ \checkmark \end{array}$$

Remember: Quotient × Divisor = Dividend

When the divisor contains two or more digits, we solve division problems by following the same steps as when the divisor contains one digit:

EXAMPLE 2.   **EXAMPLE 3.**

$$\begin{array}{r} 1\,6 \\ 16\overline{\smash{\big)}2\,5\,6} \\ 1\,6 \\ \hline 9\,6 \\ 9\,6 \\ \hline \end{array} \qquad \begin{array}{r} 2\,1 \\ 137\overline{\smash{\big)}2{,}8\,7\,7} \\ 2\ 7\,4 \\ \hline 1\,3\,7 \\ 1\,3\,7 \\ \hline \end{array}$$

When drawing the vertical line to form the first new dividend, we often move as many places in the dividend as there are digits in the divisor. In Example 3, for instance, the divisor has three digits and the new dividend also has three digits. However, there are times when we will have to move one place more in the dividend in order to make the new dividend larger than the divisor.

EXAMPLE 4. Divide: $17\overline{)1,496}$

Solution: We draw the vertical line after the *third* digit in the dividend in order to make the new dividend larger than the divisor.

$$17\overline{)1,49}6$$

Now, we complete the division as before.

$$
\begin{array}{r}
8\,8 \\
17\overline{)1,49}6 \\
1\ 36 \\
\hline
136 \\
136
\end{array}
$$

Answer: $17\overline{)1,496} = 88$

EXERCISES

In 1 to 30, divide.

1. $2\overline{)682}$ 2. $3\overline{)693}$ 3. $7\overline{)504}$ 4. $4\overline{)1,284}$

5. $5\overline{)3,155}$ 6. $7\overline{)5,243}$ 7. $6\overline{)4,584}$ 8. $5\overline{)7,490}$

9. $6\overline{)84,726}$ 10. $8\overline{)60,968}$ 11. $8\overline{)72,976}$ 12. $7\overline{)96,544}$

13. $15\overline{)45}$ 14. $16\overline{)80}$ 15. $24\overline{)96}$ 16. $27\overline{)567}$

17. $26\overline{)8,164}$ 18. $37\overline{)4,551}$ 19. $48\overline{)74,976}$ 20. $213\overline{)639}$

21. $128\overline{)640}$ 22. $640\overline{)4,480}$ 23. $173\overline{)2,422}$ 24. $321\overline{)7,383}$

25. $213\overline{)7,455}$ 26. $478\overline{)21,988}$ 27. $706\overline{)37,418}$

28. $2,324\overline{)27,888}$ 29. $3,542\overline{)85,008}$ 30. $4,306\overline{)150,710}$

APPLICATION PROBLEMS

Sample solution

If a supermarket sells 7,524 eggs in a week, how many dozens of eggs have been sold?

$$\begin{array}{r} 6\,27 \\ 12\overline{)7,5\,24} \\ 72 \\ \hline 32 \\ 24 \\ \hline 84 \\ 84 \\ \hline \end{array}$$

627

1. Mrs. Smith bought a refrigerator for $636. She paid for it with 12 equal monthly installments. How much was each payment?

2. A salesman traveled 525 miles, using 35 gallons of gasoline. How many miles did he travel on one gallon of gasoline? (Assume that each gallon gave the same mileage.)

3. A retail store bought 72 lamps for $1,296. What is the cost of each lamp?

4. How much is one yard of carpeting if 45 yards cost $405?

_____

5. If a box holds 24 cans of juice, how many boxes are needed to pack 552 cans?

_____

Unit 14. Division With a Remainder

Words to know

We know that the answer to a subtraction problem is called the **remainder**. In the preceding unit, when you performed the final subtraction in each division problem, the remainder was 0. When you perform division and the final remainder is *not* 0, we call this **division with a remainder**.

When a division problem does not "come out even," we say the problem has a **remainder**. When you are asked, "What is half of 5?" you reply, "Half of 5 is $2\frac{1}{2}$." What you have done is to divide 2 into 5 and then express the remainder as a fraction.

$$\begin{array}{r} 2 \\ 2\overline{)5} \\ 4 \\ \hline 1 \end{array} \longleftarrow \text{remainder}$$

To express the remainder as a fraction, draw a line under the remainder and write the divisor under the line:

$$\begin{array}{r} 2 \\ 2\overline{)5} \\ 4 \\ \hline \frac{1}{2} \end{array}$$

Then bring the fraction, $\frac{1}{2}$, up to the answer:

$$\begin{array}{r} 2\frac{1}{2} \\ 2\overline{)5} \\ 4 \\ \hline \frac{1}{2} \end{array}$$

Thus, $5 \div 2 = 2\frac{1}{2}$.

Now, let us do a more difficult division: $5\overline{)1,183}$
Divide as you have learned to do:

$$\begin{array}{r} 236 \\ 5\overline{)1,183} \\ 10 \\ \hline 18 \\ 15 \\ \hline 33 \\ 30 \\ \hline 3 \end{array}$$

remainder $\longrightarrow 3$

However, there is a remainder of 3.

To express the remainder as a fraction, draw a line under the remainder and write the divisor under the line:

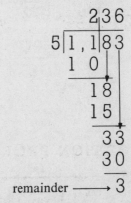

$$\begin{array}{r} 236 \\ 5\overline{)1,183} \\ 10 \\ \hline 18 \\ 15 \\ \hline 33 \\ 30 \\ \hline \frac{3}{5} \end{array}$$

Finally, you bring the $\frac{3}{5}$ up to your answer, making the fraction a part of the quotient:

Thus, $5\overline{)1,183} = 236\frac{3}{5}$.

Following are two more examples of division with a remainder.

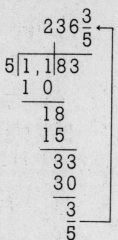

$$236\frac{3}{5}$$
$$5\overline{)1,183}$$
$$\underline{1\ 0}$$
$$18$$
$$\underline{15}$$
$$33$$
$$\underline{30}$$
$$\frac{3}{5}$$

EXAMPLE 1.

$$36\frac{13}{24}$$
$$24\overline{)877}$$
$$\underline{72}$$
$$157$$
$$\underline{144}$$
$$13$$
$$\longrightarrow \overline{24}$$

EXAMPLE 2.

$$12\frac{1}{210}$$
$$210\overline{)2,521}$$
$$\underline{2\ 10}$$
$$421$$
$$\underline{420}$$
$$1$$
$$\longrightarrow \overline{210}$$

EXERCISES

In 1 to 32, divide. Express each remainder as a fraction.

1. $4\overline{)929}$ 2. $6\overline{)829}$ 3. $5\overline{)748}$ 4. $3\overline{)275}$ 5. $5\overline{)317}$

6. $4\overline{)945}$ 7. $6\overline{)967}$ 8. $8\overline{)971}$ 9. $7\overline{)799}$ 10. $6\overline{)851}$

11. $3\overline{)821}$ 12. $4\overline{)939}$ 13. $5\overline{)747}$ 14. $7\overline{)886}$ 15. $6\overline{)923}$

16. $9\overline{)733}$ 17. $6\overline{)247}$ 18. $8\overline{)257}$ 19. $14\overline{)327}$ 20. $23\overline{)590}$

21. $18\overline{)659}$ 22. $34\overline{)865}$ 23. $28\overline{)3,481}$

24. $16\overline{)3,941}$ 25. $46\overline{)9,915}$ 26. $38\overline{)8,517}$

27. $234\overline{)74,931}$ 28. $423\overline{)91,483}$ 29. $186\overline{)79,125}$

30. $416\overline{)142,597}$ 31. $358\overline{)223,619}$ 32. $197\overline{)126,761}$

APPLICATION PROBLEMS

In 1 to 3, show each remainder as a fraction.

1. A truck carries a load of 35 cases. If the load weighs 11,385 pounds, how much does each case weigh?

2. James averages 18 miles per gallon of gasoline. How many gallons of gasoline will he need to travel 1,139 miles?

3. An oil well produces 6,751 barrels of oil in a year. How many barrels are produced in a month? (Assume that the production is the same each month.)

   In everyday life, it is not always convenient to express a remainder as a fraction. In problems 4 and 5, your answers will be whole numbers.

Sample solution

There are 4 quarts in a gallon. How many 1-gallon containers will you need to hold 182 quarts of kerosine? (*Hint:* You will need one 1-gallon container to hold a fraction of a gallon.)

$$4)\overline{18\,2} = 45\tfrac{2}{4}$$

need 1 container to hold $\tfrac{2}{4}$ gal.

$45 + 1 = 46$

46

4. A poultry farmer produces 3,833 eggs. How many boxes that hold a dozen eggs will he need to box all the eggs? (*Hint:* The farmer will need 1 box to hold a fraction of a dozen eggs.)

5. A school has an average class size of 35 students. How many classrooms does the school need if the total number of students is 2,634? (*Hint:* The school will need 1 classroom for a group of students, even if the group is smaller than 35.)

Unit 15. Division With 0's in the Quotient: I

Words to know

We sometimes think of 0 as meaning "nothing" or as having no value. But when 0 is a digit in a number, we must be careful not to overlook it.

Consider the number 202. Although the 0 has no value in itself, its presence affects the value of the number: 202 = 2 hundreds + 0 tens + 2 ones. Suppose we accidentally leave out the 0. The number 202 becomes 22, and has a value of only 2 tens + 2 ones. The 0 makes quite a difference.

Because the digit 0 affects the value of a number by "holding the other digits in place," 0 is called a **place holder**.

A very common mistake in division problems is to forget to place a 0 in the answer when you should do so. Consider the problem $14\overline{)2,912}$.

Divide as you have learned:

$$\begin{array}{r} 2 \\ 14\overline{)2,912} \\ 2\ 8 \\ \hline \end{array}$$

new dividend ⟶ 11

Note that the new dividend, 11, is *smaller* than the divisor.

Since 14 cannot go into 11, *place a 0 in the quotient as a place holder*, *directly above the 1 you just brought down*:

$$\begin{array}{r} 20 \\ 14\overline{)2,912} \\ 2\ 8 \\ \hline 11 \end{array}$$

Now, to form a new dividend, bring down the next digit, 2, and place it next to the 11:

$$\begin{array}{r} 20 \\ 14\overline{)2,912} \\ 2\ 8 \\ \hline 112 \end{array}$$

Since the new dividend, 112, is now larger than the divisor, 14, you can complete the division:

$$\begin{array}{r} 208 \\ 14\overline{)2,912} \\ 2\ 8 \\ \hline 112 \\ 112 \end{array}$$

Part of the way through this problem, you realized that the divisor, 14, was too large to go into the new dividend, 11. You could have said, "14 goes into 11 zero times." Thinking like this will remind you to place a 0 in the quotient whenever the divisor is too large for the new dividend.

Remember: When dividing, do not leave a blank space above any digit you bring down. You *must* place a 0 in that space.

EXERCISES

In 1 to 20, divide.

1. $16\overline{)6,528}$ 2. $23\overline{)7,015}$ 3. $34\overline{)7,004}$ 4. $42\overline{)8,736}$

5. $23\overline{)9,407}$ 6. $19\overline{)5,757}$ 7. $36\overline{)7,524}$ 8. $21\overline{)8,526}$

9. $28\overline{)8,512}$ 10. $26\overline{)8,034}$ 11. $31\overline{)9,517}$ 12. $27\overline{)8,316}$

13. $36\overline{)14,616}$ 14. $53\overline{)26,924}$ 15. $64\overline{)32,320}$

16. $215\overline{)86,645}$ 17. $223\overline{)89,869}$ 18. $321\overline{)129,042}$

19. $267\overline{)1,604,136}$ 20. $254\overline{)1,018,032}$

APPLICATION PROBLEMS

Sample solution

If you are offered a job paying $5,460 a year, how much is your weekly salary? (You will be paid for 52 weeks a year.)

$$
\begin{array}{r}
105 \\
52\overline{)5,460} \\
\underline{52} \\
260 \\
\underline{260}
\end{array}
$$

$105

1. A machine, working at a constant rate, produces 2,592 articles in 24 hours. How many articles are produced in one hour?

2. A bookstore sold 3,708 dictionaries in a year. How many dictionaries did the store sell in one month? (Assume that the sales were the same each month.)

3. Cantaloupes are packed 15 to a box. How many boxes are needed to pack 4,635 cantaloupes?

4. A chandelier holds 16 bulbs. How many chandeliers can be outfitted with 4,912 bulbs?

5. How many feet are there in 2,508 inches?

Unit 16. Division With 0's in the Quotient: II

Here is another situation that requires you to place a 0 in the quotient: 15 | 4,530.

Divide as you have learned:

$$
\begin{array}{r}
3 \\
15\overline{)4{,}530} \\
4\,5 \\
\end{array}
$$

new dividend ⟶ 3

This time, when you subtract 45 from 45, there is no remainder. And, when you bring down the 3 to form the new dividend, you see that 15 will not go into 3.

You say, "15 goes into 3 zero times," and *place a 0 in the quotient as a place holder*, directly above the 3 you just brought down:

$$
\begin{array}{r}
30 \\
15\overline{)4{,}530} \\
4\,5 \\
3 \\
\end{array}
$$

To form a new dividend, bring down the next digit, 0, and place it next to the 3:

$$
\begin{array}{r}
302 \\
15\overline{)4{,}530} \\
4\,5 \\
30 \\
\end{array}
$$

Since the new dividend, 30, is now larger than 15, you can complete the division:

$$
\begin{array}{r}
302 \\
15\overline{)4{,}530} \\
4\,5 \\
30 \\
30 \\
\end{array}
$$

Do you see the similarity between this example and the one given in Unit 15?

Example from Unit 15

$$
\begin{array}{r}
208 \\
14\overline{)2{,}912} \\
2\,8 \\
112 \\
112 \\
\end{array}
$$

first new dividend ⟶ (11)2

Example from Unit 16

$$
\begin{array}{r}
302 \\
15\overline{)4{,}530} \\
4\,5 \\
30 \\
30 \\
\end{array}
$$

first new dividend ⟶ (3)0

In the example from Unit 15, the first new dividend had two digits; in the example from Unit 16, the first new dividend had only *one* digit, the digit that was brought down from the dividend. But, in both cases, the first new dividend was smaller than the divisor.

EXERCISES

In 1 to 21, divide.

1. $18\overline{)3{,}672}$ 2. $15\overline{)1{,}545}$ 3. $23\overline{)4{,}669}$ 4. $19\overline{)9{,}557}$

5. $27\overline{)10{,}854}$ 6. $24\overline{)14{,}472}$ 7. $32\overline{)12{,}896}$ 8. $35\overline{)10{,}570}$

9. $22\overline{)15,466}$ 10. $38\overline{)11,476}$ 11. $42\overline{)25,242}$ 12. $46\overline{)13,892}$

13. $49\overline{)245,147}$ 14. $37\overline{)222,148}$ 15. $52\overline{)208,312}$

16. $56\overline{)224,168}$ 17. $48\overline{)288,384}$ 18. $47\overline{)235,282}$

19. $132\overline{)396,660}$ 20. $235\overline{)1,410,705}$ 21. $345\overline{)17,251,035}$

APPLICATION PROBLEMS

Sample solution

How many 15-man squads can be formed from 1,620 men?

$$\begin{array}{r} 108 \\ 15\overline{)1,620} \\ \underline{15} \\ 120 \\ \underline{120} \end{array}$$

108

1. A jet airliner, flying at a constant speed, traveled 7,865 miles in 13 hours. How many miles did it travel in 1 hour?

2. Socks are packed 12 to a box. How many boxes are needed to pack 8,448 socks?

3. Five schools have a total of 4,535 students. If each school has the same number of students, how many students does each school have?

4. Last year, John's salary was $10,452. How much did he earn per week?

5. Four members of a family won a prize of $1,220. If they share the prize equally, how much will each member get?

Unit 17. Division With 0's in the Quotient: III

Sometimes a 0 in the dividend will require you to place a 0 in the quotient. For example, divide: 4$\overline{)1,208}$.

Divide as you have learned:

$$\begin{array}{r} 3 \\ 4\overline{)1,208} \\ \underline{1\ 2} \end{array}$$

Since the next digit to be brought down is a 0, *you don't even bother bringing it down. Place a 0 in the quotient as a place holder directly above the 0 in the dividend.*

$$\begin{array}{r} 30 \\ 4\overline{)1,208} \\ \underline{1\ 2} \end{array}$$

To form a new dividend, bring down the next digit, 8. Then, complete the division.

$$\begin{array}{r} 302 \\ 4\overline{)1,208} \\ \underline{1\ 2} \end{array}$$

new dividend ⟶ 8

8

EXAMPLE. Divide: 3,200 ÷ 8

Solution:

$$\begin{array}{r} 400 \\ 8\overline{)3,200} \\ \underline{3\ 2} \end{array}$$

Answer: 400

EXERCISES

In 1 to 18, divide.

1. 13$\overline{)6,500}$

2. 18$\overline{)72,054}$

3. 23$\overline{)1,610}$

4. 27$\overline{)162,081}$

5. 24$\overline{)12,000}$

6. 19$\overline{)152,076}$

7. 32$\overline{)1,280,192}$

8. 25$\overline{)1,750,100}$

9. 36$\overline{)1,440,108}$

10. 38$\overline{)1,900,114}$

11. 41$\overline{)2,460,205}$

12. 47$\overline{)1,410,282}$

13. 53⟌3,180,106

14. 44⟌1,760,220

15. 63⟌1,260,252

16. 215⟌86,001,075

17. 325⟌19,500,975

18. 340⟌136,001,700

APPLICATION PROBLEMS

Sample solution

Bolts are packed 25 to a box. How many boxes can be packed from 50,075 bolts?

```
        2,003
  25⟌50,075
     50
        75
        75
```

2,003

1. If 10,040 pounds of coal were delivered in 5 equal shipments, how much coal was delivered in each shipment?

2. William bought a new car for $2,880, to be paid for in 36 equal installments. How much will each payment be?

3. John earns $12,036 a year, on a steady salary. How much does he earn in a month?

4. The price of admission to a concert was $5. If $40,000 worth of tickets were sold, how many tickets were sold?

5. Melons are packed 12 to a box. How many boxes will be needed to pack 72,012 melons?

Unit 18. Division With 0's in the Quotient: IV

In Unit 14, you learned how to express the *remainder* of a division problem as a *fraction*. Sometimes the changing of a remainder to a fraction will require you to place a 0 in the quotient before making a fraction of the remainder.

EXAMPLE. Divide: 8 ⟌2,485

Solution: Divide as you have learned. The divisor, 8 cannot go into the new dividend, 5. Also, *there are no more digits to bring down*. Therefore, you say, "8 goes into 5 zero times."

```
      3 1
   8)2,485
     2 4
     ───
        8
        8
       ──
```
new dividend ⟶ 5

You place a 0 in the quotient as a place holder, *directly above the 5 you just brought down*. Keep in mind that the new dividend, 5, does not become a remainder *until you place a 0 in the quotient.*

```
     3 1 0
   8)2,485
     2 4
     ───
        8
        8
       ──
        5
```

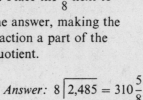

Complete the division by changing the remainder to a fraction, $\frac{5}{8}$. Place the $\frac{5}{8}$ next to the answer, making the fraction a part of the quotient.

```
          5
      3 1 0─
           8
   8)2,485
     2 4
     ───
        8
        8
       ──
        5
        ─
        8
```

Answer: 8 ⟌2,485 = $310\frac{5}{8}$

Remember: In division, do not leave a blank space above any digit you bring down. You *must* place a 0 in that space.

EXERCISES

In 1 to 23, divide.

1. 16⟌4,967   **2.** 19⟌8,178   **3.** 14⟌8,823   **4.** 21⟌6,728

5. 15⟌8,107   **6.** 26⟌8,327   **7.** 17⟌9,016   **8.** 23⟌9,895

9. 13⟌8,329   **10.** 16⟌8,485   **11.** 24⟌15,128   **12.** 48⟌19,694

13. $46\overline{)19,327}$ **14.** $28\overline{)20,168}$ **15.** $53\overline{)426,128}$

16. $48\overline{)337,449}$ **17.** $35\overline{)211,756}$ **18.** $37\overline{)260,118}$

19. $45\overline{)271,358}$ **20.** $56\overline{)281,687}$ **21.** $223\overline{)1,121,693}$

22. $315\overline{)22,062,607}$ **23.** $425\overline{)25,517,008}$

APPLICATION PROBLEMS

Sample solution _____

If Bob has 123 ounces of meat to divide equally among 6 German
shepherd dogs, how many ounces does each dog get?

$$6\overline{)123} = 20\tfrac{3}{6}$$
$$\underline{12}$$
$$\tfrac{3}{6}$$

$20\tfrac{3}{6}$

_____

1. John's car averages 18 miles to a gallon of gasoline. How many
gallons did his car use to travel 1,085 miles?

2. A bus traveled 1,153 miles in 5 days. On the average, how many
miles did the bus travel in one day?

3. A hardware store sold 1,442 pounds of plaster last year. On the average, how many pounds did the store sell each month? _____

4. Five water tanks of equal capacity hold 12,554 gallons of water. How many gallons does one tank hold? _____

5. A dealer received a shipment of cloth that cost $8,123. How many yards of cloth were received if the cost was $4 per yard? _____

Unit 19. Division of Numbers That Contain End Zeros

Words to know

When the last digits of a number are zeros, we call these digits **end zeros**.

When you divide one number that has **end zeros** by another number that has end zeros, you can simplify the division by getting rid of the end zeros.

To simplify a division problem involving end zeros, follow this rule:

Rule. Cross out the end zeros, one for one, both in the divisor and in the dividend.

Suppose you must divide: 600 ⟌ 2,400.
To simplify the division, get rid of the two zeros in the divisor and the two zeros in the dividend.

$$6\cancel{0}\cancel{0} \, \overline{)2,4\cancel{0}\cancel{0}}$$

Complete the division, ignoring all the zeros you crossed out.

$$\begin{array}{r} 4 \\ 6\cancel{0}\cancel{0} \, \overline{)2,4\cancel{0}\cancel{0}} \\ 2\ 4 \end{array}$$

What you have done by getting rid of the end zeros is to divide both the divisor and the dividend by 100.

$$\begin{array}{r} 6 \\ 100\overline{)600} \\ 600 \end{array} \qquad \begin{array}{r} 24 \\ 100\overline{)2,400} \\ 2\ 00 \\ \overline{400} \\ 400 \end{array}$$

Since $600 \div 100 = 6$ and $2400 \div 100 = 24$, then $2400 \div 600$ is the same as $24 \div 6$.

$$\begin{array}{r} 4 \\ 600\overline{)2,400} \\ 2\ 400 \end{array}$$

$$\begin{array}{r} 4 \\ 6\overline{)24} \\ 24 \end{array}$$

Remember: You must cross out an equal number of end zeros in both the divisor and the dividend.

EXAMPLE. Divide: 50 ⟌ 2,500

Solution: You get rid of one 0 in the divisor and one 0 in the dividend.

$$5\cancel{0} \, \overline{)2,50\cancel{0}}$$

Complete the division, ignoring the zeros you got rid of.

$$\begin{array}{r} 50 \\ 5\cancel{0} \, \overline{)2,50\cancel{0}} \\ 2\ 5 \end{array}$$

Answer: 50

EXERCISES

In 1 to 12, divide.

1. 30$\overline{)650}$

2. 50$\overline{)230}$

3. 80$\overline{)4,760}$

4. 200$\overline{)2,450}$

5. 300$\overline{)5,400}$

6. 240$\overline{)3,600}$

7. 300$\overline{)156,000}$

8. 370$\overline{)5,690}$

9. 5,700$\overline{)67,000}$

10. 900$\overline{)87,000}$

11. 240$\overline{)37,650}$

12. 470$\overline{)63,390}$

APPLICATION PROBLEMS

Sample solution

The distance from the earth to the moon is sometimes expressed in terms of the radius of the earth. If the earth's radius is 4,000 miles and the distance from the earth to the moon is 240,000 miles, how many "earth-radii" will be needed to express the distance from the earth to the moon?

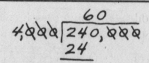

60

1. Tom's car averages 20 miles to a gallon of gasoline. How many gallons will Tom need to travel 780 miles?

2. A machine can produce 300 articles in one day. How many days will it take to produce 16,500 articles?

3. A jet airliner averages 600 miles per hour. How many hours will it take to travel 7,000 miles? _____

4. On a certain flight, astronauts averaged 2,000 miles per hour traveling to and from the moon. At this speed, how many hours will it take them to travel 656,000 miles? _____

5. A ton weighs 2,000 pounds. How many tons are there in 127,000 pounds? _____

Unit 20. Finding Averages

Words to know

The word **average** is used in everyday language to mean "in between." An "average student" in a certain school is somewhere between the best student and the worst student. The "average income" of an office worker is neither the highest income nor the lowest income of a group of office workers.

The word **average** also has a special mathematical meaning. Suppose you say, "My math tests average 85%." You mean that you added together all of your math test grades, divided this sum by the number of grades, and got a result of 85%.

To find the average of a group of numbers:

Step 1: Add all the numbers in the group.

Step 2: Divide the sum obtained in step 1 by the number of items in the group.

EXAMPLE. Find the average of the following group of test marks:

75% 90% 80% 65% 70%

Step 1: Add all the numbers in the group. (For convenience, add horizontally.)

$$75 + 90 + 80 + 65 + 70 = 380$$

Step 2: Since there are 5 marks in the group, divide the sum, 380, by 5.

$$
\begin{array}{r}
76 \\
5\overline{)380} \\
35 \\
\hline
30 \\
30 \\
\hline
\end{array}
$$

Answer: The average of all the test marks is 76%.

EXERCISES

In 1 to 6, find the average of each group of numbers.

1. 35 46 27 40

2. 87 93 76 80 74

3. 158   210   163   185   **4.** 84   75   60   90   80

5. 330   365   390   380   **6.** 12   28   15   14   19   17   19

APPLICATION PROBLEMS

Sample solution

In a football game, halfback Terry Reid made the following gains: 5 yards, 1 yard, 8 yards, 2 yards, 5 yards, 21 yards. What was his average gain per carry?

$$5+1+8+2+5+21=42$$

$$6\overline{)42}$$
$$\underline{42}$$

7 yd.

1. A salesman traveled the following number of miles: Monday, 87; Tuesday, 115; Wednesday, 95; Thursday, 130; Friday, 110. What is the average number of miles he traveled on any one day?

2. During the 21 school days last March, the total attendance in a school was 23,688. What was the average daily attendance?

3. In preparing for her vacation, Mary bought five dresses at the following prices: $23, $19, $32, $26, $15. What was the average price of each dress?

4. John's car traveled 810 miles on 45 gallons of gasoline. How many miles did his car average per gallon?

5. The weights in pounds of the seven linemen of the Centerville Chiefs football team are as follows: 198, 179, 210, 220, 189, 205, 213. What is the average weight of a Centerville lineman?

6. The six art classes in a school have the following numbers of students: 32, 26, 34, 22, 33, and 27. What is the average class size?

7. An airliner traveled 9,750 miles in 15 hours. What is the average number of miles traveled in one hour?

8. A salesman earned the following commissions in the last four weeks: $168 $194 $216 $186
What is his average weekly commission?

9. Last June, the Jones family was billed for 270 telephone calls. Find the average number of calls made each day. (June has 30 days.)

10. Jane typed 225 words in 5 minutes. What is the average number of words typed per minute?

Review of Part V (Units 13 to 20)

In 1 to 15, divide. Show any remainder as a fraction.

1. $24\overline{)5,160}$

2. $27\overline{)9,748}$

3. $48\overline{)16,416}$

4. $34\overline{)7,867}$

5. $63\overline{)12,373}$

6. $52\overline{)22,427}$

7. $40\overline{)13,600}$

8. $260\overline{)53,580}$

9. $65\overline{)26,076}$

10. $35\overline{)17,558}$

11. $64\overline{)192,074}$

12. $23\overline{)115,035}$

13. $28\overline{)11,485}$

14. $510\overline{)260,140}$

15. $750\overline{)157,500}$

In 16 to 19, find the average of each group. When necessary, round off to the nearest whole number.

16. Test grades: 85%　　90%　　70%　　80%

17. Ages: 18　　15　　19　　16　　17　　18

18. Weights: 165 lb.　　180 lb.　　195 lb.　　170 lb.　　150 lb.

19. Temperatures: 87°　　93°　　89°　　82°　　80°

Part VI. Word Problems/Fractions

Unit 21. Solving Word Problems

Words to know

In everyday life, it is often necessary to figure out problems such as the total cost of a purchase or how long it will take to make a trip. In such situations, you are not told whether to *add*, *subtract*, *multiply*, or *divide*. Rather, you must decide what arithmetic process to use. A problem in which you must decide *how* to solve it is called a **word problem.**

In order to solve a **word problem,** you must find the facts of the problem, understand what the problem is asking you to find, and then decide on the arithmetic process you will use in solving the problem.

To solve a word problem step by step, ask yourself the following questions:

Question 1: Do you understand what the problem is telling you? It may be necessary to read the problem several times in order to understand it.

Question 2: What are the facts given in the problem? Write down the known facts in the problem. This will help you to understand how they are related.

Question 3: What is the problem asking you to find? Have a clear understanding of what you must find.

Question 4: What arithmetic process will you have to use to solve the problem? Study the given information and decide whether you should *add*, *subtract*, *multiply*, or *divide* to solve the problem. Then perform the calculation.

Question 5: Is your solution correct? Does it seem reasonable? Check your answer, the unknown fact, against the known facts in the problem.

Most students find Question 4 to be the most difficult to answer. To help you decide which arithmetic process to use, keep in mind that every problem has *key words* that will tell you whether to add, subtract, multiply, or divide.

Use *addition* if the problem uses phrases like these:
1. Find the *sum* . . . .
2. What is the *total* . . . .
3. Determine the cost of *all* . . . .

Use *subtraction* if the problem uses phrases like these:
1. What is the *difference* . . . .
2. How much *more* . . . .
3. How much *less* . . . .

Use *multiplication* if the problem uses phrases like these:
1. Find the cost of *ten items* if the cost of *one item* is . . . .
2. If *each item* costs . . . , how much will *all* of them cost?
3. If the *monthly* cost is . . . , find the *annual* cost . . . .

Use *division* if the problem uses phrases like these:
1. How much is *each* . . . .
2. Find the cost *per* . . . .
3. Find the cost of *one* . . . .

No matter how difficult a problem may seem, there are only *four* arithmetic processes to choose from.

EXAMPLE 1. John worked 40 hours last week and his rate of pay was $4 per hour. Find his wages for the entire week.

Solution: Solve this word problem step by step by answering the preceding five questions:

1. The problem tells you John's hourly rate of pay and the number of hours he has worked.

2. The given facts are: (1) John worked 40 hours and (2) his rate of pay is $4 per hour.

3. The unknown fact is John's total wages for last week.

4. You must use *multiplication* since the number of hours worked multiplied by the rate per hour will equal the total wages for the week. Multiplying:

$$\begin{array}{r} 40 \\ \$4 \\ \hline \$160 \end{array}\quad\begin{array}{l}\text{hours worked}\\\text{rate per hour}\\\text{total wages}\end{array}$$

John's total wages last week were $160.

5. Check your answer by dividing the total wages for the week by 40 hours. You get an hourly rate of $4, which is the same as the given fact.

$$\begin{array}{r} 4 \\ 4\not{0}\,\overline{)16\not{0}} \\ 16 \\ \hline \end{array}$$

In each of the following examples, tell how you would solve the problem by using addition, subtraction, multiplication, or division. Then answer the question.

EXAMPLE 2. Sally bought a loaf of bread for 39¢, a jar of peanut butter for 79¢, and a jar of jelly for 45¢. How much did she spend?

Solution: Add the three costs:

$$.39 + .79 + .45 = 1.63$$

Answer: $1.63

EXAMPLE 3. Sally paid for her purchases in Example 1 with a $5 bill. How much change did she receive?

Solution: Subtract the total cost of $1.63 from $5.00:

$$\begin{array}{r} 5.00 \\ -1.63 \\ \hline 3.37 \end{array}$$

Answer: $3.37

EXAMPLE 4. Aaron earns $100 a week. How much does he earn in a year?

Solution: Since there are 52 weeks in a year, multiply 52 by $100:

$$52 \times 100 = 52.00 = 5200$$

Answer: $5,200

EXAMPLE 5. A dozen pencils cost 96¢. How much does one pencil cost?

Solution: Divide the cost of 96¢ by 12:

$$\begin{array}{r} 8 \\ 12\,\overline{)96} \\ 96 \\ \hline \end{array}$$

Answer: 8¢

EXERCISES

In 1 to 10, complete each sentence, telling whether you must use *addition*, *subtraction*, *multiplication*, or *division* to solve the problem. **Do not actually compute the answer.**

Sample solution

A radio originally priced at $11 was marked down to $7. To find the amount saved, *subtract the marked-down price from the original price*.

1. To find the price of one shirt if 3 shirts cost $21, _____

2. A television set sells for $232 and the sales tax is $13. To find the total cost, _____

3. To find the cost of 8 pairs of socks at a price of 85¢ per pair, _____

4. A coat selling for $85 was reduced to $65. To find the amount of the reduction, _____ _____.

5. To find the amount of savings on a dress that was reduced from $37 to $24, _____ _____.

6. To find the cost of 4 tires if one tire costs $21, _____ _____.

7. Tom earns $10,650 a year and his brother earns $8,750 a year. To find how much more Tom earns than his brother, _____ _____.

8. To find the monthly rent of a family that pays $1,620 in rent each year, _____ _____.

9. To find the number of inches in 52 feet, _____ _____.

10. To find the number of yards in 72 feet, _____ _____.

In 11 to 15, you must use *two steps* to solve each problem. Complete each sentence, telling which two mathematical steps you must use. **Do not actually compute the answer.**

Sample solution _____

For a party, Bess bought 48 bottles of soda at 25¢ each. She paid $8 down and promised to pay the rest next week. How much does she owe? *Multiply the number of bottles by the cost per bottle, 48 × $.25. Then subtract $8.00 from this product.*

11. Harry bought a sports jacket for $40, a hat for $10, and three ties for $2 each. He agreed to pay for the clothing in four equal payments. How much is each payment? _____ _____ _____.

12. The Jensens bought a freezer for $250. They paid $70 down and agreed to pay the balance in 12 equal monthly payments. What is the amount of each monthly payment? _____ _____ _____.

13. Each month, Sam pays $150 in rent, $12 for his telephone, and $8 for gas and electricity. What is the annual cost of his rent, telephone, gas, and electricity? _____ _____ _____.

14. Mr. Lipsky is entitled to half of the profits of a grocery store. Last year, the store took in $55,000 and had operating expenses of $40,000. How much is Mr. Lipsky's share of the profits? _____

_____

_____.

15. Three girls agree to share equally the rent of an apartment. If the total monthly rent is $180, how much will each girl pay in rent over one entire year? _____

_____

_____.

APPLICATION PROBLEMS

In these problems, compute the required answer.

1. Mr. Gold bought a refrigerator for $310 and made a down payment of $130. If the balance will be paid for in 12 equal monthly installments, how much will each payment be?   _____

2. Last year, a salesman earned a salary of $6,567 together with commissions in the amount of $7,829. What is his total salary?   _____

What is his average weekly salary?   _____

3. John drove 585 miles. If he averaged 45 miles an hour, how many hours did he drive?   _____

4. Mrs. Brown bought 45 yards of carpeting at $9 per yard. If she put down a deposit of $175, how much must she pay when the carpeting is delivered? (There is no delivery charge.)   _____

5. A refrigerator selling for $327 was reduced by $81. What will the monthly payments be if the refrigerator is to be paid for in $1\frac{1}{2}$ years?   _____

6. A washing machine selling for $235 was reduced to $180. Find the amount of the reduction.

If the washing machine will be paid for in 12 equal installments, how much will each payment be?   _____

7. A taxi company bought four taxis for $14,000. How much did each taxi cost?   _____

8. Mr. Wilson borrowed $2,500 from his bank. If he paid back $865, how much does he still owe? (Disregard any interest or finance charges.)   _____

9. Mrs. Stanford bought a living room set for $1,265. Her down payment was $350 and she made two payments of $45 each. How much does she still owe for the set?   _____

10. How much will eight typewriters cost priced at $165 each?   _____

Unit 22. Understanding Fractions

Words to know

In everyday language, a *fraction* is a "part of something." We talk of "a fraction of an inch" or of a new track record that beat the old record by "a fraction of a second."

In mathematics, we call the inch or the second a **unit**. Units may be inches, seconds, pounds, cartons of eggs, or anything at all that we can count or measure.

We define a **fraction** as a "part of a unit."

Recall how we express the remainder of a division problem as a fraction:

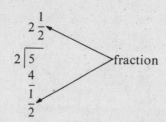

A fraction consists of two separate numbers written with the aid of a **fraction bar**. The top number is called the **numerator**. The bottom number is called the **denominator**.

$$\text{numerator} \longrightarrow \frac{1}{2} \longleftarrow \text{fraction bar}$$
$$\text{denominator} \longrightarrow$$

Thus far, you have worked mostly with whole numbers. In your application problems, you have often used whole *units* such as miles, gallons, and television sets. Many of your answers "came out even." If you found that a dealer bought "$12\frac{1}{2}$ television sets," you realized that something was wrong.

However, parts of units are very common. You can buy $\frac{1}{2}$ of a gallon of milk, jog for $\frac{3}{4}$ of a mile, or pitch for $\frac{2}{3}$ of an inning. Parts of units are called **fractions**.

We write fractions as two numbers separated by a **fraction bar**, like this: $\frac{3}{4}$

The top number, the **numerator**, tells you *how many parts are represented*. In the fraction $\frac{3}{4}$, the numerator tells you that *three* quarters are represented.

The bottom number, the **denominator**, tells you into *how many equal parts* the original unit has been divided. In the fraction $\frac{3}{4}$, the denominator tells you that the unit has been divided into *four* equal parts, or into *fourths*.

If you jog for a distance of $\frac{3}{4}$ mile, the fraction $\frac{3}{4}$

66

tells you that the mile has been divided into *four* equal parts and that you jogged for *three* of these quarter-miles.

Suppose you have a pie and you cut it into two equal parts. You now have a whole pie that is made up of two half-pies. If you take one piece (one half-pie) from the two half-pies, you have one half-pie left:

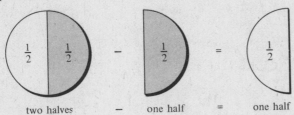

two halves   −   one half   =   one half

In fractions:

$$\frac{2}{2} - \frac{1}{2} = \frac{1}{2}$$

When you add the two half-pies together, you again have a whole pie made of two half-pies:

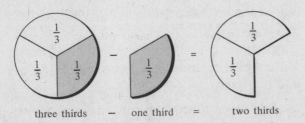

one half   +   one half   =   two halves

In fractions:

$$\frac{1}{2} + \frac{1}{2} = \frac{2}{2}$$

$\left(\text{Note that 2 half-pies equal a whole pie, or } \frac{2}{2} = 1.\right)$

Take another pie and cut it into three equal parts. If you take away one piece $\left(\frac{1}{3} \text{ of the pie}\right)$, you have $\frac{2}{3}$ of the pie left:

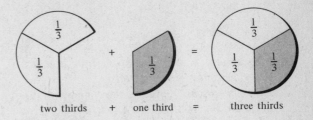

three thirds   −   one third   =   two thirds

In fractions:

$$\frac{3}{3} - \frac{1}{3} = \frac{2}{3}$$

And, when you add the $\frac{1}{3}$ back to the $\frac{2}{3}$, you have $\frac{3}{3}$, or the whole pie:

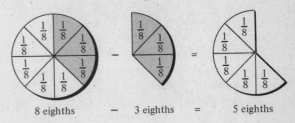

two thirds   +   one third   =   three thirds

In fractions:

$$\frac{2}{3} + \frac{1}{3} = \frac{3}{3}$$

$\left(\text{Note that 3 thirds equal a whole pie, or } \frac{3}{3} = 1.\right)$

Cut another pie into 8 equal parts and take away 3 pieces. When you take $\frac{3}{8}$ from $\frac{8}{8}$, you have $\frac{5}{8}$ left:

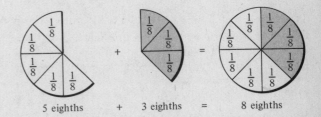

8 eighths   −   3 eighths   =   5 eighths

In fractions:

$$\frac{8}{8} - \frac{3}{8} = \frac{5}{8}$$

Finally, when you add the $\frac{3}{8}$ back to the $\frac{5}{8}$, you get $\frac{8}{8}$, the whole pie:

5 eighths   +   3 eighths   =   8 eighths

In fractions:

$$\frac{3}{8} + \frac{5}{8} = \frac{8}{8}$$

$\left(\text{Note that 8 eighths is equal to a whole pie, or } \frac{8}{8} = 1.\right)$

From the preceding examples, you can see that $\frac{2}{2} = 1$, that $\frac{3}{3} = 1$, and that $\frac{8}{8} = 1$. In general, when any fraction has the same top number and bottom number, that fraction is equal to 1 (a whole unit).

Remember: A fraction tells you two things:

1. The *bottom number* tells you into how many parts the unit has been divided.
2. The *top number* tells you how many of those parts are represented by the fraction.

REPRESENTING DIVISION

When you studied how to divide (Unit 13), you used the symbols ÷ and ⌐ to indicate division. In a fraction, *the fraction bar also represents the division of one number by another number.*

If 3 pounds of steak are to be divided into 4 equal portions, each portion will weigh $\frac{3}{4}$ of a pound. In symbols, $3 \div 4 = \frac{3}{4}$.

In the fraction $\frac{3}{4}$, the top number represents the 3 pounds of steak (the amount to be divided). The bottom number represents the number of portions, 4, into which the steak is to be divided. The fraction bar means "divided by," and the fraction $\frac{3}{4}$ is read, "3 divided by 4" or "three pounds divided into four portions."

Remember: The fraction bar and the division symbol ÷ both mean "divided by."

$$\frac{3}{4} = 3 \div 4$$

COMPARING TWO NUMBERS

A fraction may be used to *compare two numbers by division.*

If, on a test, you score 17 right answers out of 20 problems, you have answered correctly $\frac{17}{20}$ of the test. The fraction $\frac{17}{20}$ compares *the number of questions answered correctly with the total number of questions.*

There are many times when two numbers are compared by division:

"Nine out of ten Sophomores will graduate," may be represented by the fraction $\frac{9}{10}$.

"One student in five is on the honor roll," may be represented by the fraction $\frac{1}{5}$.

"9 hits for 28 times at bat," may be represented by the fraction $\frac{9}{28}$.

Notice that the larger number is always the bottom number. When comparing two numbers by division, it is usual to put the larger number (the "all" or "total" number) in the denominator.

EXERCISES

In 1 to 14, fill in the correct word or phrase that will best complete the statement or answer the question.

1. The top number of a fraction is called the _____.

2. The bottom number of a fraction is called the _____.

3. A fraction represents a _____ unit.

4. The bottom number of a fraction tells you _____ _____.

5. The top number of a fraction tells you _____ _____.

6. If a whole unit is divided into five equal parts, the bottom number of the fraction will be _____.

7. If you took two of the parts in Exercise 6, you would write this fraction as _____.

8. If the top number of a fraction is the same as the bottom number, that fraction is equal to _____ _____ .

9. If you divide a unit into eight equal parts, what will the bottom number of the fraction be? _____ _____

10. If you divide a unit into *sevenths* and take $\frac{3}{7}$ away, how many parts will remain? _____ _____

11. In Exercise 10, if you took $\frac{4}{7}$ more away, how many *sevenths* have you taken all together? _____ _____

12. Write a fraction that represents a whole unit. (A whole unit has a value of 1.) _____

13. In the fraction $\frac{5}{16}$, into how many parts has the unit been divided? _____ How many parts were taken (from the whole unit)? _____ How many parts of the whole unit remain? _____

14. How many *sixteenths* have a value of 1? $\left(\frac{?}{16} = 1\right)$ _____

In 15 to 20, represent the given facts as fractions.

Sample solution

Seven out of ten doctors recommend "Paladin, the wonder drug." _____ $\frac{7}{10}$ _____ .

15. Tarkington completed 19 passes in 29 attempts. _____

16. The National Safety Council predicted that 50,000,000 motorists would be on the road, and that there would be 400 traffic fatalities. _____

17. The Lakers have won only 3 of their last 10 games. _____

18. You have one chance in a million of winning the prize. _____

19. Because of the influenza epidemic, only 20 pupils were present, while 15 pupils were absent. Compare the number of pupils present to the total class. (*Hint:* The total class consists of the sum of the number of pupils present and the number of pupils absent.) _____

20. The betting was "5 to 4" in favor of the Chiefs. Express the Chiefs' winning chances as a fraction. (*Hint:* "5 to 4" means that, out of 9 chances, there are 5 chances of winning and 4 chances of losing. The Chiefs have 5 winning chances out of 9 chances.) _____

APPLICATION PROBLEMS

1. Ten students are absent from a class of 35. Write as a fraction the number of students absent, compared to the total number of students.

_____

Write as a fraction the number of students present, compared to the total number of students.

_____

2. A coat selling for $90 is on a " $\frac{1}{3}$ off" sale. Write as a fraction the sales price of the coat (compared to the original price).

_____

3. A team lost 1 out of 3 games. If the team played 96 games, how many games did the team win? (*Hint:* A team that has lost " 1 out of 3 " games has lost 1 game for every 3 games played. Therefore, they have *won* 2 out of 3 games. Use "2 out of 3" to calculate your answer.)

_____

4. Mr. Wilson earns $150 a week. He spends $45 on food, deposits $35 in his savings account, and deposits the rest of his money in his checking account. Write the above amounts as fractions by comparing each item with Mr. Wilson's weekly salary.

Food: _____

Savings: _____

Checking: _____

5. A bushel basket contains 150 pieces of fruit consisting of apples and pears. If there are 85 apples, what fraction of the bushel is apples?

What fraction of the bushel is pears?

_____

_____

Unit 23. Reducing Fractions to Lowest Terms

Words to know

The numerator and the denominator of a fraction are called the **terms** of the fraction. The fractions $\frac{2}{4}$ and $\frac{1}{2}$ have the same *value*, but they are written with different *terms*.

Expressing $\frac{2}{4}$ of a pound as $\frac{1}{2}$ of a pound is *reducing* the $\frac{2}{4}$ to its *lowest terms* of $\frac{1}{2}$.

In general, when you change fractions to simplest forms, you **reduce fractions to lowest terms**.

When you cut a pizza into 8 equal pieces and eat 4 of them, you have eaten $\frac{4}{8}$ of the pizza. However, you have also eaten $\frac{1}{2}$ of the pizza because $\frac{4}{8} = \frac{1}{2}$. But it is easier to say you ate "half a pizza" than "four eighths of a pizza." When you change $\frac{4}{8}$ to $\frac{1}{2}$, you **reduce the fraction to its lowest terms**. Whenever you simplify a fraction (reduce it), you do not change the value of the fraction.

The following rule will enable you to reduce fractions:

Rule: You can divide the numerator and the denominator of a fraction by the *same number* without changing the value of that fraction.

See how using this rule enables you to reduce $\frac{4}{16}$ by dividing the numerator and the denominator by 4.

$$\frac{4}{16} = \frac{4 \div 4}{16 \div 4} = \frac{1}{4}$$

We say that when $\frac{4}{16}$ is *reduced to lowest terms*, it is written as $\frac{1}{4}$.

EXAMPLE 1. Reduce $\frac{5}{15}$ to lowest terms.

Solution: You must find a number that will divide into both the top and bottom numbers *evenly*, without any remainder. Find this number by trial and error:

Will 2 go into 5 and 15? No.
Will 3 go into 5 and 15? No; into 15 only.
Will 4 go into 5 and 15? No.
Will 5 go into 5 and 15? Yes: $5 \div 5 = 1$ and $15 \div 5 = 3$.

Using the preceding rule: $\frac{5}{15} = \frac{5 \div 5}{15 \div 5} = \frac{1}{3}$

Answer: $\frac{5}{15} = \frac{1}{3}$

Alternate Solution: The most popular method of reducing a fraction to lowest terms is to draw a vertical line to the left of the fraction to indicate division. To reduce $\frac{5}{15}$ to lowest terms, you would write $\left|\frac{5}{15}\right.$. The notation $\left|\frac{5}{15}\right.$ means, "What number divides evenly into 5 and 15?"

Some people prefer to use this more detailed notation:

$$? \longleftarrow \frac{5}{15}$$

When the divisor is found by trial and error, write it to the left of the vertical line, as shown:

$$5 \left| \frac{5}{15} \right.$$

Then, indicate the two divisions with this notation:

"5 into 5 goes 1" is indicated as $5 \left| \frac{\cancel{5}}{15} \right.^{1}$

"5 into 15 goes 3" is indicated as $5 \left| \frac{5}{\cancel{15}} \right._{3}$

This notation permits you to write the solution very compactly. Here is how the entire solution of

"Reduce $\frac{5}{15}$ to lowest terms" would appear:

Solution:

$$5 \left| \frac{\cancel{5}}{\cancel{15}} \right. = \frac{1}{3}$$

Answer: $\frac{5}{15} = \frac{1}{3}$

EXAMPLE 2. Reduce $\frac{9}{24}$ to lowest terms.

Solution:

$$3 \left| \frac{\cancel{9}}{\cancel{24}} \right. = \frac{3}{8}$$

Answer: $\frac{9}{24} = \frac{3}{8}$

Whenever the top and bottom numbers of a fraction are even numbers (2, 4, 8, 10, 36, 50, ...), you can always divide by 2 to reduce the fraction. However, you must keep dividing by 2 until 2 no longer divides into the top and bottom numbers.

EXAMPLE 3. Reduce $\frac{16}{24}$ by dividing by 2.

Solution:

$$2 \left| \frac{\cancel{16}}{\cancel{24}} \right. = \frac{8}{12} \qquad 2 \left| \frac{\cancel{8}}{\cancel{12}} \right. = \frac{4}{6} \qquad 2 \left| \frac{\cancel{4}}{\cancel{6}} \right. = \frac{2}{3}$$

When reducing a fraction by this method, your solution could be written in one step, as shown:

$$2 \left| \frac{\cancel{16}}{\cancel{24}} \right. = \frac{2}{3}$$

Answer: $\frac{16}{24} = \frac{2}{3}$

Note: If, in Example 3, you see that 8 divides evenly into both 16 and 24, you can reduce $\frac{16}{24}$ much more easily:

$$8\,\bigg|\,\frac{\overset{2}{\cancel{16}}}{\underset{3}{\cancel{24}}} = \frac{2}{3}$$

Be sure to look at each answer carefully to make certain your new fraction cannot be reduced still more.

EXAMPLE 4. Reduce $\frac{36}{48}$ to lowest terms.

Solution:

$$2\,\bigg|\,\frac{\overset{\overset{9}{\cancel{18}}}{\cancel{36}}}{\underset{\underset{12}{\cancel{24}}}{\cancel{48}}} = \frac{9}{12}$$

The fraction $\frac{9}{12}$ is not the answer, since $\frac{9}{12}$ can be reduced further.

$$3\,\bigg|\,\frac{\overset{3}{\cancel{9}}}{\underset{4}{\cancel{12}}} = \frac{3}{4}$$

Answer: $\frac{36}{48} = \frac{3}{4}$

As in division, you can *eliminate end zeros* when reducing a fraction. (Recall that eliminating end zeros is the same as dividing by 10 or powers of 10.)

EXAMPLE 5. What fraction of the distance from the earth to the moon is 20,000 miles? (Use 240,000 miles as the distance.)

Solution: Get rid of end zeros, one for one, in the numerator and in the denominator.

$$\frac{20,\cancel{000}}{240,\cancel{000}} = \frac{2}{24} \qquad 2\,\bigg|\,\frac{\overset{1}{\cancel{2}}}{\underset{12}{\cancel{24}}} = \frac{1}{12}$$

Answer: $\frac{1}{12}$

Remember: To reduce a fraction to lowest terms, you must find a number that divides *evenly* into both the numerator and the denominator.

EXERCISES

In 1 to 32, reduce each fraction to lowest terms.

Sample solutions ————————————————

$$3\,\bigg|\,\frac{\overset{1}{\cancel{3}}}{\underset{3}{\cancel{9}}} = \frac{1}{3} \qquad 4\,\bigg|\,\frac{\overset{2}{\cancel{8}}}{\underset{3}{\cancel{12}}} = \frac{2}{3} \qquad 6\,\bigg|\,\frac{\overset{1}{\cancel{600}}}{\underset{3}{\cancel{1800}}} = \frac{1}{3} \qquad 2\,\bigg|\,\frac{\overset{18}{\cancel{36}}}{\underset{42}{\cancel{84}}} = 6\,\bigg|\,\frac{\overset{3}{\cancel{18}}}{\underset{7}{\cancel{42}}} = \frac{3}{7}$$

————————————————

1. $\quad \dfrac{4}{8} =$

2. $\quad \dfrac{7}{14} =$

3. $\quad \dfrac{16}{32} =$

4. $\dfrac{10}{30} =$ 5. $\dfrac{15}{20} =$ 6. $\dfrac{9}{36} =$

7. $\dfrac{45}{60} =$ 8. $\dfrac{16}{24} =$ 9. $\dfrac{12}{16} =$

10. $\dfrac{15}{60} =$ 11. $\dfrac{13}{52} =$ 12. $\dfrac{24}{32} =$

13. $\dfrac{24}{64} =$ 14. $\dfrac{8}{18} =$ 15. $\dfrac{4}{14} =$

16. $\dfrac{24}{38} =$ 17. $\dfrac{102}{106} =$ 18. $\dfrac{212}{214} =$

19. $\dfrac{35}{45} =$ 20. $\dfrac{16}{60} =$ 21. $\dfrac{8}{48} =$

22. $\dfrac{72}{84} =$ 23. $\dfrac{45}{54} =$ 24. $\dfrac{42}{70} =$

25. $\dfrac{42}{63} =$ 26. $\dfrac{22}{24} =$ 27. $\dfrac{36}{54} =$

28. $\dfrac{120}{360} =$ 29. $\dfrac{36}{144} =$ 30. $\dfrac{25}{150} =$

31. $\dfrac{35}{75} =$ 32. $\dfrac{48}{110} =$

APPLICATION PROBLEMS

Sample solution

What fraction of a 24-hour day is 20 minutes?

1 hr. = 60 min.

$$\begin{array}{r} 24 \\ \times 60 \\ \hline 1{,}440 \text{ min. per day} \end{array}$$

$$2\overline{)\begin{array}{c} \overset{1}{\cancel{20}} \\ \cancel{1{,}440} \\ 72 \end{array}} = \dfrac{1}{72}$$

$\dfrac{1}{72}$

In 1 to 5, reduce all answers to lowest terms.

1. Jane walked for 15 minutes. What fraction of an hour did she walk? (60 minutes = 1 hour)

2. Mary opened a box of 24 dishes and found that four of them were broken. What fraction of the dishes were broken?

3. Debra needed 24 inches of material to add sleeves to a blouse. What fraction of a yard does she need? (36 inches = 1 yard)

4. John spent 6 hours at the beach. What fraction of a day did he spend at the beach? (24 hours = 1 day)

5. Sandy had $35 and spent $15. What fraction of her money did she spend?

Unit 24. Raising Fractions to Higher Equivalents

Words to know

When fractions have the same value, we call them **equivalent fractions** or simply **equivalents**. Thus, $\frac{1}{4}$ and $\frac{4}{16}$ are equivalent fractions. The fraction with the larger numerator and denominator is called the **higher equivalent**.

When fractions are added and subtracted, it is often necessary to raise a given fraction to a **higher equivalent fraction**.

To raise a fraction to an equivalent fraction, use the following rule:

Rule: You can multiply the numerator and the denominator of a fraction by the same number without changing the value of that fraction.

The fraction $\frac{2}{4}$ is the higher equivalent of the fraction $\frac{1}{2}$ because it has a larger numerator and denominator. You change $\frac{1}{2}$ to $\frac{2}{4}$ by multiplying the numerator and denominator by 2:

$$\frac{1}{2} = \frac{1 \times 2}{2 \times 2} = \frac{2}{4}$$

Now you will use a procedure, based on the rule, that will enable you to raise a fraction to a higher equivalent that has a given denominator.

EXAMPLE 1. Raise $\frac{3}{4}$ to a higher equivalent that has a denominator of 16.

Solution: To raise $\frac{3}{4}$ to 16ths, you must find how many 16ths are contained in $\frac{3}{4}$. Set up the problem like this:

$$\frac{3}{4} \qquad = \frac{}{16}$$

To find how the 4 $\left(\text{the denominator of } \frac{3}{4}\right)$ is changed to 16, divide the 4 into 16. The quotient is 4.

$$\frac{3}{4} \xrightarrow[\text{into}]{} 16 \xrightarrow[\text{is}]{} 4$$

Multiply the numerator, 3, by the quotient you just found, 4. The product is 12. Write this product over the 16.

$$\frac{3}{4} \times 4 \xrightarrow[\text{into}]{\text{is} \atop =} \frac{12}{16} \longrightarrow 4$$

Answer: $\frac{3}{4} = \frac{12}{16}$

EXAMPLE 2. Raise $\frac{4}{5}$ to 20ths.

Solution: Set up the problem as before, and divide the denominator of $\frac{4}{5}$ into 20. The quotient is 4. Multiply the numerator, 4, by the quotient you just found, 4. The product is 16. Write this product over the 20.

$$\frac{4}{5} \times 4 \xrightarrow[\text{into}]{\text{is} \atop =} \frac{16}{20} \longrightarrow 4$$

Answer: $\frac{4}{5} = \frac{16}{20}$

Remember: To raise a fraction to a higher equivalent that has a given denominator:
1. **Divide the denominator of the fraction into the given denominator of the higher equivalent.**
2. **Multiply the numerator of the fraction by the quotient you found in step 1, and write this product over the given denominator.**

RAISING FRACTIONS MENTALLY

Because raising fractions to higher equivalents is used over and over again in the addition and subtraction of fractions, it is useful to be able to perform the operation **mentally**.

EXAMPLE 3. Raise $\frac{2}{3}$, $\frac{3}{4}$, and $\frac{5}{6}$ to 12ths.

Solution: Set up each problem as before, writing 12 as the given denominator.

Think: "3 into 12 = 4, and 4 × 2 = 8." Write the 8 over the 12.

$$\frac{2}{3} = \frac{8}{12}$$

Think: "4 into 12 = 3, and 3 × 3 = 9." Write the 9 over the 12.

$$\frac{3}{4} = \frac{9}{12}$$

Think: "6 into 12 = 2, and 2 × 5 = 10." Write the 10 over the 12.

$$\frac{5}{6} = \frac{10}{12}$$

Answer: $\frac{2}{3} = \frac{8}{12}$, $\frac{3}{4} = \frac{9}{12}$, $\frac{5}{6} = \frac{10}{12}$

EXERCISES

In 1 to 12, change each fraction to a higher equivalent that has the given denominator.

1. $\frac{2}{3} = \frac{}{12}$

2. $\frac{1}{4} = \frac{}{12}$

3. $\frac{2}{5} = \frac{}{20}$

4. $\frac{4}{7} = \frac{}{14}$

5. $\frac{3}{5} = \frac{}{20}$

6. $\frac{7}{16} = \frac{}{32}$

7. $\frac{1}{3} = \frac{}{9}$

8. $\frac{4}{5} = \frac{}{20}$

9. $\frac{3}{4} = \frac{}{12}$

10. $\frac{5}{24} = \frac{}{48}$

11. $\frac{7}{12} = \frac{}{36}$

12. $\frac{5}{8} = \frac{}{16}$

In 13 to 24, change:

13. $\frac{5}{8}$ to 32 nds

14. $\frac{7}{15}$ to 30 ths

15. $\frac{5}{24}$ to 48 ths

16. $\frac{8}{17}$ to 34 ths

17. $\frac{23}{32}$ to 64 ths

18. $\frac{17}{28}$ to 56 ths

19. $\frac{23}{33}$ to 66 ths

20. $\frac{7}{10}$ to 50 ths

21. $\frac{9}{15}$ to 45 ths

22. $\frac{5}{9}$ to 27 ths   **23.** $\frac{8}{11}$ to 44 ths   **24.** $\frac{19}{24}$ to 72 nds

APPLICATION PROBLEMS

Sample solution

How many half-pints are there in $\frac{7}{8}$ of a gallon?   *1 gal. = 4 qt. and 1 qt. = 2 pt. Thus,*

$\frac{7}{8} = \frac{?}{16}$, $\frac{7}{8} = \frac{14}{16}$ *1 gal. = 4 × 2 = 8 pt. or 16 $\frac{1}{2}$-pt.*

14 half-pints

1. How many 32nds of an inch are there in $\frac{3}{4}$ of an inch?

2. Change $\frac{1}{4}$ of a pound to ounces (16ths).

3. Mrs. Smith bought $\frac{3}{4}$ of a yard of velvet. How many inches (36ths) did she buy?

4. How many inches (12ths) are there in half of a foot?

5. How many sheets of paper are there in $\frac{3}{4}$ of a ream? (A ream contains 500 sheets of paper.)

Unit 25. Comparing Fractions

To compare two or more fractions means to determine which fraction has the largest value.

To compare the values of two or more fractions:

Step 1: Change the given fractions to equivalent fractions that have the *same denominator*.

Step 2: Compare the *numerators*. The fraction that has the largest numerator has the largest value.

Solution:

Step 1: $\frac{1}{2} = \frac{4}{8}$ and $\frac{3}{8} = \frac{3}{8}$.

Step 2: Since 4 is larger than 3, then $\frac{4}{8}$ is larger than $\frac{3}{8}$.

EXAMPLE 1. Which fraction is larger, $\frac{1}{2}$ or $\frac{3}{8}$?

Answer: $\frac{1}{2}$ is larger than $\frac{3}{8}$

EXAMPLE 2. Which fraction is smaller, $\frac{1}{4}$ or $\frac{5}{16}$?

Solution:

Step 1: $\frac{1}{4} = \frac{4}{16}$ and $\frac{5}{16} = \frac{5}{16}$.

Step 2: $\frac{4}{16}$ is smaller than $\frac{5}{16}$.

Answer: $\frac{1}{4}$ is smaller than $\frac{5}{16}$

EXAMPLE 3. Arrange the following fractions in descending order of size (largest first): $\frac{3}{4}$ $\frac{7}{8}$ $\frac{2}{3}$

Solution:

Step 1: $\frac{3}{4} = \frac{18}{24}, \frac{7}{8} = \frac{21}{24}$, and $\frac{2}{3} = \frac{16}{24}$.

Step 2: Arrange the equivalent fractions in descending order of size according to their numerators.

$$\frac{21}{24} \qquad \frac{18}{24} \qquad \frac{16}{24}$$

Substitute the given fractions:

$$\frac{21}{24} = \frac{7}{8} \qquad \frac{18}{24} = \frac{3}{4} \qquad \frac{16}{24} = \frac{2}{3}$$

Answer: $\frac{7}{8}$ $\quad$ $\frac{3}{4}$ $\quad$ $\frac{2}{3}$

EXERCISES

In 1 to 6, circle the *larger* fraction.

Sample solutions _____

a. $\frac{1}{2}$ $\left(\frac{5}{8}\right)$ $\frac{1}{2} = \frac{4}{8}$, *smaller than* $\frac{5}{8}$

b. $\frac{9}{16}$ $\left(\frac{5}{8}\right)$ $\frac{5}{8} = \frac{10}{16}$, *larger than* $\frac{9}{16}$

_____

1. $\frac{4}{5}$ $\frac{13}{15}$ 2. $\frac{5}{7}$ $\frac{9}{14}$ 3. $\frac{3}{5}$ $\frac{5}{10}$ 4. $\frac{5}{9}$ $\frac{13}{18}$

5. $\frac{8}{10}$ $\frac{15}{20}$ 6. $\frac{9}{12}$ $\frac{15}{24}$

In 7 to 16, circle the *smaller* fraction.

Sample solutions _____

c. $\left(\frac{3}{4}\right)$ $\frac{13}{16}$ $\frac{3}{4} = \frac{12}{16}$, *smaller than* $\frac{13}{16}$

d. $\left(\frac{5}{8}\right)$ $\frac{3}{4}$ $\frac{3}{4} = \frac{6}{8}$, *larger than* $\frac{5}{8}$

_____

7. $\frac{3}{5}$ $\frac{7}{15}$ 8. $\frac{7}{9}$ $\frac{15}{18}$ 9. $\frac{9}{12}$ $\frac{17}{24}$ 10. $\frac{2}{6}$ $\frac{2}{12}$

11. $\dfrac{3}{7}$ $\dfrac{8}{21}$ **12.** $\dfrac{7}{13}$ $\dfrac{15}{23}$ **13.** $\dfrac{3}{8}$ $\dfrac{8}{24}$ **14.** $\dfrac{5}{6}$ $\dfrac{13}{18}$

15. $\dfrac{4}{5}$ $\dfrac{15}{20}$ **16.** $\dfrac{5}{7}$ $\dfrac{21}{28}$

APPLICATION PROBLEMS

Sample solution

In the final week of the baseball season, catcher Mike Mahoney had 9 hits for 28 times at bat and pitcher Larry Schultz had 2 hits for 7 times at bat. Who had the better batting average?

Mahoney: 9 for 28 = $\dfrac{9}{28}$

Schultz: 2 for 7 = $\dfrac{2}{7}$ = $\dfrac{8}{28}$

$\dfrac{9}{28}$ is larger than $\dfrac{8}{28}$ *Mahoney*

1. John lives $\dfrac{7}{8}$ of a mile from school and James lives $\dfrac{13}{16}$ of a mile from school. Who lives closer to the school?

2. Two brands of coffee are priced at $1.29. If brand A contains $\dfrac{6}{7}$ of a pound and brand B contains $\dfrac{11}{14}$ of a pound, which brand has more coffee?

3. One piece of pipe measures $8\dfrac{3}{8}$ inches in diameter and another piece of pipe measures $8\dfrac{15}{32}$ inches in diameter. Which pipe has the larger diameter?

4. One savings bank offers $5\dfrac{3}{4}\%$ interest and another bank offers $5\dfrac{5}{8}\%$ interest. Which rate of interest is higher?

5. John ran a race in $4\dfrac{7}{10}$ minutes and Tom ran the same race in $4\dfrac{3}{5}$ minutes. Who won the race?

Unit 26. Improper Fractions and Mixed Numbers

Words to know

We have defined a fraction as a part of a unit. However, there are times when a fraction means *more* than a unit. When you buy 6 quarts of milk, for example, you have $\frac{6}{4}$ of a gallon. But $\frac{6}{4}$ of a gallon is the same as $1\frac{1}{2}$ gallons (1 gallon = 4 quarts). We call $\frac{6}{4}$ an **improper fraction**, and define an improper fraction as a fraction whose numerator is *as large as or larger than* its denominator.

We call $1\frac{1}{2}$ a **mixed number,** and define a mixed number as a number made up of whole units plus a fraction of a unit.

A fraction that is a part of a unit (whose numerator is smaller than its denominator) is sometimes called a **proper fraction**.

Since fractions represent parts of whole units, it is said to be "improper" to write a fraction that contains more than one whole unit. Suppose you want to watch a television drama that lasts for 90 minutes, and you want to know what time the show will be over. Before figuring out the problem, you change the time from $\frac{90}{60}$ of an hour to $1\frac{1}{2}$ hours.

What you have done is to change an *improper fraction* to a *mixed number*.

When a fraction has a numerator that is as large as or larger than the denominator, it is called an **improper fraction**. Examples of improper fractions are $\frac{6}{4}$, $\frac{5}{4}$, and $\frac{4}{4}$.

When a number contains both whole units and a fraction of a unit, it is called a **mixed number**. Examples of mixed numbers are $3\frac{2}{3}$, $2\frac{1}{4}$, and $1\frac{1}{8}$.

When writing the answer to any calculation, it is usual to change any improper fractions to mixed numbers or to whole numbers. To change an improper fraction to a mixed number or to a whole number, *divide the denominator into the numerator.*

A good way to remember which part of the fraction goes inside the division box is to draw the division box next to the bottom number of the fraction and let the top number "fall into" the division box.

EXAMPLE 1. Change $\frac{12}{3}$ to a whole number.

Solution:

Step 1: Draw the division box next to the denominator and let the numerator "fall in."

$$3\overline{)12}$$

Step 2: Do the division.

$$3\overline{)12} \quad \begin{array}{r} 4 \\ \underline{12} \end{array}$$

Answer: $\frac{12}{3} = 4$

EXAMPLE 2. Change $\frac{19}{4}$ to a mixed number.

Solution: $\quad 4\overline{)19} \qquad 4\overline{)19} \quad \begin{array}{r} 4\frac{3}{4} \\ \underline{16} \\ 3 \\ \to 4 \end{array}$

Answer: $\frac{19}{4} = 4\frac{3}{4}$

There are times when it is necessary to change a mixed number to an improper fraction.

EXAMPLE 3. Change $5\frac{3}{8}$ to an improper fraction.

Solution: To do this problem, you are really finding how many eighths are contained in $5\frac{3}{8}$. Set up the problem by rewriting the same denominator:

$$5\frac{3}{8} = \frac{}{8}$$

To find the new numerator, *multiply the denominator in the fraction part of the mixed number by the whole number*. The denominator of $\frac{3}{8}$ is 8. Therefore, $8 \times 5 = 40$.

$$8 \times 5 = 40 \quad 5\frac{3}{8} = \frac{}{8}$$

Now, *add the numerator of the fraction part of the mixed number* to the product you just got: $40 + 3 = 43$. Write this new numerator over the same denominator.

$$8 \times 5 = 40 \quad 5\frac{3}{8} = \frac{43}{8} \quad 40 + 3 = 43$$

Answer: $5\frac{3}{8} = \frac{43}{8}$

With practice, you can find the new numerator mentally. In the above problem, you would say: "$8 \times 5 = 40$, and $40 + 3 = 43$."

$$5\frac{3}{8} = \frac{43}{8}$$

EXAMPLE 4. Change $6\frac{2}{3}$ to an improper fraction.

Solution: Set up the problem: $\qquad 6\frac{2}{3} = \frac{}{3}$

Say: "$3 \times 6 = 18$, and $18 + 2 = 20$." $\qquad 6\frac{2}{3} = \frac{}{3}$

Write the 20 over the same denominator.

Answer: $6\frac{2}{3} = \frac{20}{3}$

Remember:

1. **To change an improper fraction to a mixed number: Divide the denominator into the numerator.**

2. **To change a mixed number to an improper fraction: Multiply the denominator by the whole number and add the numerator. This gives you the new numerator, which you write over the same denominator.**

EXERCISES

In 1 to 10, change each improper fraction to a mixed number or to a whole number.

Sample solutions

a. $\dfrac{17}{5}$ $\quad 5\overline{)17} \quad 3\frac{2}{5}$
$\qquad\qquad \underline{15}$
$\qquad\qquad\ \ \frac{2}{5}$

b. $\dfrac{12}{4}$ $\quad 4\overline{)12} \quad 3$
$\qquad\qquad \underline{12}$

1. $\dfrac{11}{8}$

2. $\dfrac{15}{3}$

3. $\dfrac{16}{15}$

4. $\dfrac{17}{8}$

5. $\dfrac{18}{3}$

6. $\dfrac{23}{6}$

7. $\dfrac{17}{7}$

8. $\dfrac{23}{8}$

9. $\dfrac{32}{6}$

10. $\dfrac{15}{4}$

In 11 to 20, change each mixed number to an improper fraction.

Sample solutions

a. $3\dfrac{2}{3} = \dfrac{11}{3}$ b. $1\dfrac{5}{8} = \dfrac{13}{8}$

    $3 \times 3 = 9 + 2 = 11$ $8 \times 1 = 8 + 5 = 13$

11. $5\dfrac{5}{6}$ 12. $12\dfrac{2}{3}$ 13. $6\dfrac{3}{4}$ 14. $4\dfrac{3}{7}$ 15. $15\dfrac{1}{2}$

16. $7\dfrac{4}{5}$ 17. $6\dfrac{5}{16}$ 18. $3\dfrac{9}{12}$ 19. $8\dfrac{1}{3}$ 20. $10\dfrac{3}{4}$

APPLICATION PROBLEMS

Sample solution

A film version of *War and Peace* runs for 390 minutes. Using the fact that 1 minute $= \dfrac{1}{60}$ of an hour, change the running time to hours.

$390 \, min. = \dfrac{390}{60} = \dfrac{39}{6} \, hr.$

$\dfrac{39}{6} = 6\overline{)39} \quad 6\tfrac{1}{2}$

$\dfrac{36}{}$

$\dfrac{3}{6}$

$6\tfrac{1}{2} \, hr.$

1. Mr. Wilson gave out 12 quarters to his grandchildren. How much money in dollars did he give out? (*Hint:* one quarter $= \dfrac{1}{4}$ of a dollar.)

2. Tom needs 15 half-inch-thick boards. How many inches thick are all of the boards? $\left(Hint: 15 \ \dfrac{1}{2}\text{'s} = 15 \times \dfrac{1}{2} = \dfrac{15}{1} \times \dfrac{1}{2} = \dfrac{15}{2}\right)$

3. How many $\dfrac{1}{8}$-inch-thick slices of cheese can be cut from a piece of cheese that measures $4\dfrac{3}{8}$ inches?

4. How many $\dfrac{1}{4}$ cups of flour can you get from a bag that holds $6\dfrac{3}{4}$ cups?

5. How many $\dfrac{1}{2}$ teaspoons of honey can be poured from a jar that holds $12\dfrac{1}{2}$ teaspoons?

Review of Part VI (Units 21 to 26)

In 1 to 5, tell how you would solve each word problem. Do not actually compute the answers.

1. Stanley can buy a camera for $75 cash or he can make a down payment of $25 and then pay $6 a month for a year. How much will he save if he pays cash? _____

_____

2. If each of 200 million Americans spends an average of one minute brushing his teeth, how many hours are spent by all of these Americans in brushing their teeth? _____

_____

3. In 1970, there were 558,392 telephones in Baltimore. If the population of the city that year was 905,759, how many people were there for each telephone? _____

_____

4. On the average, each person in the state of Delaware earned $4,324 in 1970. That year, the population of the state was 548,104. What was the total income earned in 1970 by all the people living in Delaware?

_____

5. New Orleans had a population of 593,471 in 1970. In 1960, its population was 627,525. By how much had the population decreased? What was the average yearly decrease in population between 1960 and 1970? _____

_____

_____

In 6 to 15, change each fraction to a higher equivalent that has the given denominator.

6. $\dfrac{4}{5} = \dfrac{}{20}$

7. $\dfrac{3}{7} = \dfrac{}{28}$

8. $\dfrac{3}{5} = \dfrac{}{30}$

9. $\dfrac{5}{8} = \dfrac{}{40}$

10. $\dfrac{5}{6} = \dfrac{}{42}$

11. $\dfrac{9}{15} = \dfrac{}{45}$

12. $\dfrac{7}{12} = \dfrac{}{48}$

13. $\dfrac{11}{16} = \dfrac{}{48}$

14. $\dfrac{5}{24} = \dfrac{}{72}$

15. $\dfrac{7}{8} = \dfrac{}{64}$

In 16 to 25, reduce each fraction to lowest terms.

16. $\dfrac{5}{15} =$ 17. $\dfrac{14}{28} =$ 18. $\dfrac{12}{60} =$ 19. $\dfrac{24}{48} =$

20. $\dfrac{30}{40} =$ 21. $\dfrac{16}{18} =$ 22. $\dfrac{20}{34} =$ 23. $\dfrac{25}{75} =$

24. $\dfrac{35}{45} =$ 25. $\dfrac{18}{27} =$

In 26 to 33, circle the larger fraction.

26. $\dfrac{3}{7}$ $\dfrac{7}{21}$ 27. $\dfrac{4}{5}$ $\dfrac{17}{20}$ 28. $\dfrac{3}{4}$ $\dfrac{10}{16}$ 29. $\dfrac{21}{28}$ $\dfrac{5}{7}$

30. $\dfrac{3}{4}$ $\dfrac{4}{5}$ 31. $\dfrac{5}{6}$ $\dfrac{7}{8}$ 32. $\dfrac{2}{3}$ $\dfrac{3}{5}$ 33. $\dfrac{3}{8}$ $\dfrac{4}{7}$

(Use 20ths.)   (Use 48ths.)   (Use 15ths.)   (Use 56ths.)

In 34 to 41, change each improper fraction to a whole number or to a mixed number.

34. $\dfrac{23}{5} =$ 35. $\dfrac{15}{3} =$ 36. $\dfrac{19}{4} =$ 37. $\dfrac{43}{8} =$

38. $\dfrac{57}{12} =$ 39. $\dfrac{48}{14} =$ 40. $\dfrac{37}{3} =$ 41. $\dfrac{65}{16} =$

In 42 to 49, change each mixed number to an improper fraction.

42. $6\dfrac{3}{5} =$ 43. $8\dfrac{2}{3} =$ 44. $12\dfrac{1}{4} =$ 45. $15\dfrac{3}{8} =$

46. $13\dfrac{4}{5} =$ 47. $11\dfrac{5}{8} =$ 48. $7\dfrac{5}{16} =$ 49. $14\dfrac{5}{6} =$

Part VII. Adding and Subtracting Fractions

Unit 27. Addition of Fractions That Have the Same Denominator

When two or more fractions are added, the sum is another fraction that is larger than any of the addends. Whenever the sum is an improper fraction, change it to a mixed number or a whole number.

The easiest fractions to add are those with the same denominator. To add fractions that have the same denominator, *add the numerators and rewrite the same denominator*.

EXAMPLE 1. Add: $\dfrac{3}{16} + \dfrac{5}{16} + \dfrac{7}{16}$.

Solution: To add these fractions, you are really finding how many 16ths there are in all the fractions to be added.

Add the numerators: $3 + 5 + 7 = 15$

Rewrite the same denominator with this sum over it.

Answer: $\dfrac{3}{16} + \dfrac{5}{16} + \dfrac{7}{16} = \dfrac{15}{16}$

EXAMPLE 2. Add: $\dfrac{5}{8} + \dfrac{7}{8} + \dfrac{3}{8} + \dfrac{5}{8}$

Solution: Add the numerators: $5 + 7 + 3 + 5 = 20$

Rewrite the same denominator, 8, with this sum over it.

$$\frac{20}{8}$$

Since the answer is an improper fraction, change it to a mixed number.

$$\frac{20}{8} \quad \begin{array}{r} 2\frac{1}{2} \\ 8\overline{\smash{)}20} \\ \underline{16} \\ \frac{4}{8} = \frac{1}{2} \end{array}$$

Answer: $\dfrac{5}{8} + \dfrac{7}{8} + \dfrac{3}{8} + \dfrac{5}{8} = 2\dfrac{1}{2}$

Remember: When adding fractions that have the same denominator, add only the top numbers.

EXERCISES

In 1 to 16, add. Change improper fractions to mixed numbers or to whole numbers.

Sample solution

a. $\dfrac{3}{5} + \dfrac{2}{5} + \dfrac{4}{5} = \dfrac{9}{5} = 1\dfrac{4}{5}$

$$\frac{9}{5} \quad \begin{array}{r} 1\frac{4}{5} \\ 5\overline{\smash{)}9} \\ \underline{5} \\ \frac{4}{5} \end{array}$$

b. $\dfrac{1}{4} + \dfrac{2}{4} + \dfrac{3}{4} + \dfrac{2}{4} = \dfrac{\cancel{8}^{2}}{\cancel{4}_{1}} = \dfrac{2}{1} = 2$

1. $\dfrac{3}{7} + \dfrac{5}{7} + \dfrac{2}{7} + \dfrac{6}{7}$

2. $\dfrac{5}{8} + \dfrac{3}{8} + \dfrac{1}{8} + \dfrac{7}{8}$

3. $\dfrac{3}{6} + \dfrac{5}{6} + \dfrac{1}{6} + \dfrac{5}{6}$

4. $\dfrac{3}{9} + \dfrac{7}{9} + \dfrac{5}{9} + \dfrac{4}{9}$

5. $\dfrac{5}{12} + \dfrac{7}{12} + \dfrac{9}{12} + \dfrac{13}{12}$

6. $\dfrac{4}{11} + \dfrac{5}{11} + \dfrac{8}{11} + \dfrac{10}{11}$

7. $\dfrac{13}{24} + \dfrac{7}{24} + \dfrac{9}{24} + \dfrac{21}{24}$

8. $\dfrac{8}{15} + \dfrac{12}{15} + \dfrac{7}{15} + \dfrac{14}{15}$

9. $\dfrac{8}{18} + \dfrac{11}{18} + \dfrac{15}{18} + \dfrac{10}{18}$

10. $\dfrac{13}{20} + \dfrac{17}{20} + \dfrac{11}{20} + \dfrac{15}{20}$

11. $\dfrac{18}{25} + \dfrac{19}{25} + \dfrac{13}{25} + \dfrac{21}{25}$

12. $\dfrac{21}{30} + \dfrac{15}{30} + \dfrac{18}{30} + \dfrac{25}{30}$

13. $\dfrac{25}{32} + \dfrac{19}{32} + \dfrac{27}{32} + \dfrac{30}{32}$

14. $\dfrac{15}{36} + \dfrac{28}{36} + \dfrac{25}{36} + \dfrac{34}{36}$

15. $\dfrac{27}{35} + \dfrac{32}{35} + \dfrac{30}{35} + \dfrac{19}{35}$

16. $\dfrac{35}{40} + \dfrac{28}{40} + \dfrac{21}{40} + \dfrac{36}{40}$

APPLICATION PROBLEMS

Sample solution

In Pete's Pizza Parlor, each whole pizza is cut into 8 equal slices. Find how many pizzas Pete needs to fill the following orders: 3 slices, 5 slices, 2 slices, 1 slice, 1 slice.

1 slice is $\frac{1}{8}$ of a pizza, so 3 slices = $\frac{3}{8}$, 5 slices = $\frac{5}{8}$, 2 slices = $\frac{2}{8}$, 1 slice = $\frac{1}{8}$, 1 slice = $\frac{1}{8}$

$$\frac{3}{8} + \frac{5}{8} + \frac{2}{8} + \frac{1}{8} + \frac{1}{8} = \frac{\cancel{12}^{\,3}}{\cancel{8}_{\,2}} = \frac{3}{2}$$

$1\frac{1}{2}$ pizzas

1. Mary baked a cake and added $\frac{1}{2}$ cup of sugar, $\frac{1}{2}$ cup of shortening, $\frac{1}{2}$ cup of chocolate, and $\frac{1}{2}$ cup of milk. How many cups did she add?

2. A plumber cut off the following pieces of pipe: $\frac{3}{8}$ inches, $\frac{7}{8}$ inches, $\frac{5}{8}$ inches, and $\frac{7}{8}$ inches. How many inches of pipe did he cut off?

3. Tom needs the following pieces of lumber to finish a bookcase: $\frac{3}{4}$ foot, $\frac{1}{4}$ foot, $\frac{2}{4}$ foot. How many feet of lumber does he need?

4. Jane is making a dress and needs the following pieces of material: $\frac{1}{5}$ of a yard for the collar, $\frac{4}{5}$ of a yard for the front, $\frac{4}{5}$ of a yard for the back, and $\frac{3}{5}$ of a yard for the sleeves. How many yards of material does she need?

5. A clerk sold the following weights of cheese: $\frac{5}{16}$ of a pound, $\frac{7}{16}$ of a pound, $\frac{13}{16}$ of a pound, and $\frac{9}{16}$ of a pound. What is the total weight sold?

Unit 28. Addition of Fractions That Have Unlike Denominators

Words to know

In Unit 24, you learned how to raise fractions to *higher equivalents*. This skill will now be used to enable you to add fractions that do not have the same denominator. When you change a group of fractions to equivalent fractions that all have the *same denominator*, we call this bottom number a **common denominator**.

In order to add a group of fractions that have unlike denominators, you must make the fractions "alike." That is, you must find a **common denominator** and change each given fraction to an equivalent fraction that has this same denominator.

Many times the largest denominator in the problem can be used as the common denominator.

EXAMPLE 1. Add: $\dfrac{3}{4} + \dfrac{5}{8} + \dfrac{5}{16}$

Solution: Arrange the given fractions, one under the other, as shown. To the right, draw the fraction bars for the equivalent fractions and for the sum.

$$\frac{3}{4} = \underline{\quad}$$

$$\frac{5}{8} = \underline{\quad}$$

$$\frac{5}{16} = \underline{\quad}$$

Notice that the denominator of $\dfrac{5}{16}$ is the largest denominator in the problem. Therefore, you will raise $\dfrac{3}{4}$ and $\dfrac{5}{8}$ to equivalent fractions that have a denominator of 16. You can do this because the denominator of $\dfrac{3}{4}$ divides evenly into 16 (without a remainder) and the denominator of $\dfrac{5}{8}$ divides evenly into 16. Write 16 as the common denominator for all the fractions, including the fraction that will be your answer.

$$\frac{3}{4} = \frac{}{16}$$

$$\frac{5}{8} = \frac{}{16}$$

$$\frac{5}{16} = \frac{}{16}$$

$$\frac{}{16}$$

Next, divide each given denominator into the common denominator and then multiply the quotient by each numerator. The final product is the new numerator of each equivalent fraction.

$$\frac{3 \times 4 \rightarrow 12}{4 \longrightarrow 16 \rightarrow 4}$$

Think: "4 into $16 = 4$, and $3 \times 4 = 12$." Write the 12.

$$\frac{5 \times 2 \rightarrow 10}{8 \longrightarrow 16 \rightarrow 2}$$

Think: "8 into $16 = 2$, and $5 \times 2 = 10$." Write the 10.

$$\frac{5 \times 1 \rightarrow 5}{16 \longrightarrow 16 \rightarrow 1}$$

Think: "16 into $16 = 1$, and $5 \times 1 = 5$." Write the 5.

$$\frac{}{16}$$

Now, add the top numbers of the equivalent fractions and put this sum over the common denominator, 16. Your final answer is $\dfrac{27}{16}$, an improper fraction. Change $\dfrac{27}{16}$ to a mixed number.

$$\frac{3}{4} = \frac{12}{16}$$
$$\frac{5}{8} = \frac{10}{16}$$
$$\frac{5}{16} = \frac{5}{16}$$
$$\frac{27}{16} = 1\frac{11}{16}$$

Answer: $\frac{3}{4} + \frac{5}{8} + \frac{5}{16} = 1\frac{11}{16}$

EXAMPLE 2. Add: $\frac{2}{3} + \frac{1}{4} + \frac{5}{12}$

Solution: Raise the addends to 12ths mentally.

$$\frac{2}{3} \rightarrow \frac{8}{12}$$
$$\frac{1}{4} \rightarrow \frac{3}{12}$$
$$\frac{5}{12} \rightarrow \frac{5}{12}$$
$$\frac{16}{12} = 1\frac{1}{3}$$

Answer: $\frac{2}{3} + \frac{1}{4} + \frac{5}{12} = 1\frac{1}{3}$

At times, the largest denominator in the problem cannot be used as a common denominator because one or more of the given denominators will not divide evenly into it. When this happens, you multiply the largest denominator by 2, 3, 4, 5, 6, etc., until you get a number that can be used as a common denominator.

EXAMPLE 3. Add: $\frac{3}{4} + \frac{1}{2} + \frac{3}{5}$

Solution: Note that neither 4 nor 2 will divide evenly into 5. Thus, 5 cannot be used as the common denominator. Multiply the 5 to get trial common denominators:

$5 \times 2 = 10$, which cannot be used.
$5 \times 3 = 15$, which cannot be used.
$5 \times 4 = 20$. Use 20 as the common denominator, because all the given denominators (4, 2, and 5) divide evenly into 20.

Set up the problem as in examples 1 and 2 and solve:

$$\frac{3}{4} = \frac{15}{20}$$
$$\frac{1}{2} = \frac{10}{20}$$
$$\frac{3}{5} = \frac{12}{20}$$
$$\frac{37}{20} = 1\frac{17}{20}$$

Answer: $\frac{3}{4} + \frac{1}{2} + \frac{3}{5} = 1\frac{17}{20}$

EXERCISES

In 1 to 16, add. Change improper fractions to mixed numbers or to whole numbers.

Sample solutions

$$\frac{3}{4} = \frac{6}{8}$$
$$\frac{5}{8} = \frac{5}{8}$$
$$\frac{11}{8} = 1\frac{3}{8}$$

$$8\overline{)11} \quad 1\frac{3}{8}$$
$$\underline{8}$$
$$\overline{3}$$

$$\frac{1}{2} = \frac{6}{12}$$
$$\frac{2}{3} = \frac{8}{12}$$
$$\frac{3}{4} = \frac{9}{12}$$
$$\frac{23}{12} = 1\frac{11}{12}$$

$$12\overline{)23} \quad 1\frac{11}{12}$$
$$\underline{12}$$
$$\overline{11}$$

1. $\dfrac{5}{8}$
$\dfrac{9}{16}$

2. $\dfrac{2}{3}$
$\dfrac{5}{6}$

3. $\dfrac{3}{4}$
$\dfrac{11}{16}$

4. $\dfrac{5}{7}$
$\dfrac{19}{21}$

5. $\dfrac{5}{6}$
$\dfrac{15}{18}$

6. $\dfrac{2}{5}$
$\dfrac{3}{15}$

7. $\dfrac{2}{3}$
$\dfrac{3}{9}$

8. $\dfrac{3}{7}$
$\dfrac{9}{28}$

9. $\dfrac{4}{5}$
$\dfrac{7}{15}$
$\dfrac{13}{20}$

10. $\dfrac{4}{5}$
$\dfrac{7}{10}$
$\dfrac{13}{20}$

11. $\dfrac{5}{8}$
$\dfrac{7}{16}$
$\dfrac{25}{32}$

12. $\dfrac{5}{8}$
$\dfrac{3}{5}$
$\dfrac{9}{10}$

13. $\dfrac{2}{3}$
$\dfrac{5}{8}$
$\dfrac{7}{12}$

14. $\dfrac{3}{4}$
$\dfrac{7}{8}$
$\dfrac{4}{5}$

15. $\dfrac{5}{8}$
$\dfrac{3}{4}$
$\dfrac{9}{12}$

16. $\dfrac{3}{4}$
$\dfrac{5}{16}$
$\dfrac{7}{12}$

APPLICATION PROBLEMS

Sample solution ──

Mrs. Brown needed $\frac{3}{4}$ cup of flour, $\frac{2}{3}$ cup of milk, and $\frac{1}{6}$ cup of butter for a mixture she made to breaded pork chops. How many cups did the mixture contain?

$$\frac{3}{4} = \frac{9}{12}$$
$$\frac{2}{3} = \frac{8}{12}$$
$$\frac{1}{6} = \frac{2}{12}$$
$$\frac{19}{12}$$

$$12\overline{)19} \quad 1\frac{7}{12}$$
$$\underline{12}$$
$$\frac{7}{12}$$

$$1\frac{7}{12}$$

──

1. Helen bought $\frac{1}{2}$ of a pound of candy, $\frac{3}{4}$ of a pound of nuts, and $\frac{5}{8}$ of a pound of raisins. How many pounds did she buy altogether?

2. John walked $\frac{3}{4}$ of a mile to school, $\frac{1}{3}$ of a mile to town, and $\frac{1}{2}$ of a mile to a friend's house. How many miles did he walk?

3. Mrs. Brown needs the following pieces of material to make a blouse: $\frac{2}{7}$ of a yard for the front and back, $\frac{1}{3}$ of a yard for the sleeves, and $\frac{1}{6}$ of a yard for the collar. How much material is needed for the blouse?

4. The following pieces were cut from a pipe: $\frac{1}{5}$ foot, $\frac{2}{3}$ foot, $\frac{1}{6}$ foot. How many feet of pipe were cut? (Disregard the waste.)

5. Henry spent $\frac{1}{2}$ an hour on his arithmetic homework, $\frac{1}{3}$ of an hour on history, and $\frac{1}{6}$ of an hour on English. How long did it take him to do all of his homework?

Unit 29. Addition of Mixed Numbers

Since a mixed number consists of a whole number and a fraction, you add mixed numbers in separate steps.

To add mixed numbers:

Step 1: Add the whole numbers.

Step 2: Add the fractions.

Step 3: Combine the two answers into a final sum.

EXAMPLE 1. Add: $12\frac{3}{4} + 15\frac{7}{8} + 14\frac{1}{2}$

Solution: Add the whole numbers first. Then add the fractions.

Step 1:

$$12\,\Big|\,\frac{3}{4}$$
$$15\,\Big|\,\frac{7}{8}$$
$$14\,\Big|\,\frac{1}{2}$$
$$\overline{41\,\Big|\,}$$

Step 2:

$$12\,\Big|\,\frac{3}{4} = \frac{6}{8}$$
$$15\,\Big|\,\frac{7}{8} = \frac{7}{8}$$
$$14\,\Big|\,\frac{1}{2} = \frac{4}{8}$$
$$\overline{41\,\Big|\,\quad \frac{17}{8} = 2\frac{1}{8}}$$

Step 3: Combine the two answers:

$$41 + 2\frac{1}{8} = 43\frac{1}{8}$$

Answer: $12\frac{3}{4} + 15\frac{7}{8} + 14\frac{1}{2} = 43\frac{1}{8}$

EXAMPLE 2. Add: $2\frac{1}{3} + 5\frac{1}{2} + 7\frac{1}{4}$

Solution:

$$2\,\Big|\,\frac{1}{3} = \frac{4}{12}$$
$$5\,\Big|\,\frac{1}{2} = \frac{6}{12}$$
$$7\,\Big|\,\frac{1}{4} = \frac{3}{12}$$
$$\overline{14\,\Big|\,\quad \frac{13}{12} = 1\frac{1}{12}}$$
$$+1\frac{1}{12} \longleftarrow$$
$$\overline{15\frac{1}{12}}$$

Answer: $2\frac{1}{3} + 5\frac{1}{2} + 7\frac{1}{4} = 15\frac{1}{12}$

EXERCISES

In 1 to 12, add. Change improper fractions to mixed numbers or to whole numbers.

Sample solution

$$5\,\Big|\,\frac{2}{3} = \frac{12}{18}$$
$$7\,\Big|\,\frac{5}{6} = \frac{15}{18}$$
$$4\,\Big|\,\frac{7}{9} = \frac{14}{18}$$
$$\overline{16\,\Big|\,\quad \frac{41}{18} = 2\frac{5}{18}}$$

$$\frac{41}{18}\quad 18\overline{\big)41}\,2\frac{5}{18}$$
$$\underline{36}$$
$$\frac{5}{18}$$

$$16 + 2\frac{5}{18} = 18\frac{5}{18}$$

92

1. $8\frac{3}{4}$

$11\frac{3}{8}$

$9\frac{1}{2}$

2. $13\frac{3}{4}$

$7\frac{4}{5}$

$15\frac{1}{2}$

3. $15\frac{2}{3}$

$12\frac{1}{4}$

$14\frac{5}{6}$

4. $23\frac{9}{16}$

$15\frac{5}{8}$

$24\frac{30}{32}$

5. $19\frac{4}{5}$

$10\frac{15}{20}$

$7\frac{3}{4}$

6. $25\frac{5}{7}$

$23\frac{10}{14}$

$47\frac{19}{28}$

7. $17\frac{1}{3}$

$15\frac{5}{6}$

$18\frac{5}{8}$

8. $12\frac{4}{5}$

$9\frac{12}{15}$

$11\frac{5}{6}$

9. $18\frac{2}{3}$

$21\frac{4}{5}$

$25\frac{7}{10}$

10. $14\frac{11}{16}$

$9\frac{3}{4}$

$15\frac{25}{64}$

11. $23\frac{3}{4}$

$15\frac{5}{8}$

$19\frac{4}{5}$

12. $24\frac{5}{7}$

$19\frac{2}{3}$

$25\frac{11}{14}$

APPLICATION PROBLEMS

1. A plumber needs 3 lengths of pipe measuring $6\frac{3}{16}$ inches, $8\frac{5}{8}$ inches, and $4\frac{1}{2}$ inches. What length of pipe does he need to cut the 3 pieces? (Disregard any waste.)

_____

2. A salesgirl sold the following pieces of velvet: $3\frac{1}{3}$ yards, $5\frac{3}{4}$ yards, $4\frac{1}{2}$ yards. How many yards did she sell?

_____

3. Mary bought $2\frac{1}{2}$ pounds of apples, $1\frac{3}{4}$ pounds of cherries, and $2\frac{3}{8}$ pounds of pears. How many pounds of fruit did she buy?

_____

4. A carpenter needs 3 pieces of board measuring $24\frac{3}{4}$ inches, $15\frac{7}{8}$ inches, and $13\frac{15}{16}$ inches. How many inches of board does he need?

_____

5. Jane is making a 2-piece dress and needs $2\frac{1}{5}$ yards for one part and $3\frac{2}{3}$ yards for the other part. How much material does she need?

_____

Unit 30. Subtraction of Fractions

Subtracting fractions is very similar to adding fractions. Arrange the fractions, one under the other, find the common denominator, and raise to equivalent fractions. Then, you *subtract the numerators.* (Recall that in addition you *added* the numerators.) Write this answer over the common denominator to get your final remainder.

EXAMPLE 1. Subtract: $\frac{3}{4} - \frac{2}{3}$

Solution: Set up the problem as for the addition of fractions, find the common denominator, and raise to equivalent fractions. (Be sure to write the common denominator in the space where your answer will be.)

$$\frac{3}{4} = \frac{9}{12}$$
$$-\frac{2}{3} = \frac{8}{12}$$
$$\overline{\frac{}{12}}$$

Now, *subtract* the numerators.

$$\frac{3}{4} = \frac{9}{12}$$
$$-\frac{2}{3} = \frac{8}{12}$$
$$\frac{1}{12}$$

Answer: $\frac{3}{4} - \frac{2}{3} = \frac{1}{12}$

EXAMPLE 2. Subtract: $\frac{7}{8} - \frac{5}{16}$

Solution:

$$\frac{7}{8} = \frac{14}{16}$$
$$-\frac{5}{16} = \frac{5}{16}$$
$$\frac{9}{16}$$

Answer: $\frac{7}{8} - \frac{5}{16} = \frac{9}{16}$

EXERCISES

In 1 to 22, subtract the lower fraction from the upper fraction.

Sample solutions

a.
$$\frac{2}{3} = \frac{4}{6}$$
$$\frac{1}{6} = \frac{1}{6}$$
$$\frac{3}{6} = \frac{1}{2}$$

b.
$$\frac{3}{4} = \frac{15}{20}$$
$$\frac{3}{5} = \frac{12}{20}$$
$$\frac{3}{20}$$

Trial denominator:
$5 \times 2 = 10$ (no)
$5 \times 3 = 15$ (no)
$5 \times 4 = 20$ (yes)

1. $\frac{7}{8}$ $\frac{3}{4}$

2. $\frac{1}{2}$ $\frac{1}{3}$

3. $\frac{2}{3}$ $\frac{3}{5}$

4. $\frac{5}{6}$ $\frac{3}{8}$

5. $\frac{5}{8}$ $\frac{7}{12}$

6. $\frac{4}{5}$ $\frac{3}{4}$

7. $\frac{2}{3}$ $\frac{5}{16}$

8. $\frac{3}{5}$ $\frac{5}{12}$

9. $\frac{2}{3}$ $\frac{3}{7}$

10. $\frac{4}{5}$ $\frac{4}{6}$

11. $\dfrac{1}{4}$ 12. $\dfrac{2}{3}$ 13. $\dfrac{5}{6}$ 14. $\dfrac{3}{4}$ 15. $\dfrac{5}{7}$

    $\dfrac{1}{5}$ $\dfrac{5}{9}$ $\dfrac{5}{8}$ $\dfrac{2}{3}$ $\dfrac{1}{3}$

16. $\dfrac{5}{8}$ 17. $\dfrac{1}{3}$ 18. $\dfrac{7}{9}$ 19. $\dfrac{3}{5}$ 20. $\dfrac{7}{8}$

    $\dfrac{30}{64}$ $\dfrac{1}{5}$ $\dfrac{1}{4}$ $\dfrac{2}{6}$ $\dfrac{2}{3}$

21. $\dfrac{7}{12}$ 22. $\dfrac{5}{9}$

    $\dfrac{1}{4}$ $\dfrac{3}{7}$

APPLICATION PROBLEMS

1. The Wilsons bought $\dfrac{3}{4}$ ton of coal and used up $\dfrac{1}{2}$ ton. How much coal is still left?

2. Jane bought $\dfrac{7}{8}$ of a yard of material to make a pair of shorts. If she only used $\dfrac{3}{4}$ of a yard, how much material is left?

3. Mary had $\dfrac{3}{4}$ pound of sugar and used $\dfrac{9}{16}$ pound. How much sugar is left?

4. John lives $\dfrac{9}{10}$ of a mile from school and Tom lives $\dfrac{4}{5}$ of a mile from school. How much closer does Tom live to the school?

5. Carol used $\dfrac{3}{4}$ cup of milk and $\dfrac{1}{2}$ cup of sugar to bake a cake. How much more milk than sugar did she use?

Unit 31. Subtraction of Mixed Numbers

Subtracting mixed numbers is very similar to the adding of mixed numbers. However, because subtraction often involves *borrowing*, you must *subtract the fractions first*. Then you subtract the whole numbers.

EXAMPLE 1. Subtract: $7\dfrac{5}{8} - 5\dfrac{7}{16}$

Solution: Set up the mixed numbers, one under the other, and find the common denominator. Subtract the equivalent fractions first. Then subtract the whole numbers and combine these two answers into the final remainder.

$$
\begin{array}{r|l}
7 & \dfrac{5}{8} = \dfrac{10}{16} \\[2ex]
-\,5 & \dfrac{7}{16} = \dfrac{7}{16} \\[2ex]
\hline
2 & \dfrac{3}{16}
\end{array}
$$

Answer: $7\dfrac{5}{8} - 5\dfrac{7}{16} = 2\dfrac{3}{16}$

EXAMPLE 2. Subtract: $15\dfrac{1}{5} - 8\dfrac{3}{4}$

Solution:

$$
\begin{array}{r|l}
15 & \dfrac{1}{5} = \dfrac{4}{20} \\[2ex]
-\,8 & \dfrac{3}{4} = \dfrac{15}{20} \\[2ex]
\hline
 & \dfrac{}{20}
\end{array}
$$

Notice that the numerator of $\dfrac{15}{20}$ is *larger* than the numerator of $\dfrac{4}{20}$. Since you cannot take away 15 from 4, *borrow* 1 from the 15, and change it to 14. Place the borrowed 1 in front of $\dfrac{4}{20}$, getting the mixed number $1\dfrac{4}{20}$.

$$
\begin{array}{r|l}
\overset{14}{\cancel{15}} & \dfrac{1}{5} = 1\dfrac{4}{20} \\[2ex]
-\,8 & \dfrac{3}{4} = \dfrac{15}{20} \\[2ex]
\hline
 & \dfrac{}{20}
\end{array}
$$

Change $1\dfrac{4}{20}$ to an improper fraction:

$$1\dfrac{4}{20} = \dfrac{24}{20}$$

Think: "$20 \times 1 = 20$ and $20 + 4 = 24$."

Replace $1\dfrac{4}{20}$ with $\dfrac{24}{20}$ in the problem and subtract $\dfrac{15}{20}$ from $\dfrac{24}{20}$. Then subtract the whole numbers and combine the two answers into the final remainder.

$$
\begin{array}{r|l}
\overset{14}{\cancel{15}} & \dfrac{1}{5} = 1\dfrac{4}{20} \longrightarrow \dfrac{24}{20} \\[2ex]
-\,8 & \dfrac{3}{4} = \dfrac{15}{20} \longrightarrow \dfrac{15}{20} \\[2ex]
\hline
6 & \dfrac{}{20} \longrightarrow \dfrac{9}{20} = 6\dfrac{9}{20}
\end{array}
$$

Answer: $15\dfrac{1}{5} - 8\dfrac{3}{4} = 6\dfrac{9}{20}$

Alternate Solution: Another way of borrowing from the whole number is to change the borrowed 1 to an equivalent fraction that has the common denominator. Let us use this method to subtract $8\dfrac{3}{4}$ from $15\dfrac{1}{5}$.

Start the problem as in the previous method.

$$
\begin{array}{r|l}
15 & \dfrac{1}{5} = \dfrac{4}{20} \\[2ex]
-\,8 & \dfrac{3}{4} = \dfrac{15}{20} \\[2ex]
\hline
 & \dfrac{}{20}
\end{array}
$$

As before, borrow 1 from the 15. However, raise the borrowed 1 to an equivalent fraction that has a denominator of 20, namely, $1 = \dfrac{20}{20}$. (Recall that the value of any fraction that has the same number in the numerator and the denominator is 1.) Add the borrowed $\dfrac{20}{20}$ to $\dfrac{4}{20}$ and subtract as before, as shown at the right.

$$\begin{array}{c|l} \overset{14}{\cancel{15}} & \dfrac{1}{5} = \dfrac{4}{20} + \dfrac{20}{20} \longrightarrow \dfrac{24}{20} \\[2ex] -8 & \dfrac{3}{4} = \dfrac{15}{20} \qquad\quad \longrightarrow \dfrac{15}{20} \\[2ex] \hline 6 & \qquad \dfrac{}{20} \qquad\quad \longrightarrow \dfrac{9}{20} = 6\dfrac{9}{20} \end{array}$$

Answer: $15\dfrac{1}{5} - 8\dfrac{3}{4} = 6\dfrac{9}{20}$

Remember: Any whole number divided by itself is an equivalent fraction that has a value of 1.

$$\dfrac{2}{2} = 1 \qquad \dfrac{5}{5} = 1 \qquad \dfrac{20}{20} = 1 \qquad \dfrac{100}{100} = 1 \qquad \text{etc.}$$

EXERCISES

In 1 to 21, subtract the lower number from the upper number.

Sample solutions

a.
$$\begin{array}{c|l} 15 & \dfrac{3}{4} = \dfrac{6}{8} \\[2ex] 7 & \dfrac{3}{8} = \dfrac{3}{8} \\[2ex] \hline 8 & \dfrac{3}{8} = 8\dfrac{3}{8} \end{array}$$

b.
$$\begin{array}{c|l} \overset{17}{\cancel{18}} & \dfrac{1}{2} = \dfrac{4}{8} + \dfrac{8}{8} = \dfrac{12}{8} \\[2ex] 7 & \dfrac{5}{8} \longrightarrow \dfrac{5}{8} \\[2ex] \hline 10 & \dfrac{7}{8} = 10\dfrac{7}{8} \end{array}$$

1. $17\dfrac{4}{5}$

   $17\dfrac{2}{3}$

2. $23\dfrac{4}{7}$

   $15\dfrac{10}{21}$

3. $18\dfrac{1}{3}$

   $15\dfrac{1}{5}$

4. $26\dfrac{11}{16}$

   $18\dfrac{3}{8}$

5. $12\dfrac{1}{2}$

   $7\dfrac{4}{9}$

6. $14\dfrac{7}{12}$

   $6\dfrac{2}{5}$

7. $27\frac{4}{5}$

   $8\frac{2}{3}$
___

8. $13\frac{5}{8}$

  $6\frac{11}{20}$
___

9. $32\frac{12}{16}$

  $8\frac{5}{8}$
___

10. $21\frac{5}{7}$

  $13\frac{2}{3}$
___

11. $18\frac{2}{3}$

  $9\frac{3}{8}$
___

12. $23\frac{5}{16}$

  $15\frac{3}{4}$
___

13. $18\frac{2}{7}$

  $17\frac{1}{3}$
___

14. $15\frac{3}{8}$

  $8\frac{2}{3}$
___

15. 20

  $7\frac{5}{8}$
___

16. 16

  $9\frac{11}{16}$
___

17. $23\frac{2}{3}$

  $15\frac{3}{12}$
___

18. $21\frac{7}{16}$

  $8\frac{35}{64}$
___

19. $24\frac{1}{5}$

  $18\frac{5}{6}$
___

20. $27\frac{3}{12}$

  $15\frac{17}{30}$
___

21. $24\frac{4}{9}$

  $13\frac{27}{45}$
___

APPLICATION PROBLEMS

1. A bolt of velvet contains $23\frac{3}{4}$ yards. If a clerk sold $4\frac{2}{3}$ yards, how much velvet is left in the bolt?

_____

2. Mrs. Wilson bought a $12\frac{1}{2}$-pound turkey. After being roasted, the turkey weighed $8\frac{5}{8}$ pounds. How much less does the turkey weigh after roasting?

_____

3. A carpenter had a board that measured $15\frac{1}{3}$ feet. He cut off a piece of board that measured $8\frac{5}{8}$ feet. How many feet of board are left?

_____

4. A baker had $8\frac{1}{2}$ dozen eggs and used up $5\frac{3}{4}$ dozen. How many eggs are left?

_____

5. Mrs. Brown had $8\frac{1}{3}$ cups of flour and used $3\frac{4}{5}$ cups to bake a cake. How many cups of flour are left?

_____

Review of Part VII (Units 27 to 31)

In 1 to 9, add. Change all improper fractions to mixed numbers.

1.
$$\frac{3}{4}$$
$$\frac{5}{8}$$
$$+\frac{11}{16}$$

2.
$$\frac{4}{5}$$
$$\frac{3}{4}$$
$$+\frac{13}{20}$$

3.
$$\frac{3}{8}$$
$$\frac{3}{4}$$
$$+\frac{7}{10}$$

4.
$$\frac{2}{3}$$
$$\frac{5}{8}$$
$$+\frac{11}{12}$$

5.
$$\frac{3}{5}$$
$$\frac{3}{4}$$
$$+\frac{7}{20}$$

6.
$$\frac{3}{4}$$
$$\frac{5}{8}$$
$$+\frac{3}{5}$$

7.
$$12\frac{2}{3}$$
$$15\frac{4}{5}$$
$$+19\frac{8}{15}$$

8.
$$24\frac{4}{5}$$
$$23\frac{13}{15}$$
$$+36\frac{2}{3}$$

9.
$$32\frac{3}{4}$$
$$27\frac{5}{6}$$
$$+42\frac{7}{9}$$

In 10 to 21, subtract.

10.
$$\frac{3}{4}$$
$$-\frac{5}{8}$$

11.
$$\frac{2}{3}$$
$$-\frac{3}{5}$$

12.
$$\frac{4}{5}$$
$$-\frac{3}{4}$$

13.
$$\frac{7}{8}$$
$$-\frac{4}{5}$$

14.
$$\frac{9}{16}$$
$$-\frac{3}{8}$$

15.
$$\frac{5}{6}$$
$$-\frac{1}{4}$$

16. $12\frac{1}{3}$

$-7\frac{3}{4}$

17. $23\frac{2}{3}$

$-17\frac{7}{8}$

18. $28\frac{3}{8}$

$-12\frac{3}{5}$

19. $35\frac{1}{6}$

$-23\frac{4}{5}$

20. $38\frac{3}{7}$

$-15\frac{5}{6}$

21. $18\frac{3}{16}$

$-5\frac{5}{8}$

Part VIII. Multiplying Fractions

Unit 32. Multiplication of Fractions

Every fraction is made up of a numerator (top number) and a denominator (bottom number). To multiply one fraction by another fraction, you must multiply the numerator by the numerator and the denominator by the denominator.

Rule: To multiply fractions, multiply the top numbers and multiply the bottom numbers to get a single fraction.

You can remember this rule as "multiply across." Whenever possible, reduce your product to lowest terms.

EXAMPLE 1. Multiply: $\frac{3}{4} \times \frac{2}{5}$

Solution: Multiply the top numbers and multiply the bottom numbers.

$$\frac{3}{4} \times \frac{2}{5} = \frac{6}{20}$$

Reduce $\frac{6}{20}$ to lowest terms.

$$2 \left| \frac{\overset{3}{\cancel{6}}}{\underset{10}{\cancel{20}}} \right. = \frac{3}{10}$$

Answer: $\frac{3}{4} \times \frac{2}{5} = \frac{3}{10}$

To simplify the multiplication of fractions, you may *divide any top number into any bottom number*, or you may *divide any bottom number into any top number*.

To simplify, see if any top number divides evenly (without a remainder) into any bottom number, or if any bottom number divides evenly into any top number. Then divide this number into both the top and bottom numbers.

EXAMPLE 2. Multiply: $\frac{3}{8} \times \frac{4}{5}$

Solution: Notice that 4 divides evenly into 8. Therefore, before multiplying, divide the *top number*, 4, into the *bottom number*, 8.

$$\frac{3}{\underset{2}{\cancel{8}}} \times \frac{\overset{1}{\cancel{4}}}{5} \qquad$$ Think: "4 into 4 goes 1, and 4 into 8 goes 2."

Multiply across.

$$\frac{3}{\underset{2}{\cancel{8}}} \times \frac{\overset{1}{\cancel{4}}}{5} = \frac{3}{10}$$

Answer: $\frac{3}{8} \times \frac{4}{5} = \frac{3}{10}$

There are times when you can divide in more than one way.

EXAMPLE 3. Multiply: $\frac{7}{8} \times \frac{4}{21}$

Solution: Notice that 7 divides evenly into 21 and that 4 divides evenly into 8. Divide *both pairs* of numbers; then multiply across.

$$\frac{\overset{1}{\cancel{7}}}{\underset{2}{\cancel{8}}} \times \frac{\overset{1}{\cancel{4}}}{\underset{3}{\cancel{21}}} = \frac{1}{6} \qquad$$ Think: "7 into 7 goes 1, and 7 into 21 goes 3. 4 into 4 goes 1, and 4 into 8 goes 2."

Answer: $\frac{7}{8} \times \frac{4}{21} = \frac{1}{6}$

Whenever *any number* divides evenly into both a top number and a bottom number, you may simplify by dividing.

EXAMPLE 4. Multiply: $\dfrac{8}{9} \times \dfrac{7}{12}$

Solution: The number 4 divides evenly into both the top number, 8, and the bottom number, 12. Therefore, you can simplify by dividing 4 into 8 and 4 into 12.

$$\dfrac{\overset{2}{\cancel{8}}}{9} \times \dfrac{7}{\underset{3}{\cancel{12}}} = \dfrac{14}{27}$$ Think: "4 into 8 goes 2, and 4 into 12 goes 3."

Answer: $\dfrac{8}{9} \times \dfrac{7}{12} = \dfrac{14}{27}$

You have already learned (Unit 19) how to simplify division by crossing out the end zeros, one for one, in the dividend and in the divisor. When multiplying fractions, you may get rid of the same number of end zeros in a top number and in a bottom number.

EXAMPLE 5. Multiply: $\dfrac{99}{100} \times \dfrac{10}{13}$

Solution: Cross out one end zero in the top number, 10; cross out one end zero in the bottom number, 100.

$$\dfrac{99}{1\cancel{0}\cancel{0}} \times \dfrac{1\cancel{0}}{13} = \dfrac{99}{130}$$

Answer: $\dfrac{99}{100} \times \dfrac{10}{13} = \dfrac{99}{130}$

Remember: You must divide into a top number and a bottom number. You must *never* divide a top number into a top number, or a bottom number into a bottom number.

By following the above rules for multiplication and for simplifying by dividing, you can multiply more than two fractions.

EXAMPLE 6. Multiply: $\dfrac{3}{8} \times \dfrac{4}{9} \times \dfrac{3}{15}$

Solution: Divide in as many ways as you can; then multiply across.

$$\dfrac{\overset{1}{\cancel{3}}}{\underset{2}{\cancel{8}}} \times \dfrac{\overset{1}{\cancel{4}}}{\underset{3}{\cancel{9}}} \times \dfrac{\overset{1}{\cancel{3}}}{\underset{5}{\cancel{15}}} = \dfrac{1}{30}$$

Answer: $\dfrac{3}{8} \times \dfrac{4}{9} \times \dfrac{3}{15} = \dfrac{1}{30}$

EXERCISES

In 1 to 24, multiply. Simplify by dividing where possible; reduce answers to lowest terms.

Sample solutions

a. $\dfrac{5}{6} \times \dfrac{7}{8} = \dfrac{35}{48}$

b. $\dfrac{2}{\cancel{3}} \times \dfrac{\overset{1}{\cancel{3}}}{5} = \dfrac{2}{5}$

c. $\dfrac{\overset{1}{\cancel{3}}}{\underset{2}{\cancel{4}}} \times \dfrac{\overset{3}{\cancel{6}}}{\underset{5}{\cancel{15}}} = \dfrac{3}{10}$

d. $\dfrac{\overset{1}{\cancel{3}}}{5} \times \dfrac{7}{\underset{3}{\cancel{9}}} \times \dfrac{\overset{1}{\cancel{4}}}{\underset{2}{\cancel{8}}} = \dfrac{7}{30}$

1. $\dfrac{4}{5} \times \dfrac{3}{4}$

2. $\dfrac{5}{6} \times \dfrac{3}{8}$

3. $\dfrac{5}{8} \times \dfrac{3}{4}$

4. $\dfrac{2}{5} \times \dfrac{5}{8}$ **5.** $\dfrac{12}{16} \times \dfrac{3}{5}$ **6.** $\dfrac{8}{9} \times \dfrac{2}{12}$

7. $\dfrac{5}{6} \times \dfrac{4}{5}$ **8.** $\dfrac{3}{4} \times \dfrac{4}{9}$ **9.** $\dfrac{5}{8} \times \dfrac{16}{25}$

10. $\dfrac{7}{8} \times \dfrac{12}{21}$ **11.** $\dfrac{3}{4} \times \dfrac{5}{8}$ **12.** $\dfrac{3}{8} \times \dfrac{4}{5}$

13. $\dfrac{9}{16} \times \dfrac{5}{6}$ **14.** $\dfrac{2}{3} \times \dfrac{1}{2} \times \dfrac{6}{7}$ **15.** $\dfrac{5}{16} \times \dfrac{4}{8} \times \dfrac{7}{10}$

16. $\dfrac{1}{4} \times \dfrac{5}{6} \times \dfrac{2}{5}$ **17.** $\dfrac{3}{4} \times \dfrac{1}{2} \times \dfrac{3}{5}$ **18.** $\dfrac{5}{12} \times \dfrac{4}{5} \times \dfrac{3}{16}$

19. $\dfrac{2}{3} \times \dfrac{5}{8} \times \dfrac{3}{10}$ **20.** $\dfrac{3}{4} \times \dfrac{5}{6} \times \dfrac{3}{5}$ **21.** $\dfrac{5}{16} \times \dfrac{2}{3} \times \dfrac{1}{7}$

22. $\dfrac{2}{5} \times \dfrac{3}{4} \times \dfrac{15}{16}$ **23.** $\dfrac{3}{8} \times \dfrac{4}{7} \times \dfrac{5}{6}$ **24.** $\dfrac{3}{16} \times \dfrac{7}{12} \times \dfrac{3}{4}$

APPLICATION PROBLEMS

Sample solution

If the width of a river is $\dfrac{5}{8}$ of a mile, how far from either shore is a boat located exactly in midstream?

$$\frac{1}{2} \text{ of } \frac{5}{8} = \frac{1}{2} \times \frac{5}{8} = \frac{5}{16} \qquad\qquad \underline{\frac{5}{16} \text{ mi.}}$$

1. Mrs. Wilson had a ham that weighed $\frac{3}{4}$ pound. If she used $\frac{1}{4}$ of the ham, what fraction of a pound did she use?

2. Mrs. Brown had $\frac{1}{2}$ dozen eggs and used $\frac{1}{3}$ of them. How many eggs did she use?

3. Jim lives $\frac{3}{4}$ of a mile from town. If he walked $\frac{2}{3}$ of the distance, what part of a mile did he walk?

4. Mr. Brown spent $\frac{3}{5}$ of his vacation money during the first week of his trip. If $\frac{2}{3}$ of the money went for food and lodging, what part of his entire vacation money went for food and lodging?

5. A truck driver had a load of $\frac{7}{8}$ ton of sand. If he delivered $\frac{4}{5}$ of the sand, what part of a ton did he deliver?

6. If one man can mow his lawn in $\frac{3}{4}$ of an hour, how long will it take two men to do the job? (Assume that the two men work at the same speed.)

7. Movie star Cliff Dangle has an agent who gets $\frac{1}{10}$ of his earnings. Last year, Cliff earned $\frac{3}{4}$ of a million dollars. What fraction of a million did the agent get?

8. What fraction of a foot is $\frac{3}{8}$ of an inch? (*Hint:* 1 inch $= \frac{1}{12}$ of a foot.)

9. A *furlong* is a distance that is equal to $\frac{1}{8}$ of a mile. How long is $\frac{3}{4}$ furlong?

Unit 33. Multiplication of Mixed Numbers and Whole Numbers by a Mixed Number

MIXED NUMBERS

To multiply a mixed number by a mixed number, *change the mixed numbers to improper fractions.* Then cancel out where possible and multiply across.

EXAMPLE 1. Multiply: $3\frac{3}{4} \times 4\frac{2}{3}$

Solution: Change the mixed numbers to improper fractions.

$3\frac{3}{4} = \frac{15}{4}$ Think: "$4 \times 3 = 12$, and $12 + 3 = 15$."

$4\frac{2}{3} = \frac{14}{3}$ Think: "$3 \times 4 = 12$, and $12 + 2 = 14$."

Cancel out and multiply across.

$$\frac{\overset{5}{\cancel{15}}}{\underset{2}{\cancel{4}}} \times \frac{\overset{7}{\cancel{14}}}{\underset{1}{\cancel{3}}} = \frac{35}{2} = 17\frac{1}{2}$$

Answer: $3\frac{3}{4} \times 4\frac{2}{3} = 17\frac{1}{2}$

WHOLE AND MIXED NUMBERS

To multiply a whole number by a mixed number, change the mixed number to an improper fraction and also *change the whole number to an improper fraction.*

Rule: To change a whole number to an improper fraction, draw a fraction bar under the whole number and insert the number 1 as the denominator.

$$2 = \frac{2}{1} \qquad 5 = \frac{5}{1} \qquad 20 = \frac{20}{1} \quad \text{etc.}$$

After you change the whole number and the mixed number to improper fractions, cancel out where possible and multiply across.

EXAMPLE 2. Multiply: $6 \times 3\frac{2}{3}$

Solution: Change both numbers to improper fractions: $6 = \frac{6}{1}$ and $3\frac{2}{3} = \frac{11}{3}$. Cancel out and multiply across.

$$\frac{\overset{2}{\cancel{6}}}{1} \times \frac{11}{\underset{1}{\cancel{3}}} = \frac{22}{1} = 22$$

Answer: $6 \times 3\frac{2}{3} = 22$

EXERCISES

In 1 to 16, multiply. Reduce answers to lowest terms.

Sample solutions

a. $2\frac{1}{2} \times 4\frac{2}{3} = \frac{5}{\cancel{2}_1} \times \frac{\cancel{14}^7}{3} = \frac{35}{3} = 11\frac{2}{3}$

b. $4\frac{3}{8} \times 8 = \frac{35}{\cancel{8}_1} \times \frac{\cancel{8}^1}{1} = \frac{35}{1} = 35$

1. $4\frac{1}{3} \times 3\frac{1}{5}$

2. $5\frac{1}{4} \times 2\frac{1}{3}$

3. $7\frac{3}{8} \times 9\frac{5}{6}$

4. $8\frac{5}{9} \times 4\frac{1}{11}$

5. $6\frac{5}{6} \times 3\frac{7}{8}$

6. $3\frac{4}{5} \times 5\frac{5}{8}$

7. $6\frac{2}{3} \times 4\frac{7}{8}$

8. $8\frac{4}{5} \times 3\frac{5}{9}$

9. $5 \times 3\frac{3}{4}$

10. $7 \times 4\frac{2}{3}$

11. $3\frac{7}{8} \times 7$

12. $6\frac{3}{16} \times 3$

13. $5 \times 6\frac{3}{5}$

14. $7 \times 4\frac{5}{6}$

15. $3 \times 5\frac{2}{5}$

16. $4\frac{4}{5} \times 8$

APPLICATION PROBLEMS

1. How many feet of lumber are needed to make 12 shelves, each measuring $5\frac{2}{3}$ feet?

2. Mary needs $3\frac{2}{5}$ yards of material to make a dress. How many yards of material will she need to make 4 dresses?

3. Tom earns $150 a week and saves $\frac{1}{3}$ of his income. How much does he save every week?

4. Velvet sells for $4 a yard. How much will $5\frac{3}{4}$ yards cost?

5. A ground beef pattie weighs $\frac{1}{4}$ pound. How many pounds will 12 patties weigh?

Unit 34. Multiplication of a Large Whole Number by a Mixed Number

Suppose you have to multiply a large whole number (a number with three or more digits) by a mixed number. The following procedure is usually easier than changing both numbers to improper fractions.

To multiply a large whole number by a mixed number, multiply the whole number by the *whole-number part of the mixed number*. Then multiply the whole number by the *fraction part of the mixed number*. Combine both answers for the final product.

EXAMPLE 1. Multiply: $235 \times 25\frac{3}{5}$

Solution: Multiply the whole number, 235, by the whole-number part of the mixed number, 25.

$$
\begin{array}{r}
235 \\
\times\ 25 \quad\dfrac{3}{5} \\
\hline
1\ 175 \\
4\ 70 \\
\hline
5,875
\end{array}
$$

Next, multiply the whole number, 235, by the fraction part of the mixed number, $\frac{3}{5}$. Combine both answers for the final product.

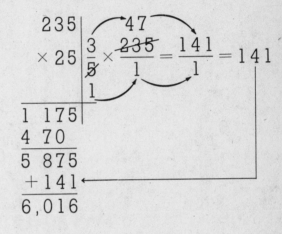

$$
\frac{3}{5} \times \frac{\overset{47}{\cancel{235}}}{1} = \frac{141}{1} = 141
$$

$$
\begin{array}{r}
235 \\
\times\ 25 \\
\hline
1\ 175 \\
4\ 70 \\
\hline
5\ 875 \\
+\ 141 \\
\hline
6,016
\end{array}
$$

Answer: $235 \times 25\frac{3}{5} = 6,016$

EXAMPLE 2. Multiply: $105 \times 79\frac{1}{3}$

Solution:

$$
\frac{1}{3} \times \frac{\overset{35}{\cancel{105}}}{1} = \frac{35}{1} = 35
$$

$$
\begin{array}{r}
105 \\
\times\ 79 \\
\hline
945 \\
7\ 35 \\
\hline
8\ 295 \\
+\ 35 \\
\hline
8,330
\end{array}
$$

Answer: $105 \times 79\frac{1}{3} = 8,330$

EXERCISES

In 1 to 15, multiply.

1. $\begin{array}{r} 135 \\ \times\, 18\frac{2}{3} \\ \hline \end{array}$

2. $\begin{array}{r} 248 \\ \times\, 26\frac{5}{8} \\ \hline \end{array}$

3. $\begin{array}{r} 326 \\ \times\, 38\frac{1}{3} \\ \hline \end{array}$

4. $\begin{array}{r} 530 \\ \times\, 45\frac{7}{10} \\ \hline \end{array}$

5. $\begin{array}{r} 262 \\ \times\, 35\frac{3}{4} \\ \hline \end{array}$

6. $\begin{array}{r} 436 \\ \times\, 18\frac{1}{2} \\ \hline \end{array}$

7. $\begin{array}{r} 342 \\ \times\, 23\frac{3}{5} \\ \hline \end{array}$

8. $\begin{array}{r} 287 \\ \times\, 32\frac{5}{7} \\ \hline \end{array}$

9. $\begin{array}{r} 416 \\ \times\, 43\frac{9}{16} \\ \hline \end{array}$

10. $\begin{array}{r} 369 \\ \times\, 37\frac{2}{3} \\ \hline \end{array}$

11. $\begin{array}{r} 535 \\ \times\, 36\frac{4}{5} \\ \hline \end{array}$

12. $\begin{array}{r} 328 \\ \times\, 43\frac{3}{4} \\ \hline \end{array}$

13. 486
$\times\, 46\frac{1}{3}$
_____

14. 484
$\times\, 26\frac{5}{16}$
_____

15. 460
$\times\, 34\frac{4}{5}$
_____

APPLICATION PROBLEMS

1. A can of green beans weighs $4\frac{1}{2}$ ounces. How many ounces will 235 cans weigh?

_____

2. A car averages $18\frac{1}{2}$ miles to a gallon of gasoline. How many miles will be traveled on 237 gallons?

_____

3. A hotel needs $21\frac{3}{4}$ yards of carpeting to cover the floor of one room. How many yards of carpeting will be needed to cover the floors of 253 rooms? (All the rooms are the same size.)

_____

4. A bottle of salad oil holds $12\frac{2}{3}$ ounces. How many ounces will 345 bottles hold?

_____

5. A brick weighs $3\frac{1}{5}$ pounds. How much will 460 bricks weigh?

_____

Review of Part VIII (Units 32 to 34)

In 1 to 18, multiply. Where possible, simplify by dividing numerators and denominators by the same number. Express all improper fractions as mixed numbers.

1. $\dfrac{3}{4} \times \dfrac{3}{5} =$

2. $\dfrac{4}{5} \times \dfrac{3}{8} =$

3. $\dfrac{2}{3} \times \dfrac{3}{10} =$

4. $\dfrac{5}{8} \times \dfrac{12}{15} =$ 5. $\dfrac{3}{7} \times \dfrac{5}{6} \times \dfrac{21}{30} =$ 6. $\dfrac{3}{8} \times \dfrac{2}{5} \times \dfrac{5}{6} =$

7. $\dfrac{5}{16} \times \dfrac{4}{15} \times \dfrac{3}{4} =$ 8. $\dfrac{2}{5} \times \dfrac{3}{4} \times \dfrac{5}{6} =$ 9. $3\dfrac{1}{2} \times 5\dfrac{3}{4} =$

10. $7 \times 6\dfrac{4}{5} =$ 11. $4\dfrac{2}{3} \times 6 =$ 12. $5\dfrac{3}{5} \times 4\dfrac{2}{3} =$

13. $6\dfrac{1}{3} \times 4 =$ 14. $3\dfrac{3}{8} \times 4\dfrac{1}{4} =$

15. $\begin{array}{r} 563 \\ \times\, 67\frac{2}{3} \\ \hline \end{array}$ 16. $\begin{array}{r} 848 \\ \times\, 85\frac{3}{4} \\ \hline \end{array}$ 17. $\begin{array}{r} 470 \\ \times\, 37\frac{4}{5} \\ \hline \end{array}$ 18. $\begin{array}{r} 650 \\ \times\, 78\frac{7}{10} \\ \hline \end{array}$

Part IX. Dividing Fractions

Unit 35. Division of Fractions

Words to know

When we **invert** something, we turn it upside down. When we **invert a fraction**, we turn it upside down by putting the top number on the bottom and the bottom number on top.

When a division problem with fractions is indicated with the ÷ symbol, the second fraction (the right-hand fraction) is the divisor. Thus, in the problem $\frac{1}{2} \div \frac{1}{4}$, the divisor is $\frac{1}{4}$.

To divide one fraction by another fraction, indicate the division with the ÷ symbol. Then follow this rule:

Rule: To divide fractions, *invert the divisor* (the second fraction) and change the problem to multiplication.

To **invert a fraction**, reverse the numerator and the denominator.

When you invert $\frac{2}{3}$, you get $\frac{3}{2}$.

When you invert $\frac{7}{8}$, you get $\frac{8}{7}$.

When you invert $\frac{99}{100}$, you get $\frac{100}{99}$.

Remember: The symbol ÷ means "divided by."

EXAMPLE 1. Divide: $\frac{3}{4} \div \frac{3}{8}$

Solution: First, bring down the left-hand fraction exactly as it is written. Then, change the ÷ symbol to a × symbol. Finally, *invert* the second fraction (the divisor).

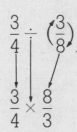

Solve the multiplication problem.

$$\frac{\overset{1}{\cancel{3}}}{\underset{1}{\cancel{4}}} \times \frac{\overset{2}{\cancel{8}}}{\underset{1}{\cancel{3}}} = \frac{2}{1} = 2$$

Answer: $\frac{3}{4} \div \frac{3}{8} = 2$

Recall (Unit 13) that a division problem asks how many times the divisor is contained in the dividend. Example 1 asks, "How many $\frac{3}{8}$'s are there in $\frac{3}{4}$?" Applying the rule, the answer is 2. Does this make sense? Do 2 $\frac{3}{8}$'s make $\frac{3}{4}$? As you can see, they do: 2 $\frac{3}{8}$'s $= 2 \times \frac{3}{8} = \frac{2}{1} \times \frac{3}{8} = \frac{6}{8} = \frac{3}{4}$.

We check division problems with fractions just as we do with whole numbers: The answer (quotient) multiplied by the divisor should equal the dividend.

113

EXAMPLE 2. Divide and check: $\frac{7}{8} \div 4$

Solution: Rewrite the whole number, 4, as $\frac{4}{1}$. Then invert the divisor and multiply.

$$\frac{7}{8} \div \left(\frac{4}{1}\right)$$

$$\frac{7}{8} \times \frac{1}{4} = \frac{7}{32}$$

Check: The quotient, $\frac{7}{32}$, times the divisor, 4, should equal the dividend, $\frac{7}{8}$.

$$\frac{7}{\underset{8}{\cancel{32}}} \times \frac{\overset{1}{\cancel{4}}}{1} = \frac{7}{8} \quad \checkmark$$

Answer: $\frac{7}{8} \div 4 = \frac{7}{32}$

EXAMPLE 3. Divide $\frac{3}{4}$ into $\frac{1}{2}$ and check.

Solution: Recall that the number doing the dividing is the divisor. Thus, $\frac{3}{4}$ is the divisor. (Mentally change "divide $\frac{3}{4}$ into $\frac{1}{2}$" to "$\frac{1}{2} \div \frac{3}{4}$.")

$$\frac{1}{2} \div \frac{3}{4}$$

$$\underset{1}{\frac{1}{\cancel{2}}} \times \frac{\overset{2}{\cancel{4}}}{3} = \frac{2}{3}$$

Check:

$$\underset{1}{\overset{1}{\frac{\cancel{2}}{3}}} \times \overset{1}{\underset{2}{\frac{\cancel{3}}{\cancel{4}}}} = \frac{1}{2} \quad \checkmark$$

Answer: $\frac{3}{4}$ divided into $\frac{1}{2}$ is $\frac{2}{3}$.

EXERCISES

In 1 to 16, divide.

1. $\frac{3}{5} \div \frac{3}{4}$ 　　2. $\frac{2}{7} \div \frac{4}{21}$ 　　3. $\frac{5}{8} \div \frac{7}{8}$ 　　4. $\frac{3}{16} \div \frac{4}{9}$

5. $\frac{3}{5} \div \frac{9}{10}$ 　　6. $\frac{5}{6} \div \frac{7}{12}$ 　　7. $\frac{1}{2} \div \frac{7}{16}$ 　　8. $\frac{11}{12} \div \frac{4}{7}$

9. $\frac{2}{3} \div \frac{4}{5}$ 　　10. $\frac{5}{6} \div \frac{7}{8}$ 　　11. $\frac{5}{8} \div \frac{5}{12}$ 　　12. $\frac{5}{8} \div \frac{5}{8}$

13. $\frac{7}{8} \div \frac{3}{16}$ 　　14. $\frac{3}{4} \div \frac{4}{5}$ 　　15. $\frac{1}{3} \div \frac{7}{8}$ 　　16. $\frac{3}{8} \div \frac{7}{8}$

APPLICATION PROBLEMS

In 1 to 5, check your answers.

1. How many $\frac{1}{8}$'s of a pound are there in $\frac{3}{4}$ of a pound?

_____

2. How many barrels of sand can be filled with $\frac{3}{4}$ ton of sand if each barrel can hold $\frac{1}{16}$ of a ton?

_____

3. If you have $\frac{7}{8}$ gallon of alcohol, how many pint-size containers can you fill? (*Hint:* There are 8 pints to a gallon.)

_____

4. A bus is dispatched every 3 minutes. How many buses are dispatched in $\frac{3}{4}$ of an hour? $\left(Hint: 3 \text{ minutes} = \frac{3}{60} \text{ of an hour.}\right)$

_____

5. How many 6-inch pieces of pipe can be cut from a length of pipe measuring $\frac{2}{3}$ yard? $\left(Hint: 6 \text{ inches} = \frac{1}{6} \text{ of a yard.}\right)$

_____

Unit 36. Division of Mixed and Whole Numbers by Mixed Numbers

MIXED NUMBERS

To divide one mixed number by another mixed number, *change the mixed numbers to improper fractions*. Then divide, as shown in the preceding unit, by inverting the divisor and multiplying.

EXAMPLE 1. Divide: $3\frac{2}{3} \div 4\frac{1}{2}$

Solution: Change $3\frac{2}{3}$ to $\frac{11}{3}$ and change $4\frac{1}{2}$ to $\frac{9}{2}$. Then divide.

$$\frac{11}{3} \div \left(\frac{9}{2}\right)$$

$$\frac{11}{3} \times \frac{2}{9} = \frac{22}{27}$$

Answer: $3\frac{2}{3} \div 4\frac{1}{2} = \frac{22}{27}$

WHOLE AND MIXED NUMBERS

To divide a whole number by a mixed number, *change both the mixed number and the whole number to improper fractions*. Then divide.

EXAMPLE 2. Divide: $5 \div 1\frac{1}{2}$

Solution: Change 5 to $\frac{5}{1}$ and change $1\frac{1}{2}$ to $\frac{3}{2}$.

$$\frac{5}{1} \div \left(\frac{3}{2}\right)$$

$$\frac{5}{1} \times \frac{2}{3} = \frac{10}{3} = 3\frac{1}{3}$$

Answer: $5 \div 1\frac{1}{2} = 3\frac{1}{3}$

EXERCISES

In 1 to 14, divide.

1. $4\frac{3}{4} \div 5\frac{1}{2}$

2. $3\frac{2}{3} \div 6\frac{3}{5}$

3. $5\frac{3}{16} \div 2\frac{1}{2}$

4. $2\frac{1}{12} \div 3\frac{3}{4}$

5. $4\frac{2}{3} \div 4\frac{4}{6}$

6. $6\frac{2}{3} \div 3\frac{1}{5}$

7. $3\frac{3}{4} \div 2\frac{2}{5}$

8. $14\frac{1}{2} \div 3\frac{5}{8}$

9. $2\frac{2}{3} \div 7\frac{1}{2}$

10. $8 \div \frac{3}{4}$

11. $3\frac{4}{5} \div 8$

12. $5\frac{3}{4} \div 5$

13. $8 \div 2\frac{2}{5}$

14. $6 \div 7\frac{7}{8}$

APPLICATION PROBLEMS

In 1 to 5, check your answers.

1. If a dress requires $3\frac{1}{5}$ yards of material, how many dresses can be made with 30 yards of material?

    _____

2. A plane flies 845 miles in $1\frac{2}{3}$ hours. How many miles does the plane average in one hour?

    _____

3. Tom drove 153 miles in $3\frac{1}{2}$ hours. How many miles did he average in one hour?

_____

4. If $1\frac{3}{4}$ ounces of butter are used to make a box of cookies, how many boxes of cookies can be made with 12 pounds of butter?

_____

5. If a board $10\frac{1}{4}$ feet long is cut into 6 equal pieces, how long will each piece be?

_____

Unit 37. Simplifying Complex Fractions

Words to know

So far, in our work with fractions, numerators and denominators have always been whole numbers. It is possible for the numerator or the denominator, or both, to be a fraction or a mixed number. When this happens, the fraction is a **complex fraction**.

The process of division can be indicated in three ways. Thus, "3 divided by 4" can be shown by:

(1) the division box, $4\overline{)3}$.

(2) the division symbol, $3 \div 4$.

(3) the fraction bar, $\frac{3}{4}$.

The fraction bar, between the numerator and the denominator, can be read as "divided by." You will use this fact to simplify **complex fractions**, which are fractions that have a fraction in the numerator or in the denominator, or in both.

To "simplify" a complex fraction means to change it to a proper fraction or a mixed number that has the same value.

EXAMPLE 1. Simplify: $\dfrac{\frac{1}{2}}{\frac{2}{3}}$

Solution: Instead of reading this complex fraction

as "$\frac{1}{2}$ over $\frac{2}{3}$," read it as "$\frac{1}{2}$ divided by $\frac{2}{3}$." In symbols:

$$\frac{\frac{1}{2}}{\frac{2}{3}} = \frac{1}{2} \div \frac{2}{3}$$

To simplify the complex fraction, do the indicated division.

$$\frac{1}{2} \div \frac{2}{3} = \frac{1}{2} \times \frac{3}{2} = \frac{3}{4}$$

Answer: $\dfrac{\frac{1}{2}}{\frac{2}{3}} = \frac{3}{4}$

Rule: To simplify a complex fraction, rewrite the fraction as a division problem with the fraction in the numerator divided by the fraction in the denominator. Then do the division.

EXAMPLE 2. Simplify: $\dfrac{3\frac{1}{4}}{5}$

Solution: Rewrite the complex fraction as a division problem.

$$\dfrac{3\frac{1}{4}}{5} = 3\frac{1}{4} \div 5 = \dfrac{13}{4} \div \dfrac{5}{1}$$

Do the division.

$$\dfrac{13}{4} \div \dfrac{5}{1} = \dfrac{13}{4} \times \dfrac{1}{5} = \dfrac{13}{20}$$

Answer: $\dfrac{3\frac{1}{4}}{5} = \dfrac{13}{20}$

EXERCISES

In 1 to 12, simplify the complex fraction.

1. $\dfrac{\frac{3}{8}}{\frac{2}{3}}$

2. $\dfrac{\frac{3}{4}}{\frac{7}{8}}$

3. $\dfrac{\frac{3}{5}}{5}$

4. $\dfrac{16\frac{2}{3}}{100}$

5. $\dfrac{6}{3\frac{3}{4}}$

6. $\dfrac{\frac{3}{8}}{\frac{5}{16}}$

7. $\dfrac{3\frac{2}{3}}{4\frac{4}{5}}$

8. $\dfrac{27\frac{1}{2}}{36\frac{4}{7}}$

9. $\dfrac{37\frac{1}{2}}{100}$

10. $\dfrac{12\frac{5}{6}}{8\frac{2}{3}}$

11. $\dfrac{12\frac{1}{2}}{100}$

12. $\dfrac{\frac{3}{5}}{4\frac{1}{3}}$

Unit 38. Finding a Number When a Fractional Part of It Is Known

Suppose that 5 students in a class are absent, and this represents $\frac{1}{5}$ of the number of students in the class. How would you find the total number of students?

Rule: To find a number when you know a fractional part of it: Divide the known fractional part, which is a given number, by the fraction. The quotient will be the unknown number.

Applying the rule, we divide 5 by $\frac{1}{5}$:

$$5 \div \frac{1}{5} = \frac{5}{1} \times \frac{5}{1} = \frac{25}{1} = 25$$

There are 25 students in the class.

EXAMPLE 1. If a family spends $50 a week on food, and this is $\frac{2}{5}$ of the family's income, what is the total family income?

Solution: Since you know that $50 is $\frac{2}{5}$ of the total income, divide the $50 by $\frac{2}{5}$ to find the income.

$$50 \div \frac{2}{5} = \frac{\overset{25}{\cancel{50}}}{1} \times \frac{5}{\cancel{2}} = 125$$

Check: If the answer is correct, then $\frac{2}{5}$ of $125 should equal $50.

$$\frac{2}{\cancel{5}} \times \frac{\overset{25}{\cancel{125}}}{1} = 50 \quad \checkmark$$

Answer: The total family income is $125.

Remember: In a word problem, always check your answer against the *given facts*.

EXAMPLE 2. If $\frac{3}{16}$ of a number is 12, find the number.

Solution: To find the unknown number, divide the known fractional part, 12, by the fraction, $\frac{3}{16}$.

$$12 \div \frac{3}{16} = \frac{\overset{4}{\cancel{12}}}{1} \times \frac{16}{\cancel{3}} = 64$$

Check: Is $\frac{3}{16}$ of 64 equal to 12?

$$\frac{3}{\cancel{16}} \times \frac{\overset{4}{\cancel{64}}}{1} = 12 \quad \checkmark$$

Answer: 64

THE $\frac{IS}{OF}$ FRACTION

In solving word problems that deal with fractional parts of an unknown number, many students have difficulty remembering which given number should be divided into which. A good way to remember which number becomes the divisor and which number becomes the dividend is to think of the "fraction" $\frac{IS}{OF}$.

The number in the problem related to IS is written as the numerator, and will be the dividend when the fraction is simplified.

The number related to OF is written as the denominator, and will be the divisor when the fraction is simplified.

The given facts in Example 1 can be expressed as: "$50 is $\frac{2}{5}$ of what amount?" Using the $\frac{IS}{OF}$ method, write a fraction using the 50 ("$50 is") as the numerator and the $\frac{2}{5}$ ("$\frac{2}{5}$ of") as the denominator. You get $\frac{50}{\frac{2}{5}}$. Carry out the division.

$$\frac{IS}{OF} = \frac{50}{\frac{2}{5}} = 50 \div \frac{2}{5} = \frac{\overset{25}{\cancel{50}}}{1} \times \frac{5}{\cancel{2}} = 125$$

The given facts in Example 2 may be stated as: "12 is $\frac{3}{16}$ of what number?" Write the fraction 12 (IS) over $\frac{3}{16}$ (OF) to get $\frac{12}{\frac{3}{16}}$. Carry out the division.

$$\frac{IS}{OF} = \frac{12}{\frac{3}{16}} = 12 \div \frac{3}{16} = \frac{\overset{4}{\cancel{12}}}{1} \times \frac{16}{\cancel{3}} = 64$$

No matter what the actual wording may be, all problems about fractional parts of unknown numbers can be reworded so that one number is related to IS and the other is related to OF. You can then use the fraction $\frac{IS}{OF}$ to write a numerical fraction that will solve the problem.

EXERCISES

In 1 to 10, find the unknown number.

Sample solutions ──

a. $\frac{1}{2}$ of what number is 12?

$$\frac{IS}{OF} = \frac{12}{\frac{1}{2}} = \frac{12}{1} \times \frac{2}{1} = \frac{24}{1} = 24$$

b. 16 is $\frac{1}{2}$ of what number?

$$\frac{IS}{OF} = \frac{16}{\frac{1}{2}} = \frac{16}{1} \times \frac{2}{1} = \frac{32}{1} = 32$$

──

1. $\frac{3}{4}$ of what number is 26?

2. $\frac{2}{3}$ of what number is 14?

3. $\frac{5}{8}$ of what number is 20?

4. $\frac{2}{5}$ of what number is 42?

5. $\frac{3}{8}$ of what number is 12?

6. 35 is $\frac{1}{3}$ of what number?

7. 30 is $\frac{5}{8}$ of what number?

8. 27 is $\frac{2}{3}$ of what number?

9. 23 is $\frac{1}{4}$ of what number?

10. 40 is $\frac{1}{12}$ of what number?

APPLICATION PROBLEMS

Sample solution ──

At Newton High School, $\frac{1}{6}$ of the cheerleaders are Sophomores. Find the total number of cheerleaders if the number of Sophomores is 4.

$$\frac{IS}{OF} = \frac{4}{\frac{1}{6}} = \frac{4}{1} \times \frac{6}{1} = \frac{24}{1} = 24$$

24

──

1. Tom received 976 votes for G.O. President. If this represents $\frac{4}{5}$ of all the votes, how many students voted in the election?

_____

2. If the school baseball team won 22 games, which is $\frac{2}{3}$ of the games played, what was the total number of games played?

_____

3. A stadium has 20,088 general admission seats. Find the total number of seats if this represents $\frac{2}{3}$ of the stadium seats.

_____

4. John saves $45 a week. If he is saving $\frac{5}{8}$ of his weekly income, how much does he earn in a week?

_____

5. Mary spent $35, which is $\frac{1}{6}$ of her weekly income, on food. What is her weekly income?

_____

Unit 39. Finding What Fractional Part One Number Is of Another Number

Rule: To find what fractional part one number is of another number, write a fraction with the *total amount as the denominator* and the *partial amount as the numerator*.

EXAMPLE 1. If you had $25 and you spent $15, what fractional part of your money did you spent?

Solution: You spent $15 out of a total of $25. Therefore, write a fraction with 15 as the numerator and 25 as the denominator. Then reduce the fraction.

$$\frac{\text{amount spent}}{\text{total}} = \frac{\overset{3}{\cancel{15}}}{\underset{5}{\cancel{25}}} = \frac{3}{5}$$

Check: Does $\frac{3}{5}$ of $25 equal $15?

$$\frac{3}{\underset{1}{\cancel{5}}} \times \frac{\overset{5}{\cancel{25}}}{1} = \frac{15}{1} = 15 \quad \checkmark$$

Answer: You spent $\frac{3}{5}$ of your money.

Alternate Solution: You may use the $\frac{\text{IS}}{\text{OF}}$ method to solve this example. The problem asks: "15 is what fractional part of 25?" Write the fraction $\frac{\text{IS}}{\text{OF}} = \frac{15}{25}$ and reduce to lowest terms, $\frac{3}{5}$.

EXAMPLE 2. What part of 49 is 42?

Solution: Since 42 is the "part" and 49 is the "total," form a fraction with 42 as the numerator and 49 as the denominator. Reduce.

$$7 \,\Big|\, \frac{\overset{6}{\cancel{42}}}{\underset{7}{\cancel{49}}} = \frac{6}{7}$$

Check: Does $\frac{6}{7}$ of 49 equal 42?

$$\frac{6}{\underset{1}{\cancel{7}}} \times \frac{\overset{7}{\cancel{49}}}{1} = \frac{42}{1} = 42 \quad \checkmark$$

Answer: $\frac{6}{7}$

Alternate Solution: You may use the $\dfrac{IS}{OF}$ method to solve this example. The problem asks: "42 is what part of 49?" Write the fraction $\dfrac{IS}{OF} = \dfrac{42}{49}$ and reduce to lowest terms, $\dfrac{6}{7}$.

Note: In all word problems, look for *key words* to help you. When you are finding what fractional part one number is of another number, words such as *total*, *complete*, and *all* indicate the larger number (that will form the denominator). Words such as *part*, *portion*, and *amount spent* indicate the smaller number (that will form the numerator).

EXERCISES

In 1 to 14, find the fractional part.

Sample solutions

    a. 6 is what part of 12? $\dfrac{IS}{OF} = \dfrac{6}{12} = \dfrac{1}{2}$ **b.** What part of 18 is 3? $\dfrac{IS}{OF} = \dfrac{3}{18} = \dfrac{1}{6}$

1. 12 is what part of 18?   **2.** 16 is what part of 20?

3. 28 is what part of 42?   **4.** 49 is what part of 56?

5. 75 is what part of 100?   **6.** 35 is what part of 85?

7. 24 is what part of 64?   **8.** What part of 64 is 16?

9. What part of 75 is 25?   **10.** What part of 80 is 10?

11. What part of 72 is 30?   **12.** What part of 70 is 21?

13. What part of 144 is 36?   **14.** What part of 150 is 75?

APPLICATION PROBLEMS

Sample solution

Of 500 Seniors who entered the 12th grade at Washington High School, 475 received diplomas in June. What fraction of the Seniors graduated?

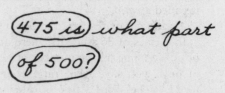

$$\frac{IS}{OF} = \frac{475}{500} \qquad 25\,\overline{\smash{\big)}\,\frac{\cancel{475}}{\cancel{500}}} \genfrac{}{}{0pt}{}{^{19}}{_{20}} = \frac{19}{20} \qquad\qquad \frac{19}{20}$$

1. There are 20 girls in a class of 36 students. What part of the class is girls?

_____

2. A car radiator holds 20 quarts. If it contains 8 quarts of antifreeze, what part of the contents is antifreeze?

_____

3. There are 8 students absent in a class of 32 students. What fractional part of the class is absent?

_____

4. Tom bought a television set for $125 and made a down payment of $50. What fractional part of the price is the down payment?

_____

5. John is 24 years old. If he spent 4 years in college, what part of his life did he spend in college?

_____

Unit 40. Ratios and Proportions

Words to know

We often compare two numbers by subtraction. Suppose the State University football team beats Tech by a score of 21 to 7. We say, "State beat Tech by 14 points," since $21 - 7 = 14$.

We can also compare two numbers by division. In the football game, we can say, "State scored 3 times as much as Tech," since $21 \div 7 = 3$.

When two numbers are compared by _division_, the indicated division is called a **ratio**.

When two ratios are equal, these two ratios form a **proportion**.

RATIOS

When a newspaper article tells us, "In River City, there are 3 registered Democrats for every 2 registered Republicans," we do not know how many Democrats or Republicans there are. The article tells us how the number of Democrats is _related_ to the number of Republicans. It does not tell us the actual numbers. Such a relationship between two numbers is called a _ratio_.

A **ratio** compares two numbers by division.

In a class of 36 students, there are 12 girls and 24 boys. To compare the number of girls to the number of boys, you say, "The ratio of girls to boys is 12 to 24." The word "to" is often represented by a colon (:). Thus, "12 to 24" may be written as "12 : 24."

In fact, the colon (:) is simply another division symbol ($\div$). Any ratio can also be written as a fraction, since the fraction bar itself is a symbol for division. Thus, "12 : 24" and "$\frac{12}{24}$" are both read as "12 to 24."

You know that when a fraction is reduced to lowest terms, the value of the fraction does not change. Since 12 to 24 can be written as $\frac{12}{24}$, you can reduce the ratio to lower terms _without changing the ratio of girls to boys._ Note that $\frac{12 \text{ girls}}{24 \text{ boys}}$ is the same ratio as $\frac{6 \text{ girls}}{12 \text{ boys}}$, which is the same ratio as $\frac{3 \text{ girls}}{6 \text{ boys}}$, which is the same ratio as $\frac{1 \text{ girl}}{2 \text{ boys}}$.

Remember: Reducing a ratio to lower terms does not change the value of the ratio.

Similarly, the ratio of boys to girls is 24 to 12, which is written as $24:12$ or as $\frac{24}{12}$. The ratio $\frac{24}{12}$ can be reduced to $\frac{12}{6}$ or $\frac{6}{3}$ or $\frac{2}{1}$. A ratio *must* have a denominator. Always write the "1" in the denominator when necessary.

The ratio of girls to the total number of students is 12 to 36, which is written as $12:36$ or as $\frac{12}{36}$. The ratio of boys to the total number of students is 24 to 36, which is written as $24:36$ or as $\frac{24}{36}$.

In everyday language, the words "out of" are often used when a part of something is compared to the whole. Thus, "12 *out of* 36 students are girls" or "24 *out of* 36 students are boys."

Although the above examples dealt with only *two* groups of students (24 boys and 12 girls), there were many different ratios:

girls to boys	$12:24$ or	$\frac{12}{24}$
boys to girls	$24:12$ or	$\frac{24}{12}$
girls to total students	$12:36$ or	$\frac{12}{36}$
boys to total students	$24:36$ or	$\frac{24}{36}$

You could also write the ratio of total students to girls ($36:12$) or the ratio of total students to boys ($36:24$).

In word problems involving ratios, be sure you read the problem carefully in order to write the correct ratio. It is usually easier to solve ratio problems when you write the ratios as fractions. As with all word problems, look for *key words* to help you. Such phrases as "7 out of 10 voters" and "3 girls to 4 boys" tell you that a *ratio* is involved.

EXAMPLE 1. A school bus carries 35 students. If the ratio of girls to boys is $2:3$, how many girls are on the bus?

Solution: Since the ratio of girls to boys is $2:3$, you know that there are 2 girls for every 3 boys. In other words, *for every 5 students there are 2 girls and 3 boys.* Write these facts as ratios:

$$\frac{\text{number of girls}}{\text{total students}} = \frac{2}{5} \qquad \frac{\text{number of boys}}{\text{total students}} = \frac{3}{5}$$

Your problem asks for the number of *girls* on the bus. Therefore, choose the ratio of *girls* to the total number of students, $\frac{2}{5}$. Since a ratio is a fraction, your problem is now simply, "Find $\frac{2}{5}$ of 35."

$$\frac{2}{5} \times \frac{\overset{7}{\cancel{35}}}{1} = 14$$

Check: If "14 girls" is the correct answer, then there should be 21 boys on the bus ($35 - 14 = 21$). Does this agree with the given ratio of $2:3$?

$$\frac{14 \text{ girls}}{21 \text{ boys}} = \frac{14}{21} = \frac{2}{3} \quad \checkmark$$

Answer: 14 girls

EXAMPLE 2. The Centreville Drum and Bugle Corps has 60 members. A member plays either a drum or a bugle. If 3 out of 5 members play bugles, how many members play drums?

Solution: Of every 5 members, 3 play bugles and 2 play drums. From this information, write the ratio of members that play *drums* to the total number of members:

$$\frac{\text{members that play drums}}{\text{total members}} = \frac{2}{5}$$

Find $\frac{2}{5}$ of the total members.

$$\frac{2}{5} \times \frac{\overset{12}{\cancel{60}}}{1} = 24$$

Check: If 24 members play drums, 36 members play bugles ($60 - 24 = 36$). Does a ratio of "36 out of 60" agree with the given ratio of "3 out of 5"?

$$6\,\overline{)\underset{10}{\overset{6}{\cancel{\frac{36}{60}}}}} = \frac{6}{10} \qquad 2\,\overline{)\underset{5}{\overset{3}{\cancel{\frac{6}{10}}}}} = \frac{3}{5} \quad \checkmark$$

Answer: 24 members play drums.

EXAMPLE 3. Change each of the following expressions to a ratio in fraction form. Reduce the ratio to lowest terms: **a.** 12 voters out of 60 voters; **b.** 18 inches to 1 yard; **c.** 3 quarts to 2 gallons

Solutions:

a. $\dfrac{12}{60} = \dfrac{1}{5}$

b. Since you have inches and yards to compare, change both numbers to inches.

$$\frac{18 \text{ inches}}{1 \text{ yard}} = \frac{18 \text{ inches}}{36 \text{ inches}} = \frac{18}{36} = \frac{1}{2}$$

c. There are 4 quarts in a gallon. Thus,

$$\frac{3 \text{ quarts}}{2 \text{ gallons}} = \frac{3 \text{ quarts}}{8 \text{ quarts}} = \frac{3}{8}$$

Answers: **a.** $\dfrac{1}{5}$ **b.** $\dfrac{1}{2}$ **c.** $\dfrac{3}{8}$

PROPORTIONS

We know that the ratio 8 : 12 has the same value as the ratio 2 : 3, because reducing a ratio to lower terms does not change its value. Thus, we may write the following **proportion**:

$$8 : 12 = 2 : 3$$

This proportion tells us that the two ratios are equal. The two numbers at the ends of the proportion are called the **extremes**:

$$8 : 12 = 2 : 3$$
⌐ extremes ⌐

In the above proportion, the extremes are the numbers 8 and 3.

The two numbers inside the proportion (next to the equals sign) are called the **means**:

$$8 : 12 = 2 : 3$$
means

In the above proportion, the means are 12 and 2. In this proportion, the product of the extremes (8 × 3) is 24; the product of the means (12 × 2) is also 24. Thus, the product of the means equals the product of the extremes.

Rule: In a proportion, the product of the means equals the product of the extremes.

EXAMPLES. From the information that is given, write a proportion. Then tell whether the proportion is *true* or *false*.

a. On Saturday, Cal drove 400 miles in 10 hours. On Sunday, at the same speed, he drove 200 miles in 5 hours.

Solution: 400 : 10 = 200 : 5
extremes: 400 × 5 = 2,000 ⎫ products
means: 10 × 200 = 2,000 ⎭ are equal
The proportion is *true*.

b. Patricia feeds 12 cats with 4 quarts of milk. She can feed 25 cats with 8 quarts of milk.

Solution: 12 : 4 = 25 : 8
extremes: 12 × 8 = 96 ⎫ products are
means: 4 × 25 = 100 ⎭ not equal
The proportion is *false*.

c. George has an LP record that plays music for 15 minutes. With 5 such records, he can listen to 75 minutes of music.

Solution: 1 : 15 = 5 : 75
extremes: 1 × 75 = 75 ⎫ products
means: 15 × 5 = 75 ⎭ are equal
The proportion is *true*.

EXERCISES

In 1 to 20, change each expression to a ratio in fraction form. Reduce each ratio to lowest terms.

1. 6 to 8

2. 9 to 12

3. 5 to 5

4. 15 to 9

5. 10 in. to 1 ft.

6. 25 : 40

7. 50 : 30

8. 24 : 3

9. 4 oz. to 1 lb.

10. 2 pt. : 1 gal.   **11.** 7 out of 28   **12.** 15 out of 45

13. 6 out of 48   **14.** 4 out of 10   **15.** 12 out of 50

16. 24 to 24   **17.** 28 in. : 4 ft.   **18.** 9 out of 45

19. 6 in. to $1\frac{1}{2}$ ft.   **20.** 20 : 60

In 21 to 25, write a proportion from the information that is given. Tell whether the proportion is *true* or *false*.

21. A salesman earns a commission of $100 on sales of $2,000. He will earn a commission of $150 on sales of $3,000.

22. Last year, Mr. Davis paid $800 in income tax on earnings of $4,800. This year he paid $1,000 in income tax on earnings of $5,600.

23. Jane earned $7.15 for $5\frac{1}{2}$ hours of babysitting. She will earn $3.90 for 3 hours of babysitting.

24. Dewey read 6 books in $25\frac{1}{2}$ hours. He can read 5 books in $21\frac{1}{4}$ hours.

25. Dave's car traveled 98.75 miles on 6.25 gallons of gasoline. Dave's car can travel 173.8 miles on 11 gallons.

APPLICATION PROBLEMS

Sample solution

A nut mixture is made up of 3 pounds of cashews and 5 pounds of peanuts. How many pounds of each are needed to make 40 pounds of the mixture?

Of every 8 lb., 3 are cashews and 5 are peanuts.

$$\frac{cashews}{mixture} = \frac{3}{8} = \frac{15}{40}$$

$$\frac{peanuts}{mixture} = \frac{5}{8} = \frac{25}{40}$$

15 lb. cashews

25 lb. peanuts

1. The ratio of boys to girls in a school is 3 : 2. If there are 1,850 students, how many are boys and how many are girls?

_____ boys

_____ girls

2. A team won 150 games and lost 65 games. What is the ratio of games won to games played?

_____

3. If 30 students in a class are present and 5 students are absent, what is the ratio of students absent to students present?

What is the ratio of students absent to the number of students?

_____

4. Two partners in a business share profits in the ratio of 5 : 4. How much would each partner get if the profits for the year were $18,000?

_____

5. At the E-Z Cut-Rate Store, the following items are on sale:

Erasers: 2 for 35¢, 6 for $1.00
Pencils: 3 for 25¢, 12 for $1.00
Ball-Point Pens: 2 for 39¢, 6 for $1.10

Write each price as a proportion. Which proportion is _true_?

_____

Review of Part IX (Units 35 to 40)

In 1 to 12, divide.

1. $\dfrac{3}{5} \div \dfrac{3}{10}$

2. $\dfrac{5}{6} \div \dfrac{2}{3}$

3. $\dfrac{3}{16} \div \dfrac{2}{7}$

4. $\dfrac{3}{4} \div \dfrac{2}{3}$

5. $\dfrac{4}{5} \div \dfrac{8}{15}$

6. $\dfrac{5}{8} \div \dfrac{10}{15}$

7. $3\dfrac{1}{3} \div 4\dfrac{3}{5}$

8. $5\dfrac{3}{4} \div 6$

9. $4 \div 5\dfrac{7}{8}$

10. $2\dfrac{2}{3} \div 1\dfrac{4}{5}$

11. $5 \div 2\dfrac{3}{16}$

12. $6\dfrac{1}{2} \div 4$

In 13 to 16, simplify the complex fraction.

13. $\dfrac{\frac{2}{3}}{\frac{4}{5}}$

14. $\dfrac{2\frac{1}{5}}{3\frac{1}{4}}$

15. $\dfrac{12\frac{1}{2}}{100}$

16. $\dfrac{5\frac{5}{8}}{6}$

In 17 to 20, find the unknown number.

17. $\dfrac{5}{8}$ of what number is 36?

18. $\dfrac{3}{5}$ of what number is 35?

19. 40 is $\dfrac{2}{3}$ of what number?

20. 32 is $\dfrac{5}{6}$ of what number?

In 21 to 24, find the fractional part.

21. 16 is what part of 48?

22. 24 is what part of 72?

23. What part of 35 is 7?

24. What part of 85 is 25?

25. A bowl of fruit contains 4 apples, 6 peaches, and 5 pears.

    a. What is the ratio of apples to pears? _____

    b. What is the ratio of peaches to apples? _____

    c. What is the ratio of pears to apples and peaches combined? _____

    d. What is the ratio of apples to all of the fruit? _____

26. Dorothy says that she can type 6 pages an hour, or 48 pages during an eight-hour day. Express these facts as a proportion. Is the proportion true? _____

Part X. Decimal Fractions

Unit 41. Understanding Decimal Fractions

Words to know

Proper fractions, improper fractions, and mixed numbers are all written with a fraction bar. Fractions written with a fraction bar are called **common fractions**.

When a common fraction has a denominator of 10 or a power of 10, it can be expressed as a **decimal fraction.** In decimal fractions, the fraction bar is replaced with the **decimal point.**

A mixed fraction consists of a whole number and a common fraction. Similarly, when a whole number and a decimal fraction are combined, you have a **mixed decimal**.

Perhaps you have noticed that amounts of money on personal checks are often written as **common fractions.** Nine dollars and fifty cents is written as $9 $\frac{50}{100}$. When you write the amount $9 $\frac{50}{100}$ as $9.50, you express the common fraction, $\frac{50}{100}$, as a **decimal fraction,** .50. Also, you express the mixed fraction, 9 $\frac{50}{100}$, as the **mixed decimal**, 9.50. In either example, the fraction bar is replaced by the **decimal point**.

A decimal fraction is similar to a common fraction, because it represents a part of a unit. A common fraction can have any number as its denominator, but a decimal fraction must have a denominator that is 10 or a power of 10. Powers of 10, you recall, are 100, 1,000, 10,000, and so on.

When you write a decimal fraction, you do not write the denominator. *The denominator of a decimal fraction is never written down.* Rather, it is determined by the number of digits to the right of the decimal point.

Here are some examples of common fractions written as decimal fractions:

$\frac{7}{10}$ = .7 Read ".7" as "seven *tenths*." Note that the 7 is *one place* to the right of the decimal point.

$\frac{13}{100}$ = .13 Read ".13" as "thirteen *hundredths*." Note that the right-hand digit is *2 places* to the left of the decimal point.

$\frac{135}{1,000}$ = .135 Read ".135" as "one hundred thirty-five *thousandths*." Note that the right-hand digit is *3 places* to the right of the decimal point.

As you move to the right of the decimal point, the value of each digit is divided by 10. Thus, a value of *tenths* is divided by 10 to get a value of *hundredths*; a value of hundredths is divided by 10 to get a value of *thousandths*; etc.

Remember: When you read the name of a decimal fraction, you *say the denominator* even though the denominator is not actually written down.

The following table will enable you to read the names of decimal fractions:

Table II: *Names of Decimal Fractions*

Number of Digits to the Right of the Decimal Point	Name of the Decimal Fraction	Example	Name of the Example
1 digit	tenths	.5	five tenths
2 digits	hundredths	.18	eighteen hundredths
3 digits	thousandths	.101	one hundred one thousandths
4 digits	ten–thousandths	.0004	four ten–thousandths
5 digits	hundred–thousandths	.00022	twenty–two hundred–thousandths
6 digits	millionths	.000001	one millionth

In addition to indicating the denominators of decimal fractions, the decimal point separates the whole unit from the decimal fraction in a mixed decimal. Mixed decimals are read by adding the names of decimal fractions to the names of whole numbers. For example, "5.06" is read "five and six hundredths," and "99.44" is read "ninety-nine and forty-four hundredths."

EXERCISES

1. Read the following decimal fractions and mixed decimals out loud and write them as word statements:

   a. .4 _____

   b. 2.07 _____

   c. .15 _____

   d. .125 _____

   e. 7.025 _____

   f. .0623 _____

   g. 5.50 _____

   h. .070 _____

   i. .045 _____

   j. 1.0063 _____

   k. 16.24 _____

   l. .08 _____

2. Write each of the following word statements as a decimal fraction:

   a. six hundredths _____

   b. eight tenths _____

   c. twenty-three hundredths _____

   d. two hundred twenty-three thousandths _____

   e. thirty hundredths _____

   f. four and forty-seven thousandths _____

   g. three thousand two hundred twenty-seven ten-thousandths _____

   h. five hundred twenty-eight ten-thousandths _____

i. one and nine thousandths _____

j. eight hundredths _____

k. seven tenths _____

l. ten and twenty-three ten-thousandths _____

APPLICATION PROBLEMS

Sample solution

John earns $100 each week and has a deduction of $5 for medical insurance. Write the deduction as a decimal fraction.

(5 is) what part (of 100?) $\frac{IS}{OF} = \frac{5}{100} = .05$ .05

1. Tom had $10 and spent $7. Write as a decimal fraction the part of the money he spent.

   _____

2. A coat selling for $100 was reduced by $20. Write the reduction as a decimal fraction.

   _____

3. A salesman earns $15 for every $100 of sales. Write his earnings as a decimal fraction.

   _____

4. A retailer received a shipment of 1,000 drinking glasses and found 115 of them to be broken. Write the number of broken glasses as a decimal fraction.

   _____

Unit 42. Comparing Decimals

Words to know

In our discussions of decimal fractions, we will use the word **decimal** to mean "decimal fraction." Thus, "comparing decimals" means "comparing decimal fractions."

When you compared the values of common fractions (Unit 25), you found a *common denominator*.

To compare the values of **decimals** that have different numbers of decimal places, you must make them alike by changing them to decimals that have the *same number of decimal places*. When two decimals have the same number of decimal places, they have a common denominator. Thus, .07 and .67 have a common denominator of 100. The decimals .018 and .180 have a common denominator of 1,000.

To compare decimals:

Step 1: Change the given decimals to decimals that have the same number of decimal places. To do this, *place zeros to the right of the last digit* until the desired number of decimal places is reached.

Step 2: Compare the resulting numbers. The higher number is the decimal with the larger value.

EXAMPLE 1. Which is larger, .5 or .45?

Solution: To compare .5 and .45, change them to 2-place decimals: .5 = .50 and .45 = .45. The decimal .50 (50 *hundredths*) is larger than the decimal .45 (45 *hundredths*).

Answer: .5 is larger than .45

EXAMPLE 2. Which is smaller, .4 or .04?

Solution: Change .4 and .04 to 2-place decimals: .4 = .40 and .04 = .04. The decimal .04 (4 *hundredths*) is smaller than the decimal .40 (40 *hundredths*).

Answer: .04 is smaller than .4

EXAMPLE 3. Arrange the following decimals in order of descending values (largest first):

.01   .1   .001

Solution: Change the given numbers to 3-place decimals: .01 = .010, .1 = .100, and .001 = .001. The largest decimal is .100 (100 thousandths), followed by .010 (10 thousandths), followed by .001 (1 thousandth).

Answer: .1   .01   .001

EXERCISES

In 1 to 6, circle the largest decimal.

1. .7   .07   .070

2. .013   .0115   .12

3. .05   .50   .0050

4. .60   .8   .900

5. .45   .045   .405

6. .4   .05   .008

In 7 to 10, underline the decimals that have the same value.

7. .04   .040   .0050

8. .8   .08   .80

9. .03   .003   .0300

10. .17   .170   .0170

In 11 to 14, arrange the decimals in ascending order of size (smallest value first).

Sample solutions

.400   .150   .235   *.15   .235   .4*

.0300   .0230   .4000 .0415   *.023   .03   .0415   .4*

11. .125   .1259   .2   .02   ___ ___ ___ ___

12. .6   .605   .006   .07   ___ ___ ___ ___

13. .025   .205   .250   .0025   ___ ___ ___ ___

14. .75   .075   .0780   .8   ___ ___ ___ ___

APPLICATION PROBLEMS

1. John walked .6 mile and Tom walked .58 mile. Who walked farther?

2. Which weighs more, .64 pound or .5 pound?

3. Two brands of coffee are priced at $1.15 a can. If one can weighs 1.25 pounds and the other weighs 1.2 pounds, which brand is the better buy?

4. Harry earned a commission of 5.5% and Tom earned a commission of 5.25%. Who earned a higher commission?

5. Bank A pays 5.95% interest and Bank B pays 5.9% interest. Which bank pays a higher interest?

Unit 43. Rounding Off Decimals

When a whole number is *rounded off*, its actual value is changed to an approximate value. In Unit 2, you learned how to round off whole numbers to any given place, such as the ten's place or the hundred's place.

To round off decimals, you follow the same steps you used to round off whole numbers. However, in the final step, you omit all digits inside the parentheses.

After deciding on the value to be rounded off to, do the following steps:

Step 1: Place parentheses around all digits to the right of this value.

Step 2: A. If the left-hand digit inside the parentheses is 5 or more, add "1" to the part outside the parentheses. *Note:* In this step, the actual value of "1" will vary. If you round off to *tenths*, then "1" will have a value of .1; if you round off to *thousandths*, then "1" will have a value of .001; etc.
B. If the left-hand digit inside the parentheses is less than 5, do not add "1."

Step 3: Omit all digits inside the parentheses.

EXAMPLE 1. Round off .2645 to the nearest *tenth*.

Step 1: Place parentheses around all digits to the right of the *tenth* place.

$$.2(645)$$

Step 2: Since the left-hand digit inside the parentheses is greater than 5, add "1" to the part outside the parentheses. (In this example, "1" is one *tenth*.)

$$\begin{array}{r} .2(645) \\ +.1 \\ \hline .3(645) \end{array}$$

Step 3: Omit all digits inside the parentheses.

$$.3(645)$$

Answer: .2645 = .3, to the nearest tenth.

EXAMPLE 2. Round off .2645 to the nearest *hundredth*.

Step 1: Place parentheses around all digits to the right of the *hundredths* place.

$$.26(45)$$

Steps 2 and 3: Since the left-hand digit inside the parentheses is less than 5, do not add "1." Then omit all digits inside the parentheses.

$$\begin{array}{r} .26(45) \\ +0 \\ \hline .26(45) \end{array}$$

Answer: .2645 = .26, to the nearest hundredth.

EXAMPLE 3. Round off .2645 to the nearest *thousandth*.

Step 1: Place parentheses around all digits to the right of the *thousandth* place.

.264(5)

Steps 2 and 3: Since the digit inside the parentheses is 5, add "1" to the part outside the parentheses. (In this example, "1" is one *thousandth*.) Then omit the digit inside the parentheses.

.264(5)
+.001
—————
.265(5̶)

Answer: .2645 = .265, to the nearest thousandth.

EXERCISES

In 1 to 8, round off to the nearest *tenth*.

1. .37   2. .43   3. .55   4. .86

5. .158   6. .638   7. .456   8. .076

In 9 to 16, round off to the nearest *hundredth*.

9. .344   10. .248   11. .295   12. .305

13. .125   14. .238   15. .3264   16. .3485

In 17 to 24, round off to the nearest *thousandth*.

17. .2452   18. .0348   19. .1153   20. .00085

21. .0042   22. .23965   23. .0346   24. .2508

APPLICATION PROBLEMS

1. The diameter of a rod is .678. What is the measurement to the nearest *hundredth*?

2. A package of meat weighs 2.53 pounds. Rounded off to the nearest *tenth*, what is the weight of the package?

3. The thickness of a disc measures .1256 of an inch. Round off the measurement to the nearest *thousandth*.

_____

4. A metal bar measures 5.347 inches. Round off the measurement to the nearest *hundredth*.

_____

5. Round off 3.25 billion to the nearest *tenth* of a billion.

_____

Unit 44. Changing Decimals to Common Fractions

Decimals have denominators of 10 or powers of 10.

To change a decimal to a common fraction, *rewrite the decimal as a fraction that has the equivalent denominator in 10 or powers of 10.* Reduce this common fraction to lowest terms.

A quick way of determining the denominator is to remember that the *number of digits* in the decimal is the same as the *number of zeros* in the denominator. For example:

A decimal with *one digit* changes to a fraction with *one zero* in the denominator: .8 changes to $\frac{8}{10}$.

A decimal with *two digits* changes to a fraction with *two zeros* in the denominator: .35 changes to $\frac{35}{100}$.

A decimal with *three digits* changes to a fraction with *three zeros* in the denominator: .415 changes to $\frac{415}{1,000}$.

A decimal with *four digits* changes to a fraction with *four zeros* in the denominator: .0356 changes to $\frac{356}{10,000}$.

EXAMPLE 1. Change .04 to a common fraction.

Solution: Rewrite the decimal *four hundredths* as the common fraction $\frac{4}{100}$ and reduce to lowest terms. (Notice that there are *2 digits* in the decimal .04 and *2 zeros* in the fraction $\frac{4}{100}$.)

$$.04 = \frac{4}{100} \qquad 4\overline{\smash{)}\begin{array}{c} 1 \\ \cancel{4} \\ \cancel{100} \\ 25 \end{array}} = \frac{1}{25}$$

Answer: $.04 = \frac{1}{25}$

EXAMPLE 2. Change .625 to a common fraction.

Solution: Rewrite the decimal *six hundred twenty-five thousandths* as the common fraction $\frac{625}{1,000}$ and reduce to lowest terms. (Notice that there are *3 digits* in .625 and *3 zeros* in $\frac{625}{1,000}$.)

$$.625 = \frac{625}{1,000}$$

$$25\overline{\smash{)}\begin{array}{c} 25 \\ \cancel{625} \\ \cancel{1,000} \\ 40 \end{array}} = \frac{25}{40} \qquad 5\overline{\smash{)}\begin{array}{c} 5 \\ \cancel{25} \\ \cancel{40} \\ 8 \end{array}} = \frac{5}{8}$$

Answer: $.625 = \frac{5}{8}$

EXAMPLE 3. Change $.12\frac{1}{2}$ to a common fraction.

Solution: Rewrite the decimal *twelve and one-half hundredths* as $\frac{12\frac{1}{2}}{100}$ and simplify the complex fraction.

(Notice that there are *2 digits* in $.12\frac{1}{2}$ and *2 zeros* in $\left.\dfrac{12\frac{1}{2}}{100}\right)$

(*Reminder:* To divide fractions, invert the divisor and multiply.)

$$.12\frac{1}{2} = \frac{12\frac{1}{2}}{100} = 12\frac{1}{2} \div 100$$

$$= \frac{25}{2} \div \frac{100}{1}$$

$$\frac{25}{2} \div \frac{100}{1} = \frac{\overset{1}{\cancel{25}}}{2} \times \frac{1}{\underset{4}{\cancel{100}}} = \frac{1}{8}$$

Answer: $.12\frac{1}{2} = \frac{1}{8}$

EXERCISES

In 1 to 12, change the decimal to a common fraction and reduce to lowest terms.

1. .3

2. .05

3. .23

4. .008

5. .119

6. .013

7. .60

8. .030

9. .235

10. .010

11. .255

12. .75

In 13 to 18, change the decimal to a complex fraction and simplify.

13. $.33\frac{1}{3}$

14. $.14\frac{2}{7}$

15. $.16\frac{2}{3}$

16. $.37\frac{1}{2}$

17. $.66\frac{2}{3}$

18. $.66\frac{1}{2}$

APPLICATION PROBLEMS

1. The thickness of a nail is .25 of an inch. Write the thickness as a common fraction.

              _____

2. Jane bought .87 $\frac{1}{2}$ of a pound of meat. What common fraction of a pound did she buy?

              _____

3. Write $.75 as a fraction of a dollar.

              _____

4. The decimal fraction .60 of a mile is equal to what common fraction of a mile?

              _____

5. Write .2 of a second as a common fraction.

              _____

Review of Part X (Units 41 to 44)

In 1 to 5, write each decimal as a word statement.

1. .6 _____

2. .03 _____

3. .45 _____

4. .115 _____

5. .007 _____

In 6 to 11, circle the largest decimal.

6. .8   .65   .08   .080   7. .5   .40   .050   .05

8. .12   .025   .0125   .02   9. .30   .03   .030   .0300

10. .45   .050   .05   .405   11. .705   .75   .075   .0750

In 12 to 17, round off to the nearest *hundredth*.

12. .048   **13.** .263   **14.** .005   **15.** .506   **16.** .123   **17.** .018

In 18 to 23, round off to the nearest *thousandth*.

18. .1255   **19.** .0008   **20.** .0634   **21.** .0038

22. .4653   **23.** .2365

In 24 to 32, change each decimal fraction to a common fraction and reduce to lowest terms.

24. .75   **25.** .07   **26.** .1

27. .20   **28.** .125   **29.** .375

30. .020   **31.** .002   **32.** .325

Part XI. Adding, Subtracting, and Multiplying Decimals

Unit 45. Addition of Decimals and Mixed Decimals

Adding decimals is similar to adding whole numbers. However, there are two things to remember when writing a column of decimals and mixed numbers to be added:

1. You must line up the decimal points, one under the other, in a straight line.
2. You must line up the digits to the right and to the left of each decimal point, one under the other, according to their value.

EXAMPLE 1. Add: $3.5 + 10.23 + .235$

Solution: Line up the digits and decimal points correctly, one under the other.

$$
\begin{array}{r}
3.5 \\
10.23 \\
.235 \\
\hline
\end{array}
$$

Bring down the decimal point to where your answer will be.

$$
\begin{array}{r}
3.5 \\
10.23 \\
.235 \\
\hline
\end{array}
$$

Add as with whole numbers.

$$
\begin{array}{r}
3.5 \\
10.23 \\
.235 \\
\hline
13.965 \\
\end{array}
$$

Answer: $3.5 + 10.23 + .235 = 13.965$

EXAMPLE 2. Add: $8.97 + 89.7 + 897$

Solution:

$$
\begin{array}{r}
8.97 \\
89.7 \\
897 \\
121 \\
\hline
995.67 \\
\end{array}
$$

Answer: $8.97 + 89.7 + 897 = 995.67$

EXAMPLE 3. Add: $\$7 + \$.59 + 27¢$

Solution:

$$
\begin{array}{r}
7.00 \\
.59 \\
.27 \\
1 \\
\hline
7.86 \\
\end{array}
$$

Answer: $\$7 + \$.59 + 27¢ = \$7.86$

EXERCISES

In 1 to 8, add.

1. $4.3 + .235 + 5.05$

2. $.35 + .175 + .62 + .4$

3. $22.53 + 12.05 + 9.275$

4. $16.84 + 23.246 + 34.5$

5. $18.63 + 24.075 + 237.8$

6. $115.45 + 230.125 + 452.864$

7. $357.643 + 562.48 + 763.2875$

8. $642.687 + 578.9 + 785.2576$

APPLICATION PROBLEMS

1. Tom bought a coat for $97.50, a suit for $65.95, and a shirt for $3.75. How much money did he spend?

2. John had $237.64 in the bank, and made a deposit of $63.58. How much does John have in the bank?

3. Harry earns $185.65 a week and his wife earns $97.45 a week. What is their combined weekly income?

4. Find the total of the following distances: 5.6 miles, 12.1 miles, 108.4 miles, and 15.6 miles.

5. James earned the following commissions: $33.65, $27.83, $53.42, and $43.58. Find his total commission.

Unit 46. Subtraction of Decimals and Mixed Decimals

To subtract decimals and mixed decimals, set up the subtraction problem as you did for addition:

1. Line up the decimal points, one under the other, in a straight line.
2. Line up the digits correctly, one under the other, according to their values.

Then follow the same procedure as for subtracting whole numbers.

EXAMPLE 1. Subtract: 35.68 − 15.25

Solution: Line up the digits and decimal points correctly.

$$\begin{array}{r} 35.68 \\ -15.25 \\ \hline \end{array}$$

Bring down the decimal point to where your answer will be.

$$\begin{array}{r} 35|.68 \\ -15|.25 \\ \hline \end{array}$$

Subtract as with whole numbers.

$$\begin{array}{r} 35.68 \\ -15.25 \\ \hline 20.43 \end{array}$$

Check your answer.

$$\begin{array}{r} 20.43 \\ +15.25 \\ \hline 35.68 \end{array} \checkmark$$

Answer: 35.68 − 15.25 = 20.43

EXAMPLE 2. Subtract: 125.07 − 83.48

Solution:

$$\begin{array}{r} \overset{49}{12\boxed{5.0}7} \\ -83.48 \\ \hline 41.59 \end{array} \qquad \begin{array}{c} Check: \\ \begin{array}{r} 41.59 \\ +83.48 \\ \hline 125.07 \end{array} \checkmark \end{array}$$

Answer: 125.07 − 83.48 = 41.59

EXAMPLE 3. Subtract: 7.6 − 4.528

Solution: Write 7.6 as 7.600, so that it has as many places as the subtrahend.

$$\begin{array}{r} \overset{59}{7\boxed{.60}0} \\ -4.582 \\ \hline 3.018 \end{array} \qquad \begin{array}{c} Check: \\ \begin{array}{r} 3.018 \\ +4.582 \\ \hline 7.600 \end{array} \checkmark \end{array}$$

Answer: 7.6 − 4.582 = 3.018

EXERCISES

In 1 to 20, subtract.

1.
$$\begin{array}{r} .36 \\ -.18 \\ \hline \end{array}$$

2.
$$\begin{array}{r} .44 \\ -.27 \\ \hline \end{array}$$

3.
$$\begin{array}{r} .27 \\ -.08 \\ \hline \end{array}$$

4.
$$\begin{array}{r} .237 \\ -.025 \\ \hline \end{array}$$

5.
$$\begin{array}{r} .423 \\ -.347 \\ \hline \end{array}$$

6.
$$\begin{array}{r} 27.05 \\ -23.46 \\ \hline \end{array}$$

7.
$$\begin{array}{r} 60.07 \\ -42.38 \\ \hline \end{array}$$

8.
$$\begin{array}{r} 47.163 \\ -21.687 \\ \hline \end{array}$$

9.
$$\begin{array}{r} 32.6 \\ -14.732 \\ \hline \end{array}$$

10.
$$\begin{array}{r} 28.52 \\ -13.756 \\ \hline \end{array}$$

11.
$$\begin{array}{r} .49 \\ -.17 \\ \hline \end{array}$$

12.
$$\begin{array}{r} .235 \\ -.123 \\ \hline \end{array}$$

13. $.63 - .423$ 14. $.523 - .35$ 15. $.067 - .0048$

16. $23.5 - 15.67$ 17. $47.8 - 22.9$ 18. $19.05 - 9.25$

19. $35. - 15.63$ 20. $43. - 9.316$

In 21 to 26, subtract:

21. 12.62 from 25.06 22. 27.5 from 46.628

23. 14.03 from 32.005 24. 19.325 from 28

25. 12.8 from 35.05 26. 18.005 from 23

APPLICATION PROBLEMS

1. A suit selling for $73.84 is reduced to $69.95. What is the amount of the reduction?

2. Tom earned $9,628.87 last year. This year his income is $10,745.65. How much more did he earn this year?

3. John earned $195.50 last week, and had the following deductions taken from his pay check: Federal income tax, $37.60; Social Security tax, $9.37; union dues, $1.93. Find John's net pay ("take-home" pay).

4. Tom ran the 100-yard dash in 14.30 seconds, and later ran the same distance in 12.07 seconds. By how much did he improve his time?

5. Harry bought a hat for $8.65, a sports jacket for $27.68, and a tie for $1.89. If he had $78.65 before he bought the clothes, how much does he have left?

Unit 47. Multiplication of Whole Numbers by Decimals

The multiplication of whole numbers by decimals or by mixed decimals is similar to the multiplication of whole numbers by whole numbers. However, you must determine where to insert the decimal point in the answer.

Rule: To multiply decimals and whole numbers:
1. **Set up the problem** and multiply as with whole numbers.
2. **Count the number of decimal places to the right of the decimal point in the problem** (the number of decimal places in the multiplicand or the number of decimal places in the multiplier). Moving from right to left, count as many decimal places in the product as there are decimal places in the problem, and insert the decimal point there.

EXAMPLE 1. Multiply: 23.43×25

Solution: Multiply as with whole numbers.

$$
\begin{array}{r}
\overset{\scriptstyle 1\,2\ \ 1}{23.43} \\
\times\ 25 \\
\hline
11715 \\
4686 \\
\hline
58575
\end{array}
$$

Count the number of decimal places to the right of the decimal point in the problem (in the multiplicand).

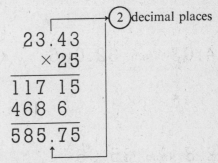

Since the multiplicand has 2 decimal places to the right of its decimal point, the product must have 2 decimal places to the right of its decimal point.

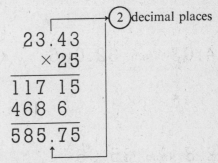

Answer: $23.43 \times 25 = 585.75$

EXAMPLE 2. Multiply: $174 \times .083$

Solution:

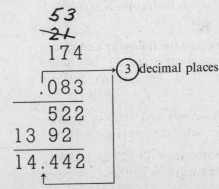

Answer: $174 \times .083 = 14.442$

143

EXERCISES

In 1 to 20, multiply.

1. 123
    × 3.5

2. 23.28
    × 14

3. 235
    × .25

4. 1473
    × .24

5. 46.05
    × 32

6. 562
    × .07

7. 2474
    × 3.6

8. 5433
    × 2.15

9. 634.24
    × 36

10. 2364
    × .19

11. 4247
    × .34

12. 56235
    × .236

13. 23.47
    × 235

14. 5628
    × .14

15. 7365
    × 4.6

16. 63.46
    × 145

17. 3468
    × 3.47

18. 53.52
    × 235

19. 243.6
    × 235

20. 4368
    × 3.06

APPLICATION PROBLEMS

1. How much will 135 floor tiles cost at $.23 each?

2. Tom earns $153.50 a week. How much does he earn in a year?

3. John bought a color television set, to be paid for by a down payment of $75 and 16 installments of $21.75 each. What is the total cost of the television set?

4. Harry bought 3 shirts at $3.75 each, 8 pairs of socks at $.79 each, and 4 ties at $1.85 each. How much did Harry spend?

5. How much will 53 yards of carpeting cost at $7.65 a yard?

Unit 48. Multiplication of Decimals by Decimals

To multiply two decimals or mixed decimals, follow the rule explained in the preceding unit. However, since both the multiplicand *and* the multiplier have decimal places to the right of the decimal point, you must count the *total* number of decimal places in the problem. Add the number of decimal places in the top number (the multiplicand) to the number of places in the bottom number (the multiplier). Moving from right to left, count as many places in the product as there are total decimal places in the problem. Insert the decimal point there.

EXAMPLE 1. Multiply: $348.25 × .16

Solution: Multiply as with whole numbers.

```
  348.25
  × .16
 ───────
  208950
  34825
 ───────
 557200
```

Count the number of decimal places to the right of the decimal point in the top number. Count the number of decimal places to the right of the decimal point in the bottom number. Add these two numbers.

```
  348.25  ────→ 2
  × .16   ────→ 2
              ─── ④ decimal places
 ───────
  208950
  34825
 ───────
 557200
```

To place the decimal point in your product, count 4 decimal places, moving from right to left.

```
  348.25  ────→ 2
  × .16   ────→ 2
              ─── ④ decimal places
 ───────
 20 8950
 34 825
 ───────
 55.7200
```

Since the answer is in dollars and cents, cross out the last two zeros, because they have no value.

$$\$55.72\cancel{00}$$

Answer: $348.25 × .16 = $55.72

EXAMPLE 2. Multiply: 53.6 × 2.02

Solution:

```
  53.6   ────→ 1
  × 2.02 ────→ 2
              ─── ③ decimal places
 ───────
  1 072
 107 20
 ───────
 108.272
```

Answer: 53.6 × 2.02 = 108.272

EXERCISES

In 1 to 20, multiply.

1.
```
 43.26
× 5.4
─────
```

2.
```
 46.3
× .025
─────
```

3.
```
 3.27
× .35
─────
```

4.
```
 .456
× .34
─────
```

5.
```
 37.64
× .037
─────
```

6. 46.38   7. 245.6   8. 38.65   9. 5.638   10. 253.48
  × .46   × .045   × .86   × 24.5   × .65

11. 437.05   12. 568.34   13. 720.62   14. 649.42   15. 482.63
   × 3.47   × .605   × .458   × 23.08   × .008

16. 574.65   17. 867.38   18. 5642.8   19. 738.36   20. 65.84
   × 20.07   × 52.7   × .539   × .075   × .427

APPLICATION PROBLEMS

1. Brand X gasoline sells for $.46 a gallon. What is the cost of 18.5 gallons?

2. How much would 4.65 yards of velvet cost if one yard sells for $4.62?

3. The average rainfall in a city is 3.425 inches per month. How much rain will fall in 4.5 months? (Since your answer will be approximate, round it off to the nearest *hundredth*.)

4. A car rental company charges $75 a week plus $.0416 per mile. If you travel 1,625.5 miles in seven days, how much would the car cost you?

5. If a package of sugar weighs 2.125 pounds, how much would 335 packages weigh?

Unit 49. Rounding Off to the Nearest Penny in Multiplication

When you obtain a product that must be expressed in dollars and cents, it is necessary to round off to the nearest *hundredth*. Since a penny is a hundredth of a dollar, you must "round off to the nearest penny."

In Example 1 of the preceding unit, you rounded off the product $55.7200 to $55.72. Most of the time, however, the digits to be rounded off will not be zeros.

EXAMPLE 1. Multiply: $362.66 × .36

Solution: Perform the multiplication and place the decimal point in the product by counting four decimal places, from right to left.

$$
\begin{array}{r}
362.66 \\
\times .36 \\
\hline
21\ 7596 \\
108\ 798 \\
\hline
130.5576
\end{array}
$$

In working with dollars and cents, your final answer must have only *two places* to the right of the decimal point. (Cents are hundredths of a dollar, and the value of the second digit to the right of the decimal point is hundredths.) Therefore, you must round off 130.5576 to the nearest hundredth. Follow the steps explained in the unit on rounding off decimals (Unit 43):

Step 1: Place parentheses around all digits to the right of the hundredth place.

$$130.55(76)$$

Step 2: Since the left-hand digit inside the parentheses is greater than 5, add "1" to the part outside the parentheses. In working with dollars and cents, the "1" will always be "1 penny," written ".01."

$$
\begin{array}{r}
130.55(76) \\
+.01 \\
\hline
130.56(76)
\end{array}
$$

Step 3: Omit all digits inside the parentheses.

$$130.56(76) = 130.56$$

Answer: $362.66 × .36 = $130.56

Since you have practiced rounding off whole numbers (Unit 2) and decimals (Unit 48), you should be able to round off a product to the nearest penny *mentally*.

Remember: When rounding off to the nearest penny, if the third digit to the right of the decimal point is 5 or more, add a penny to your answer. If the third digit is less than 5, do not add a penny.

EXAMPLE 2. Multiply: $235.45 × .25

Solution:

$$
\begin{array}{r}
235.45 \\
\times .25 \\
\hline
11\ 77\ 25 \\
47\ 09\ 0 \\
\hline
58.86(25) = 58.86
\end{array}
$$

Answer: $235.45 × .25 = $58.86

EXAMPLE 3. Find, to the nearest penny, the cost of 1.42 grams of a chemical if the price is (*a*) $2.12 per gram and (*b*) $1.90 per gram.

Solutions:

(*a*)
$$
\begin{array}{r}
1.42 \\
\times 2.12 \\
\hline
2\ 84 \\
14\ 2 \\
2\ 84 \\
\hline
3.01(04) = 3.01
\end{array}
$$

Answer: $3.01

(*b*)
$$
\begin{array}{r}
1.42 \\
\times 1.90 \\
\hline
1\ 27\ 80 \\
1\ 42 \\
\hline
2.69(80) = 2.70
\end{array}
$$

Answer: $2.70

EXERCISES

In 1 to 20, multiply and round off to the nearest penny.

1. $34.42
   × .25

2. $46.37
   × .045

3. $27.43
   × .07

4. $53.65
   × .34

5. $242.65
   × .125

6. $256.43
   × .68

7. $347.67
   × .036

8. $362.49
   × .43

9. $465.55
   × .38

10. $478.64
    × .46

11. $538.78
    × .53

12. $673.15
    × .64

13. $2,435.23
    × .25

14. $2,536.28
    × .47

15. $3,648.47
    × .54

16. $4,765.83
    × .057

17. $4,267.56
    × .48

18. $5,658.72
    × .47

19. $5,748.68
    × .54

20. $5,658.76
    × .57

APPLICATION PROBLEMS

Sample solution

Nancy bought a lamp selling for $63.85. If the sales tax is 7% (7% = .07), how much did she pay for the lamp, including tax?

63.85
× .07
_____
4.46(95) = 4.47, tax

63.85
+4.47
_____
$68.32

1. A coat selling for $135.50 was reduced by 25% (25% = .25). Find the new price.

2. Mrs. McGill bought a fur coat that cost $537.85. She paid 7% sales tax (7% = .07). How much did the coat cost?

3. A salesman earns a 15% commission on sales (15% = .15). He made the following sales: $348.63, $538.45, and $247.65. Find his total commissions.

4. How much would 87.9 gallons of heating fuel cost at $.37 a gallon?

5. At a "$\frac{1}{3}$ off" sale, Dan bought an electric heater originally priced at $39.95. If there is a 5% tax on the sales price, how much did the heater cost? $\left(\text{Use the decimal .333 for the fraction } \frac{1}{3}. \ 5\% = .05\right)$

Unit 50. Multiplication of Whole Numbers, Decimals, and Mixed Decimals by 10 and Powers of 10

WHOLE NUMBERS

To multiply a whole number by 10, place one zero to the right of the number. Thus, 23 × 10 = 23(0) = 230.

To multiply a whole number by 100, place two zeros to the right of the number. Thus, 23 × 100 = 23(00) = 2,300.

To multiply a whole number by 10, 100, 1,000, or any power of 10: Place as many 0's to the right of the given number (the multiplicand) as there are zeros in the multiplier.

EXAMPLE 1. Multiply: 253 × 100,000

Solution: Since there are five zeros in 100,000, place five zeros to the right of 253:

253(00000)

Answer: 253 × 100,000 = 25,300,000

DECIMALS

To multiply a decimal or a mixed decimal by 10 or a power of 10, move the decimal point as many places to the right as there are zeros in the multiplier.

EXAMPLE 2. Multiply: $12.35 × 10

Solution: Move the decimal point one place to the right.

$$12.35 \times 10 = 12.3.5 = 123.5$$

Because this problem deals with dollars and cents, and since cents are hundredths of a dollar, place a zero after the 5 (5 tenths) to make it 50 cents (50 hundredths).

Answer: $12.35 × 10 = $123.50

EXAMPLE 3. Multiply: 15.47 × 100

Solution: Move the decimal point two places to the right.

$$15.47 \times 100 = 15.47. = 1,547.$$

When there are no digits to the right of a decimal point, it is not necessary to include the decimal point.

Answer: 15.47 × 100 = 1,547

EXAMPLE 4. Multiply: 25.87 × 1,000

Solution: Move the decimal point three places to the right.

$$25.87 \times 1,000 = 25.87(\ ).$$

Since there are only two digits to the right of the decimal point, and since you moved the decimal point three places, insert a zero after the 7 as a place holder: 2587(0).

Answer: 25.87 × 1,000 = 25,870

EXAMPLE 5. Multiply: .006 × 100

Solution: Move the decimal point two places to the right.

$$.006 \times 100 = .00.6 = 00.6$$

Since the zeros to the left of the decimal point have no value, and since they are not needed as place holders, omit them.

Answer: .006 × 100 = .6

EXERCISES

In 1 to 24, multiply. Perform the multiplications *mentally*.

1. 235 × 10

2. 470 × 10

3. 236 × 1,000

4. 140 × 100

5. 537 × 10,000

6. 325 × 10

7. 236 × 100

8. 307 × 10,000

9. 215 × 10

10. $13.05 × 10

11. $15.23 × 100

12. $12.63 × 1,000

13. $.63 × 100

14. $29.07 × 10

15. $.059 × 100

16. $.003 × 100

17. $123.00 × 10

18. $35.75 × 1,000

19. $.005 × 10,000

20. 45.61 × 10

21. 27.35 × 100

22. 15.08 × 10

23. 27.63 × 100

24. 43.37 × 1,000

APPLICATION PROBLEMS

1. Find the price of 100 floor tiles at $.57 each.

2. Molly bought 10 yards of fabric at $3.75 a yard. Find the total amount she paid.

3. Mrs. Atkins is buying a refrigerator on the installment plan, and has 10 payments left. If each payment is $17.53, how much does she still owe for the refrigerator?

4. A certain drug costs $.42 a capsule. How much would 100 capsules cost?

5. Wallpaper sells for $6.85 a roll. How much would 10 rolls cost?

Review of Part XI (Units 45 to 50)

In 1 to 4, add.

1. $125.53 + 25.065 + 1.255 + .05$

2. $.05 + .125 + .008 + .8$

3. $15.3 + 128.75 + 8.075 + .3075$

4. $35.005 + 28.15 + 18.1 + 5.03$

In 5 to 10, subtract.

5. $157.25 - 65.06$ **6.** $24.4 - 12.53$ **7.** $65 - 43.030$

8. $27.05 - 14.165$ **9.** $38.5 - 15.125$ **10.** $150.3 - 85.5$

In 11 to 22, multiply and round off to the nearest penny.

11. $2.85
    × 15

12. $38.25
    × 36

13. $265
    × .35

14. $347
    × .06

15. $127.50
    × 4.6

16. $353
    × 8.5

17. $87.08
    × .27

18. $385
    × .10

19. $465.27
    × 6.8

20. $362.87
    × .25

21. $305.05
    × .06

22. $27.58
    × 3.8

Part XII. Dividing Decimals

Unit 51. Division When the Dividend Is a Decimal

To divide a whole number into a decimal or a mixed decimal, you proceed as in the division of whole numbers. However, you must know where to put the decimal point in your answer (the quotient).

Rule: When the dividend is a decimal, place the decimal point in your answer *directly above the decimal point in the dividend*. Then divide as with whole numbers.

EXAMPLE. Divide: 150.75 ÷ 25

Solution: Use the division box to set up the problem, as with whole numbers. Then move the decimal point up in a straight line directly above the decimal point in the dividend.

$$25\overline{)150.75}$$

Now, divide as with whole numbers.

$$
\begin{array}{r}
6.03 \\
25\overline{)150.75} \\
150 \\
\hline
75 \\
75 \\
\hline
\end{array}
$$

Answer: 150.75 ÷ 25 = 6.03

EXERCISES

In 1 to 12, divide. Round off each answer to the nearest *tenth*.

1. $21\overline{)23.19}$

2. $32\overline{)53.05}$

3. $27\overline{)46.23}$

153

4. 35 $\overline{|250.60}$ **5.** 32 $\overline{|803.07}$ **6.** 43 $\overline{|135.63}$

7. 52 $\overline{|460.85}$ **8.** 45 $\overline{|605.50}$ **9.** 37 $\overline{|475.82}$

10. 63 $\overline{|1,472.87}$ **11.** 65 $\overline{|3,417.07}$ **12.** 72 $\overline{|3,053.17}$

APPLICATION PROBLEMS

1. John bought a car for $3,280.32. If the car is to be paid for in 36 equal installments, how much will each payment be?

2. Mrs. Kelly bought 43 yards of velvet for $378.83. What was the price of the velvet per yard?

3. The Wilsons spent $1,968.75 on their 25-day vacation. What was the average cost per day?

4. Tom paid $2,317.64 in Federal income tax last year. On the average, how much income tax did he pay each week?

5. Mr. Adams paid $1,704.72 in rent last year. Find his monthly rent.

Unit 52. Division of Whole Numbers, Decimals, and Mixed Decimals by 10 and Powers of 10

WHOLE NUMBERS

Every whole number has a decimal point after the right-hand digit, whether or not the decimal point is actually written. Thus, "6" may be written "6." and "27" may be written "27."

Rule: To divide a whole number by 10, by 100, or by any power of 10, move the decimal point in the dividend to the left as many places as there are zeros in the divisor.

EXAMPLE 1. Divide: $762 \div 10$

Solution: Move the decimal point 1 place to the left: $762. \div 10 = 76.2. = 76.2$

Answer: $762 \div 10 = 76.2$

EXAMPLE 2. Divide: $762 \div 100$

Solution: Move the decimal point 2 places to the left: $762. \div 100 = 7.62. = 7.62$

Answer: $762 \div 100 = 7.62$

EXAMPLE 3. Divide: $762 \div 1,000$

Solution: Move the decimal point 3 places to the left: $762. \div 1,000 = .762. = .762$

Answer: $762 \div 1,000 = .762$

EXAMPLE 4. Divide: $762 \div 10,000$

Solution: Move the decimal point 4 places to the left and place a zero to the right of the decimal point as a place holder: $762. \div 10,000 = .0762. = .0762$

Answer: $762 \div 10,000 = .0762$

DECIMALS

To divide a decimal by 10 or a power of 10, follow the preceding rule: *Move the decimal point in the dividend to the left as many places as there are zeros in the divisor.* Be sure to include zeros as place holders when necessary.

EXAMPLE 5. Divide: $1.72 \div 100$

Solution: Move the decimal point 2 places to the left: $1.72 \div 100 = .01.72 = .0172$

Answer: $1.72 \div 100 = .0172$

EXAMPLE 6. Divide: $.06 \div 100$

Solution: Move the decimal point 2 places to the left: $.06 \div 100 = .00.06 = .0006$

Answer: $.06 \div 100 = .0006$

EXERCISES

In this set of exercises, you should perform the divisions *mentally*. In 1 to 12, divide each number by 10.

1. 85   2. 78   3. 57   4. 230   5. 460   6. 650

7. 32.5   8. 47.8   9. 4.63   10. 23.37   11. 3.2   12. .478

In 13 to 24, divide each number by 100.

13. 56   14. 80   15. 240   16. 34.8

17. 542   18. 63.8   19. 4.53   20. 67.39

21. 5,600   22. 548.7   23. 65.93   24. .768

In 25 to 36, divide each number by 1,000.

25. 3,478   **26.** 400   **27.** 2,620   **28.** 628

29. 264.5   **30.** 8.25   **31.** 5,620   **32.** 675.9

33. 520   **34.** 3,570   **35.** 89.2   **36.** .72

In 37 to 44, divide each number by 10,000.

37. 4,620   **38.** 5,729   **39.** 15,625   **40.** 24,700

41. 43,234   **42.** 275.07   **43.** 6,842.8   **44.** 852

APPLICATION PROBLEMS

1. Matt's old car averages 10 miles per gallon of gasoline. How many gallons will Matt need to travel 847 miles?

2. For the Senior Prom, 100 Seniors must pay $1,360 for the hotel hall. How much will each Senior have to pay? (Each Senior pays the same amount.)

3. A 1,000-member congregation must raise $22,640 to repair the church. If every member pays the same amount, how much must each member contribute?

4. At a benefit concert attended by 10,000 people, the total receipts were $58,500. What was the average price per ticket?

5. A construction company is building an apartment house and needs 100 floor tiles for each kitchen. How many kitchens can be tiled with 5,600 tiles?

Unit 53. Division When the Divisor Is a Decimal

Never try to divide when the divisor contains a decimal point. If there is a decimal point in your divisor, *change the divisor to a whole number*.

To do this, move the decimal point in the divisor to the right until it is "outside of the number." If the divisor is 1.62, change it to the whole number 162. by moving the decimal point *two* places to the right, If the divisor is .162, change it to the whole number 162. by moving the decimal point *three* places to the right. Recall that every whole number has a decimal point to the right of its right-hand digit.

Since you have moved the decimal point in the divisor, you must now move the decimal point in the dividend to the right *the same number of places* as you moved the decimal point in the divisor.

After moving the decimal points, divide as if the divisor were a whole number.

EXAMPLE 1. Divide: .12 | 24.36

Solution: Move the decimal point in the divisor two places to the right.

$$.12. \overline{| 24.36 }$$

Next, move the decimal point in the dividend two places to the right.

$$.12. \overline{| 24.36. }$$

What you have done is the same as multiplying both the divisor and the dividend by 100 in order to change .12 to a whole number. That is, .12 × 100 = 12. and 24.36 × 100 = 2,436.

Now you divide as with whole numbers.

$$
\begin{array}{r}
203 \\
12\overline{| 2436 } \\
24 \\
\hline
36 \\
36 \\
\hline
\end{array}
$$

Check: Does your quotient, 203, multiplied by the original divisor, .12, equal the original dividend, 24.36?

$$
\begin{array}{r}
203 \longleftarrow \text{quotient} \\
\times\ .12 \longleftarrow \text{divisor} \\
\hline
4\ 06 \\
20\ 3 \\
\hline
24.36 \longleftarrow \text{dividend}
\end{array}
$$

Answer: .12 | 24.36 = 203

EXAMPLE 2. Divide: 1.5 | 225

Solution: Move the decimal point in the divisor one place to the right (1.5 × 10 = 15).

$$1.5. \overline{| 225 }$$

Next, move the decimal point in the dividend one place to the right.

$$1.5. \overline{| 225.0. }$$

Since there are no digits to the right of the decimal point in the dividend, fill in the empty space with a zero as a place holder (225 × 10 = 2,250).

$$1.5. \overline{| 225.0. }$$

Divide as with whole numbers.

$$
\begin{array}{r}
150 \\
15\overline{| 2250 } \\
15 \\
\hline
75 \\
75 \\
\hline
\end{array}
$$

Check:
$$
\begin{array}{r}
150 \longleftarrow \text{quotient} \\
\times 1.5 \longleftarrow \text{divisor} \\
\hline
750 \\
150 \\
\hline
225.0 \longleftarrow \text{dividend}
\end{array}
$$

Answer: 1.5 | 225 = 150

EXAMPLE 3. Divide: .1848 ÷ .14

Solution: Set up the problem and move the decimal point two places to the right in both the divisor and in the dividend. Then divide as if the divisor were a whole number. After you move the decimal point in your dividend, you move it *straight up* to place the decimal point in your answer.

$$
\begin{array}{r}
1.32 \\
.14. \overline{| .18.48 } \\
14 \\
\hline
4\ 4 \\
4\ 2 \\
\hline
28 \\
28 \\
\hline
\end{array}
$$

Answer: .1848 ÷ .14 = 1.32

Remember: To perform division when there is a decimal point in the divisor:

1. **Change** the divisor to a whole number by moving the decimal point to the right. The divisor is a whole number when the decimal point is "outside" (to the right) of the divisor.
2. **Move** the decimal point in the dividend to the right the same number of places as you moved the decimal point in the divisor.
3. **Divide** as if the divisor were a whole number, placing the decimal point in your answer directly above the decimal place in your dividend.

EXERCISES

In 1 to 10, divide.

Sample solutions

a. $.15 \overline{)43.65}$ $291. = 291$

```
  291.
.15)43.65.
   30
   136
   135
    15
    15
```

b. $.32 \overline{)224.00}$ $700. = 700$

```
  700.
.32)224.00
   224
```

1. $.25 \overline{)37.75}$

2. $.08 \overline{)27.20}$

3. $3.8 \overline{)132.24}$

4. $.055 \overline{)267.3}$

5. $.042 \overline{)470.4}$

6. $5.6 \overline{)651.84}$

7. $.15 \overline{)625.5}$

8. $.075 \overline{)427.5}$

9. $.27 \overline{)2.5839}$

10. $.23 \overline{)621}$

APPLICATION PROBLEMS

1. Oranges sell at $.45 a dozen. How many dozen can you buy with $4.05?

_____

2. A wholesale butcher charged $30.52 for an order of beef. If the price of the beef was $1.09 a pound, how much did the beef weigh?

_____

3. An airplane flew 997.15 miles in 2.75 hours. What was its average speed in miles per hour?

_____

4. Gasoline sells at $.45 a gallon. How many gallons can you buy with $7.50? (Give your answer as a common fraction.)

_____

5. Mrs. Rennie paid $1.68 for a sack of potatoes. If the potatoes sold at $.06 per pound, how many pounds of potatoes did the sack hold?

_____

Unit 54. Rounding Off to the Nearest Penny in Division

In business problems, it is often necessary to divide amounts of money into smaller amounts. Sometimes the answer will contain a fraction of a penny. In actual business transactions, however, you cannot pay out or collect a fraction of a penny. Hence, in working with dollars and cents in division problems, you cannot keep a fraction of a penny in your answer. You either have to raise the fraction to a whole penny or drop the fraction out.

EXAMPLE 1. Divide $415.75 into 20 equal parts.

Solution: Set up the division problem and divide. You get a remainder of 15.

$$\begin{array}{r} 20.78 \\ 20\overline{)415.75} \\ 40 \\ \hline 15\ 7 \\ 14\ 0 \\ \hline 1\ 75 \\ 1\ 60 \\ \hline 15 \end{array}$$ ← remainder

When dividing dollars and cents, use the following rule for rounding off:

Rule: If the remainder is half or more than half of the divisor, add a penny to your answer. If the remainder is less than half of the divisor, do not add a penny to your answer.

In this example, half of the divisor is 10. Since the remainder is 15, you add a penny to your answer.

half of the divisor →

$$\begin{array}{r} 9 \\ 20.7\cancel{8} = \$20.79 \\ 20\overline{)415.75} \\ 40 \\ \hline 15\ 7 \\ 14\ 0 \\ \hline 1\ 75 \\ 1\ 60 \\ \hline 15 \end{array}$$ ← remainder

Answer: $415.75 ÷ 20 = $20.79

EXAMPLE 2. Divide: 30 $\overline{)\$536.53}$

Solution: Divide as usual, and obtain a remainder of 13.

```
        17.88
    30|536.53
       30
       ────
       236
       210
       ────
        26 5
        24 0
        ─────
         2 53
         2 40
         ─────
           13 ←── remainder
```

Because the remainder is less than half of the divisor, do not add a penny to your answer.

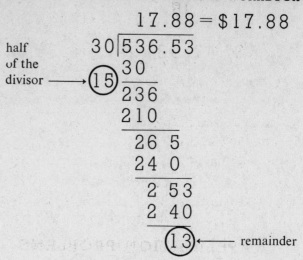

```
        17.88 = $17.88
    30|536.53
half   30
of the ⑮ ──
divisor→ 236
        210
        ────
         26 5
         24 0
         ─────
          2 53
          2 40
          ─────
            ⑬ ←── remainder
```

Answer: 30|$536.53 = $17.88

EXERCISES

In 1 to 12, divide and round off to the nearest penny.

1. 23|$695.83   **2.** 25|$1,032.30   **3.** 15|$230.52

4. 34|$690.00   **5.** 22|$749.43   **6.** 19|$820.88

7. 36|$739.20   **8.** 18|$578.85   **9.** 24|$590.52

10. $18\overline{\smash{)}\$547.98}$ **11.** $36\overline{\smash{)}\$1,153.63}$ **12.** $31\overline{\smash{)}\$1,240.07}$

APPLICATION PROBLEMS

In 1 to 5, round off your answer to the nearest penny.

1. At the A and Z Furniture Store, according to sales records, the average installment purchase is $843.71 and is paid for in 24 equal payments. What is the amount of the average payment?

2. Last year, Stanley spent $12.68 on postage. On the average, how much did he spend each month?

3. Meg has saved $505.58 for her two-week vacation. How much can she afford to spend on each day of her vacation? (Assume that the vacation is exactly 14 days.)

4. Harry spent $60 last year on newspapers. On the average, how much did he spend each day? (Use a 365-day year; $60 is 6,000 pennies.)

5. After adding up the food costs and medical expenses, Shirley found that her pet cat cost $35.75 last year. How much does Shirley spend per month on her cat?

Unit 55. Division of a Smaller Whole Number by a Larger Whole Number

There are times when you must divide a smaller number by a larger number. For example, if 5 boys want to share 2 dollars, how much should each boy get?

Because the number of dollars is smaller than the number of boys, the answer will not be in whole dollars. Rather, the answer will be in cents, which are the decimal fractions of dollars. *Cents*, you recall, are *hundredths* of dollars.

EXAMPLE 1. Divide: $2 ÷ 5 (Round off your answer to the nearest penny.)

Solution: Place two zeros after the decimal point because you want the answer in hundredths of dollars. Then move the decimal point up in a straight line.

$5\overline{\smash{)}2.00}$

Now you divide as with whole numbers.

$$
\begin{array}{r}
.40 \\
5\overline{)2.00} \\
2\ 0 \\
\hline
\end{array}
$$

Answer: Each boy will get $.40

The same method is used to divide any smaller number by a larger number. Also, the dividend can be an amount of something, such as miles, pounds, hours, etc. To divide a smaller whole number by a larger whole number, use the following rule:

Rule: To divide a smaller whole number by a larger whole number, place a decimal point to the right of the dividend. Then:

1. **For an answer to the nearest *tenth*, place *one* zero to the right of the decimal point.**

2. **For an answer to the nearest *hundredth*, place *two zeros* to the right of the decimal point.**

3. **For an answer to the nearest *thousandth*, place *three zeros* to the right of the decimal point.**

And so on.

Then divide and round off the remainder.

Since dividing a smaller number by a larger number often does not come out even, be sure you know how to round off your decimal answer. To round off a decimal answer to a given value such as tenths, hundredths, or thousandths. follow the procedure explained in the preceding unit. However, instead of rounding off to the nearest penny, round off to the given value.

EXAMPLE 2. Divide: $7 \div 12$ (Round off the answer to the nearest tenth.)

Solution: Place a decimal point and one zero after the 7. Divide and round off.

$$
\begin{array}{r}
.\overset{6}{5} = .6 \\
12\overline{)7.0} \\
6\ 0 \\
\hline
1\ 0 \\
\end{array}
$$

half of the divisor ⟶ ⑥ remainder

Since the remainder is larger than half of the divisor, you add 1 unit to the quotient. In this example, the unit is tenths, so you add .1 to .5, getting .6.

Answer: $7 \div 12 = .6$, to the nearest tenth

EXAMPLE 3. Divide: $7 \div 12$ (Round off the answer to the nearest hundredth.)

Solution: Place a decimal point and two zeros after the 7. Divide and round off.

$$
\begin{array}{r}
.58 = .58 \\
12\overline{)7.00} \\
6\ 0 \\
\hline
1\ 00 \\
96 \\
\hline
4 \\
\end{array}
$$

half of the divisor ⟶ ⑥   ④ ⟵ remainder

Answer: $7 \div 12 = .58$, to the nearest hundredth

EXAMPLE 4. Divide: $7 \div 12$ (Round off the answer to the nearest thousandth.)

Solution: Place a decimal point and three zeros after the 7. Divide and round off.

$$
\begin{array}{r}
.583 = .583 \\
12\overline{)7.000} \\
6\ 0 \\
\hline
1\ 00 \\
96 \\
\hline
40 \\
36 \\
\hline
4 \\
\end{array}
$$

half of the divisor ⟶ ⑥   ④ ⟵ remainder

Answer: $7 \div 12 = .583$, to the nearest thousandth

In all word problems involving division, you may have to round off the answers. In problems dealing with cost or price, *always round off to the nearest penny.* When other units are involved, such as yards, pounds, or hours, you must be told whether the answer is to be in whole units, tenths, hundredths, etc. If you are not told, *always round off to the nearest whole unit.*

EXAMPLE 5. A snail travels 5 inches in 7 hours. Find, to the nearest tenth of an inch, how far it travels in one hour.

Solution: To find the distance traveled in *one* hour, divide the entire distance, 5 inches, by the total time, 7 hours.

$$
\begin{array}{r}
.7 \\
7\overline{)5.0} \\
4\ 9 \\
\hline
1 \\
\end{array}
$$

half of the divisor ⟶ $3\frac{1}{2}$ ① ⟵ remainder is less than half of the divisor

Do not add .1 to the quotient.

Answer: .7 of an inch

EXERCISES

In 1 to 5, divide. Round off the quotient to the nearest *tenth*.

1. $7\overline{)4}$ **2.** $15\overline{)11}$ **3.** $8\overline{)5}$ **4.** $13\overline{)10}$ **5.** $23\overline{)19}$

In 6 to 10, divide. Round off to the nearest *hundredth*.

6. $12\overline{)8}$ **7.** $18\overline{)7}$ **8.** $28\overline{)19}$ **9.** $13\overline{)5}$ **10.** $26\overline{)23}$

In 11 to 15, divide. Round off to the nearest *thousandth*.

11. $16\overline{)5}$ **12.** $35\overline{)23}$ **13.** $27\overline{)15}$ **14.** $32\overline{)28}$ **15.** $23\overline{)21}$

APPLICATION PROBLEMS

Sample solution

For an experiment, Sandy must measure equal amounts of a chemical into 7 test tubes. If he must use 2 grams of the chemical, how much goes into each test tube? Round off your answer to the nearest hundredth of a gram. *Each tube gets*
$\frac{1}{7}$ *of 2, or* $\frac{2}{7}$ *grams.*

$$
\begin{array}{r}
9 \\
.2\!\!\!/8 = .29 \\
7\overline{)2.00} \\
1\,4 \\
\hline
60 \\
56 \\
\hline
4
\end{array}
$$

.29 gram

1. Tee shirts sell at 5 for \$4. How much is one shirt?

2. Mary needs 6 yards of material to make 7 blouses. To the nearest tenth of a yard, how much material is used to make one blouse?

3. What is the price of one pair of socks if they sell at $9.55 a dozen?

                                                     _____

4. If an electricity bill for one month is $20, what is the average cost of electricity for one day? Use a 30-day month.

                                                     _____

5. Ninety seconds is what fraction of an hour? Answer with a decimal fraction to the nearest thousandth. (*Hint:* 90 seconds is 1.5 minutes. You can use the $\frac{IS}{OF}$ fraction.)

                                                     _____

Unit 56. Changing Common Fractions to Decimal Fractions

Recall that a fraction is a "part of a unit." A *common fraction* is a part of its denominator. Thus, the fraction $\frac{3}{4}$ is "three parts out of four" or "three fourths." A *decimal fraction* is also a part of its denominator, even though the denominator is not actually written down. Thus, the fraction .75 is "75 parts out of a hundred" or "75 hundredths."

Notice that both the common fraction $\frac{3}{4}$ and the decimal fraction .75 have the same value: $\frac{3}{4} = .75$.

In money, 3 quarters is the same as $.75.

You can say that you have "half a dollar" or that you have "$.50." Both fractions have the same value, because $\frac{1}{2} = .50$. The common fraction $\frac{1}{2}$ of a dollar means that 1 dollar has been divided by 2. The fraction $\frac{3}{4}$ means that the number 3 has been divided by 4.

Rule: To change a common fraction to a decimal fraction, divide the numerator by the denominator.

Follow the rule for dividing a smaller number by a larger number that was explained in the preceding unit.

EXAMPLE 1. Change $\frac{4}{5}$ to a decimal fraction. Round off your answer to the nearest tenth.

Solution: $\frac{4}{5}$ means 4 divided by 5.

$$\begin{array}{r} .8 = .8 \\ 5\overline{)4.0} \\ \underline{4\ 0} \end{array}$$

Answer: $\frac{4}{5} = .8$

Alternate Method: Draw a division box next to the denominator and let the numerator "fall in." (You used this method in your work with improper fractions in Unit 26.) Then divide as usual.

$$\frac{4}{5}\overline{)4}$$

EXAMPLE 2. Change $\frac{2}{3}$ to a decimal fraction. Round off your answer to the nearest hundredth.

Solution: $\frac{2}{3}$ means 2 divided by 3. Or, $\frac{2}{3}\overline{)2}$.

$$\begin{array}{r} 7 \\ .66 = .67 \\ 3\overline{)2.00} \\ \underline{1\ 8} \\ 20 \\ \underline{18} \\ ② \end{array}$$

half of the divisor ⟶ $1\frac{1}{2}$

② ⟵ remainder

Answer: $\frac{2}{3} = .67$, to the nearest hundredth

EXERCISES

In 1 to 15, change the common fraction to a decimal fraction. Round off the answer to the nearest hundredth.

1. $\dfrac{5}{16}$ 2. $\dfrac{3}{16}$ 3. $\dfrac{9}{20}$ 4. $\dfrac{1}{6}$ 5. $\dfrac{3}{7}$

6. $\dfrac{5}{9}$ 7. $\dfrac{5}{12}$ 8. $\dfrac{7}{11}$ 9. $\dfrac{15}{24}$ 10. $\dfrac{21}{28}$

11. $\dfrac{13}{15}$ 12. $\dfrac{27}{30}$ 13. $\dfrac{15}{40}$ 14. $\dfrac{24}{36}$ 15. $\dfrac{12}{32}$

APPLICATION PROBLEMS

1. A nut measures $\dfrac{9}{32}$ of an inch in diameter. What is the measurement of the nut in *thousandths* of an inch?

2. John ran $\frac{4}{7}$ of a mile. How many *hundredths* of a mile did he run?

_____

3. A moon rock weighs $\frac{7}{16}$ of a pound. How many *hundredths* of a pound does it weigh?

_____

4. For an experiment, a chemist needs $\frac{5}{9}$ of a gallon of a certain chemical. How many *thousandths* of a gallon does he need?

_____

5. The time of flight of an experimental rocket is $\frac{5}{12}$ of an hour. What is the time of flight in *thousandths* of an hour?

_____

Unit 57. Changing the Fraction in a Mixed Number to a Decimal to Simplify Multiplication and Division

When you must multiply or divide a whole number by a mixed number, the problem can often be simplified by changing the common fraction to a decimal fraction.

EXAMPLE 1. Multiply: $345 \times 23\frac{1}{4}$

Solution: You may find it easier to multiply if you change $23\frac{1}{4}$ to 23.25.

$$
\begin{array}{r}
23.25 \\
\times\ 345 \\
\hline
116\ 25 \\
930\ 0 \\
6\ 975 \\
\hline
8,021.25
\end{array}
$$

Answer: $345 \times 23\frac{1}{4} = 8,021.25$

Note: To multiply 345 by $23\frac{1}{4}$ using common fractions, first change $23\frac{1}{4}$ to an improper fraction.

$$345 \times 23\frac{1}{4} = \frac{345}{1} \times \frac{93}{4}$$

Then, you must multiply the numerators, 345×93. Finally, you must divide this product by 4. In general, there is less chance for error in performing one operation than in performing several separate operations.

EXAMPLE 2. Divide: $\$125 \div 25\frac{1}{2}$

Solution: Change $25\frac{1}{2}$ to 25.5 and divide.

$$
\begin{array}{r}
4.90 = 4.90 \\
25.5.\overline{)125.0.00} \\
102\ 0 \\
\hline
23\ 00 \\
22\ 95 \\
\hline
50 \leftarrow \text{remainder}
\end{array}
$$

half of the divisor → $127\frac{1}{2}$

Answer: $\$125 \div 25\frac{1}{2} = \$4.90$

EXERCISES

In 1 to 6, change the mixed fraction to a mixed decimal and multiply.

1. $247 \times 35\frac{3}{4}$

2. $527 \times 47\frac{1}{5}$

3. $345\frac{1}{2} \times 37$

4. $638\frac{3}{5} \times 43$

5. $528 \times 124\frac{1}{4}$

6. $728 \times 46\frac{2}{8}$

In 7 to 12, change the mixed fraction to a mixed decimal and divide. If the quotient does not come out even, round off the answer to the nearest hundredth.

7. $215 \div 12\frac{1}{2}$

8. $354\frac{4}{5} \div 38$

9. $527\frac{1}{5} \div 43$

10. $1,356\frac{3}{4} \div 120$

11. $2,435 \div 15\frac{4}{5}$

12. $3,528\frac{1}{2} \div 28$

APPLICATION PROBLEMS

1. If a cinder block weighs $15\frac{1}{2}$ pounds, how many pounds will 358 cinder blocks weigh?

2. A clothing manufacturer uses $4\frac{3}{4}$ yards of material to make a suit. How many suits can he make with 475 yards of material?

3. A sewing machine weighs $23\frac{4}{5}$ pounds. How many pounds would 324 sewing machines weigh?

4. A fruit picker can pick $12\frac{1}{2}$ bushels of tomatoes in one hour. How many bushels can he pick in 138 hours?

5. Gasoline sells for $\$.38\frac{3}{5}$ a gallon. How many gallons can be bought with \$6? (Answer to the nearest tenth of a gallon.)

_____

_____

_____

_____

Review of Part XII (Units 51 to 57)

In 1 to 12, divide and round off to the nearest penny.

1. $5\overline{\smash{\big)}\$2,605.85}$

2. $24\overline{\smash{\big)}\$3,263.50}$

3. $42\overline{\smash{\big)}\$368.75}$

4. $4.5\overline{\smash{\big)}\$372.08}$

5. $.18\overline{\smash{\big)}\$680}$

6. $85.\overline{\smash{\big)}\$568.52}$

7. $.06\overline{)\$853}$ 8. $27\overline{)\$4,321.48}$ 9. $.05\overline{)\$475.68}$

10. $6.3\overline{)\$248.95}$ 11. $.38\overline{)\$874.70}$ 12. $.53\overline{)\$654.80}$

In 13 to 18, divide. Round off to the nearest *hundredth*.

13. $12\overline{)3}$ 14. $15\overline{)6}$ 15. $23\overline{)18}$

16. $65\overline{)42}$ 17. $128\overline{)85}$ 18. $350\overline{)275}$

In 19 to 24, change each fraction to a decimal. Round off to the nearest *hundredth*.

19. $\dfrac{2}{3}$ 20. $\dfrac{5}{7}$ 21. $\dfrac{12}{15}$

22. $\dfrac{25}{63}$ **23.** $\dfrac{19}{45}$ **24.** $\dfrac{48}{72}$

In 25 and 26, change the mixed number to a mixed decimal and multiply.

25. $9\dfrac{99}{100} \times 87$ **26.** $847 \times 25\dfrac{2}{5}$

In 27 and 28, change the mixed number to a mixed decimal and divide.

27. $7,128 \div 9\dfrac{9}{10}$ **28.** $54.2 \div 3\dfrac{4}{5}$

Part XIII. Percents

Unit 58. Understanding Percents

Words to know

You know that there are 100 *cents* in a dollar and 100 years in a *century*. This makes it easy to remember that **percent** means *per hundred*.

THE MEANING OF %

The word **percent** can be read "hundredths" or "out of 100." The symbol **%** is often used in place of the word **percent**. Note what the % symbol means in the following examples:

A salesman who earns a commission of "15% on sales" earns $15 for every $100 worth of merchandise he sells. He earns "$15 out of $100."

A "7% sales tax" means that you are taxed $.07 every time you spend $1.00; that is, the tax is "7¢ out of 100¢."

When a school has a student population that is "55% boys," then "55 students out of every 100 students are boys."

If the amount of spoilage in a crate of oranges is found to be "10%," this means that "10 oranges out of every 100 oranges" are spoiled.

PERCENTS WITH FRACTIONS

When a common fraction or a decimal fraction is involved in a percent problem, you usually keep the fraction in its original form. Note how the following expressions are written with the % symbol:

"$66\frac{2}{3}$ out of 100" may be expressed as "$66\frac{2}{3}\%$."

"87.5 per hundred" means "87.5%."

"$\frac{1}{3}$ hundredths" means "$\frac{1}{3}$ of 1 percent" or "$\frac{1}{3}\%$."

THE MEANING OF 100%

We use the expression "100%" to mean "*all of something*" or "*the whole group*." Note what "100%" means in each of the following:

A can labeled "100% pure juice" contains no water or coloring. The contents are "*all* pure juice."

When a theater is filled to "100% capacity," you know that "*all* the seats" are filled.

If "100% of the Sophomore Class" attended a game, then the "*whole class*" attended.

GREATER THAN 100%

When you mean *more* than the whole group or *more* than all of something, you use expressions such as "150%" or "200%."

If your income this year is "150%" of last year's income, it is 50% *greater* than it was last year. "150%" means *all* of something (100%), plus 50% more.

If the cost of something is "200%" of the old price, the new price is *twice* the old price. "200%" means two times 100%.

The expression "475%" means four times 100%, plus 75% more.

UNKNOWN PERCENTS

Since you know that *100%* means *all*, you can figure out percents that are not given in a problem. You do this by subtracting the given percent from 100%. For example:

The school that has a student population of 55% boys must have a population of 45% girls, since $100\% - 55\% = 45\%$.

The crate that has 10% of its oranges spoiled has $100\% - 10\% = 90\%$ of its oranges not spoiled.

COMMON FRACTIONS

Since percents mean *hundredths*, you can write any percent as a common fraction that has a denominator of 100. For example:

6% means "6 out of 100," or $\frac{6}{100}$.

$25\% = \frac{25}{100}$

$66\frac{2}{3}\% = \frac{66\frac{2}{3}}{100}$ (In this example, you have a complex fraction.)

DECIMAL FRACTIONS

Finally, you can write any percent as a decimal fraction. Simply rewrite the common fraction as a decimal fraction (to the hundredth place). For example:

$$6\% = \frac{6}{100} = .06$$

$$25\% = \frac{25}{100} = .25$$

$$2.5\% = \frac{2.5}{100} = .025$$

$$66\frac{2}{3}\% = \frac{66\frac{2}{3}}{100} = .66\frac{2}{3}$$

EXERCISES

In 1 to 27, fill in the blanks.

1. 25 out of 100 means _____ %

2. 5 out of 100 means _____ %

3. 87 out of 100 means _____ %

4. 100 out of 100 means _____ %

5. $12\frac{1}{2}$ out of 100 means _____ %

6. 37.5 out of 100 means _____ %

7. $4\frac{1}{2}$ out of 100 means _____ %

8. 95 out of 100 means _____ %

9. $33\frac{1}{3}$ out of 100 means _____ %

10. 8 hundredths means _____ %

11. 75 hundredths means _____ %

12. $5\frac{1}{2}$ hundredths means _____ %

13. 32.7 hundredths means _____ %

14. $\frac{1}{4}$ hundredths means _____ %

15. $33\frac{1}{3}$ hundredths means _____ %

16. 4.25 hundredths means _____ %

17. 20 hundredths means _____ %

18. $37\frac{1}{2}$ hundredths means _____ %

19. $\frac{5}{100} =$ _____ %

20. $\frac{27}{100} =$ _____ %

21. $\frac{12\frac{1}{2}}{100} =$ _____ %

22. $\frac{80}{100} =$ _____ %

23. $\frac{37.5}{100} =$ _____ %

24. $\frac{33\frac{1}{3}}{100} =$ _____ %

25. $\frac{12.5}{100} =$ _____ %

26. $\frac{75}{100} =$ _____ %

27. $\frac{100}{100} =$ _____ %

APPLICATION PROBLEMS

Sample solution

In 1971, Joe Torre of the St. Louis Cardinals won the National League Batting Championship with a .363 batting average. Write this as a percent.

$$.363 = \frac{363}{1,000} \qquad 10\overline{)\frac{363}{1,000}} = \frac{36.3}{100}$$

36.3%

1. A school has 48% girls. How many students out of every 100 are girls?

How many students out of every 100 are boys?

2. If there is a sales tax of 7%, how many dollars tax will you pay for every purchase of $100?

How many dollars for a purchase of $200?

3. If 15% of a class is absent, what is the percent of students present?

4. A family spends 25% of its income on rent and 15% on food. What percent of the income is left for other expenses?

5. A dress selling for $100 was reduced by 20%. What is the new price of the dress?

Unit 59. Changing Percents to Decimals and Decimals to Percents

PERCENTS TO DECIMALS

In many problems, you must perform multiplication and division with percents. Before you can do this, you must always change the percent to a decimal.

Rule: To change a percent to a decimal, rewrite the percent without the % sign. Then move the decimal point two places to the *left*.

EXAMPLES

$30\% = .30. = .30$ (Recall that every whole number has a decimal point, even though the decimal point is not actually written.)

$5\% = .05. = .05$ (Recall the use of zeros as place holders.)

$250\% = 2.50. = 2.50$ (When a percent exceeds 100%, it is rewritten as a mixed decimal.)

$4\frac{1}{2}\% = .04.\frac{1}{2} = .04\frac{1}{2}$ (In a mixed number, the decimal point is between the whole number and the common fraction, even though it is not actually written.)

When a percent is a mixed number, it is sometimes convenient to eliminate the common fraction from the decimal equivalent. Do this by first changing the mixed number to a mixed decimal. Then follow the above rule.

EXAMPLES

$4\frac{1}{2}\% = 4.5\% = .04.5 = .045$

(Notice that .045 and $.04\frac{1}{2}$ both have the same value.)

$99\frac{44}{100}\% = 99.44\% = .99.44$
$= .9944$

You may find it helpful to think of percents as the hundred cents contained in a dollar. To change a percent to a decimal, simply *rewrite the percents as cents of a dollar*. For example, write 25% as .25, just as you write 25¢ as $.25. Also, $7\% = .07$ (7¢ = $.07) and $150\% = 1.50$ (150¢ = $1.50).

DECIMALS TO PERCENTS

When a problem requires a percent as the answer, you will often have to change your decimal answer to a percent. To change a given decimal to a percent, you reverse the preceding rule.

Rule: To change a decimal to a percent, rewrite the decimal with the % sign. Then move the decimal point two places to the *right*.

EXAMPLES

$.65 = .65. \% = 65\%$

$.03 = .03. \% = 3\%$ (Since the zero to the left of the 3 is not needed as a place holder, you do *not* write "03%.")

$2.25 = 2.25. = 225\%$

$.875 = .87.5 = 87.5\% \text{ or } 87\frac{1}{2}\%$

$.008 = .00.8 = .8\%$

$.12\frac{1}{2} = .12.\frac{1}{2} = 12\frac{1}{2}\% \text{ or } 12.5\%$

$1.2 = 1.2.0 = 120\%$

(A mixed decimal changes to a percent that exceeds 100%.)

EXERCISES

In 1 to 20, change each percent to a decimal. When the percent is a mixed number, keep the common fraction.

1. 28% 2. 6% 3. 1% 4. 35%

5. 100%

6. $12\frac{1}{2}\%$

7. $5\frac{3}{4}\%$

8. 23.8%

9. 8%

10. 15.9%

11. $33\frac{1}{3}\%$

12. $.001\%$

13. 125%

14. 300%

15. $.008\%$

16. $.4\%$

17. 105%

18. $.5\%$

19. 3.25%

20. 6.7%

In 21 to 40, change each decimal to a percent. When the decimal contains a common fraction, keep it.

21. $.50$

22. $.28$

23. $.07$

24. $.45$

25. $.15$

26. 3.15

27. $.25\frac{1}{2}$

28. $.05\frac{1}{2}$

29. 1.35

30. $.005$

31. $.4$

32. 1.00

33. $.12\frac{3}{4}$

34. $.325$

35. $.001$

36. $.9$

37. $.68\frac{4}{5}$

38. $.025$

39. $.008$

40. $.08$

APPLICATION PROBLEMS

1. "The Cost-of-Living Index increased by 1.7%." Express the percent as a decimal.

2. During the season, a pitcher won 16 games out of 20 for an average of .800. What percent of games pitched did he win?

What percent did he lose?

3. If there is a sales tax of 7%, how many cents do you pay on a $5 purchase?

4. How many cents is 75% of a dollar?

5. A ball player has a batting average of .350. What is the percent of hits for times at bat?

Unit 60. Changing Percents to Fractions and Fractions to Percents

PERCENTS TO FRACTIONS

As you learned in Unit 58, since *percent* means *hundredth*, you can write any percent as a fraction that has a denominator of 100. You will now use this skill to change percents to fractions.

Rule: To change a given percent to a fraction, write the percent as a fraction that has a denominator of 100. Then reduce to lowest terms.

EXAMPLES

$$20\% = \frac{20}{100} = \frac{1}{5} \qquad 2\left|\frac{\overset{1}{\cancel{2}}}{\underset{5}{\cancel{10}}}\right. = \frac{1}{5}$$

$$75\% = \frac{75}{100} = \frac{3}{4} \qquad 25\left|\frac{\overset{3}{\cancel{75}}}{\underset{4}{\cancel{100}}}\right. = \frac{3}{4}$$

$$12\frac{1}{2}\% = \frac{12\frac{1}{2}}{100} = 12\frac{1}{2} \div \frac{100}{1}$$

$$= \frac{\overset{1}{\cancel{25}}}{2} \times \frac{1}{\underset{4}{\cancel{100}}} = \frac{1}{8}$$

FRACTIONS TO PERCENTS

There are two ways of changing a fraction to a percent.

First, if you can raise a given fraction to an equivalent fraction that has a denominator of 100, then you can change the given fraction to a percent.

EXAMPLE 1. Change $\frac{1}{5}$ to a percent.

Solution: Since 5 divides evenly into 100, you can raise $\frac{1}{5}$ to an equivalent fraction that has a denominator of 100.

$$\frac{1}{5} = \frac{}{100} \qquad \frac{1}{5}\!\!\nearrow\!\!\overset{20}{\underset{100}{}} \qquad \text{(Think: "5 into 100 goes}$$
$$\text{20, and } 20 \times 1 = 20.\text{")}$$

Answer: $\frac{1}{5} = \frac{20}{100} = 20\%$

When the denominator of the given fraction does not divide evenly into 100, use the following rule:

Rule: When a fraction cannot be raised to an equivalent fraction that has a denominator of 100, divide the numerator by the denominator. Then carry your answer to three places and change the decimal to a percent.

EXAMPLE 2. Change $\frac{3}{8}$ to a percent.

Solution: Since 8 will not divide evenly into 100, you must use the rule. Divide 8 into 3, and carry your answer to three places.

$$
\begin{array}{r}
.375 \\
8\overline{)3.000} \\
\underline{2\ 4} \\
60 \\
\underline{56} \\
40 \\
\underline{40} \\
\end{array}
$$

$$.375 = .37\!\!\underset{\frown}{}\!5\% = 37.5\%$$

Answer: $\frac{3}{8} = 37.5\%$

EXAMPLE 3. Change $\frac{6}{7}$ to a percent.

$$.857 = .85\!\!\underset{\frown}{}\!7\% = 85.7\%$$

$$
\begin{array}{r}
7\overline{)6.000} \\
\underline{5\ 6} \\
40 \\
\underline{35} \\
50 \\
\underline{49} \\
1 \\
\end{array}
$$

Reminder: You may write the division box next to the denominator and let the numerator "drop in."

$$\frac{6}{7}\overline{)6.00}$$

Answer: $\frac{6}{7} = 85.7\%$

Table III shows some common fractions expressed as 3-place decimal equivalents and as percents.

Table III: *Decimal Equivalents and Percents*

Fraction	Decimal Equivalent	Percent	Fraction	Decimal Equivalent	Percent
$\frac{1}{8}$	.125	12.5%	$\frac{5}{8}$	.625	62.5%
$\frac{1}{6}$	.167	16.7%	$\frac{2}{3}$	.667	66.7%
$\frac{1}{5}$	.200	20%	$\frac{3}{4}$	.750	75%
$\frac{1}{4}$	.250	25%	$\frac{4}{5}$	.800	80%
$\frac{1}{3}$	.333	33.3%	$\frac{5}{6}$	.833	83.3%
$\frac{3}{8}$	.375	37.5%	$\frac{7}{8}$	.875	87.5%
$\frac{2}{5}$	.400	40%			
$\frac{1}{2}$	.500	50%			
$\frac{3}{5}$	.600	60%			

EXERCISES

In 1 to 15, change each percent to a fraction. Reduce the fraction to lowest terms.

1. 10% **2.** 30% **3.** 90% **4.** 85%

5. 5% **6.** 32% **7.** 64% **8.** 14%

9. 38% **10.** 76% **11.** 4% **12.** $7\frac{1}{2}\%$

13. $6\frac{1}{4}\%$ **14.** $8\frac{1}{3}\%$ **15.** $42\frac{6}{7}\%$

In 16 to 30, change each fraction to a percent.

16. $\dfrac{7}{10}$ **17.** $\dfrac{3}{50}$ **18.** $\dfrac{15}{25}$ **19.** $\dfrac{17}{20}$ **20.** $\dfrac{25}{75}$

21. $\dfrac{20}{80}$ **22.** $\dfrac{12}{48}$ **23.** $\dfrac{14}{35}$ **24.** $\dfrac{7}{28}$ **25.** $\dfrac{15}{18}$

26. $\dfrac{17}{22}$ **27.** $\dfrac{23}{45}$ **28.** $\dfrac{3}{7}$ **29.** $\dfrac{32}{55}$ **30.** $\dfrac{42}{85}$

APPLICATION PROBLEMS

Reduce all fractions to lowest terms.

1. Last term, 20% of a class failed a test. What fraction of the class failed the test?

What fraction of the class passed?

2. A dress is on sale at 25% off the regular price. What fraction of the regular price is the sales price?

3. A living room set is reduced by $\frac{1}{3}$ off the regular price. What is the percent of reduction?

What percent of the original price is the sales price?

4. Tom bought a radio and gave $\frac{1}{5}$ of the full price as a down payment. What percent of the full price was the down payment?

5. John received $\frac{4}{5}$ of the votes cast for class president. What percent of the votes did he receive?

Unit 61. Fractional Parts of 1%

Percents are sometimes expressed as *fractions* of 1%. A percent such as "$\frac{1}{4}$%" means "$\frac{1}{4}$ of 1%" and "$\frac{1}{2}$%" means "$\frac{1}{2}$ of 1%," etc. When performing calculations, it is usually simpler to change fractions of percents to decimals.

Rule: To change a fraction of a percent to a decimal:

1. **Change** the "common-fraction percent" to a "decimal-fraction percent" by rewriting the common fraction as a decimal fraction.
2. **Change** the resulting percent to a decimal by moving the decimal point two places to the left and dropping the % sign.

EXAMPLE 1. Change $\frac{1}{4}$% to a decimal.

Solution: Since $\frac{1}{4} = .25$, change $\frac{1}{4}$% to .25%. Then drop the percent sign and move the decimal point two places to the left: $\frac{1}{4}\% = .25\% = .00.25 = .0025$

Answer: $\frac{1}{4}\% = .0025$

EXAMPLE 2. Change $\frac{7}{8}$% to a decimal.

Solution: Change $\frac{7}{8}$ to its decimal equivalent. Use Table III in the previous unit, or divide the denominator into the numerator.

$$
\begin{array}{r}
.875 \\
8\overline{\smash)7.000} \\
\underline{6\ 4} \\
60 \\
\underline{56} \\
40 \\
\underline{40}
\end{array}
$$

Change the decimal equivalent to a percent.

$$\frac{7}{8}\% = .875\% = .00.875$$
$$= .00875$$

Answer: $\frac{7}{8}\% = .00875$

Some fractions, when changed to decimals, do not come out even. In cases like this, you must round off the decimal equivalent to a given number of places.

EXAMPLE 3. Change $\frac{1}{3}$% to a 5-place decimal.

Solution: Change $\frac{1}{3}$ to a 3-place decimal equivalent.

(Since, in changing a percent to a decimal, we move the decimal point two places to the left, we need only three places in the decimal equivalent.) Use Table III in the previous unit, or divide the numerator into the denominator.

$$
\frac{1}{3} = 3\overline{\smash)1.000}
\begin{array}{r}
.333 \\
\end{array}
$$

$$
\begin{array}{r}
.333 \\
3\overline{\smash)1.000} \\
\underline{9} \\
10 \\
\underline{9} \\
10 \\
\underline{9} \\
1 \longleftarrow \text{less than half the divisor}
\end{array}
$$

$$\frac{1}{3}\% = .333\%$$
$$= .00.333$$
$$= .00333$$

Answer: $\frac{1}{3}\% = .00333$

EXERCISES

In 1 to 15, change each fraction of a percent to a 5-place decimal. In 1-5, you can use Table III in the preceding unit.

1. $\frac{1}{4}\%$ 2. $\frac{2}{3}\%$ 3. $\frac{3}{8}\%$ 4. $\frac{5}{6}\%$ 5. $\frac{4}{5}\%$ 6. $\frac{3}{10}\%$

7. $\frac{7}{10}\%$ 8. $\frac{44}{100}\%$ 9. $\frac{2}{7}\%$ 10. $\frac{4}{9}\%$ 11. $\frac{2}{11}\%$ 12. $\frac{13}{15}\%$

13. $\frac{8}{9}\%$ 14. $\frac{19}{20}\%$ 15. $\frac{18}{21}\%$

APPLICATION PROBLEMS

Sample solution _____

If 1% of a given number is 40, how much will $\frac{1}{4}\%$ be? $\frac{1}{4}\%$ is $\frac{1}{4}$ of 1%. Thus, $\frac{1}{4}\%$ of the number is $\frac{1}{4}$ of $40 = \frac{1}{4} \times \frac{40}{1} = 10$

_____ *10*

1. Which is a larger percent: $\frac{16}{17}\%$ or .9%?

2. If $\frac{1}{5}\%$ of a given number is equal to 25, how much is 1% of the given number?

3. Is $\frac{9}{10}\%$ larger than 1%?

4. If 1% of a given number is 50, how much is $\frac{1}{2}$% of the given

number?

_____

5. "Last month the Cost-of-Living Index rose by three-tenths of one percent." Write the percent as a decimal.

_____

Unit 62. Finding a Percent of a Given Amount

A very common problem in everyday life is figuring out the amount of sales tax you must pay for a given purchase. To do this, you must know the percent of the tax, and you must know the amount of the purchase.

A sales tax of 7% (7% means 7¢ per 100¢) tells you that you must pay $.07 for every $1.00 of purchase. A purchase of $2.00 would be taxed $.14, a purchase of $3.00 would be taxed $.21, and so on.

In general, if you know a given amount, you can find any percent of that amount by multiplying.

Rule: To find a given percent of a given amount, change the percent to a decimal. Then multiply the amount by the decimal equivalent of the percent. (If the given amount is in dollars and cents, round off to the nearest penny.)

EXAMPLE 1. Find the amount of sales tax on a purchase of $43.30 if the tax is 7%.

Solution: Since $7\% = \frac{7}{100} = .07$, multiply $43.30 by .07 and round off.

$$\begin{array}{r} 43.30 \\ \times\ .07 \\ \hline 3.03\cancel{(10)} \end{array}$$

Answer: The tax is $3.03

EXAMPLE 2. A retailer purchased 75 dresses. If he sold 80% of them, find the number of dresses sold.

Solution: Change 80% to a decimal and multiply the number of dresses, 75, by this decimal.

$$\begin{array}{r} 75 \\ \times\ .80 \\ \hline 60.00 \end{array}$$

Answer: 60 dresses were sold.

EXAMPLE 3. Find $\frac{1}{4}$% of 5,280 to the nearest whole number.

Solution: $\frac{1}{4}\% = .25\% = .0025$

Multiply: $5,280 \times .0025$

$$\begin{array}{r} 5,280 \\ \times\ .0025 \\ \hline 2\ 6400 \\ 10\ 560 \\ \hline 13.\cancel{(2000)} \end{array}$$

Answer: 13

EXAMPLE 4. Find $4\frac{1}{2}$% of $5,000.

Solution: $4\frac{1}{2}\% = 4.5\% = .04.5 = .045$

$$\begin{array}{r} .045 \\ \times 5,000 \\ \hline 225.000 \end{array}$$

Answer: $225.00

EXERCISES

In 1 to 20, find:

1. 5% of 58

2. 15% of 72

3. 6% of 125

4. 25% of $12.63

5. 21% of $47.93

6. 38% of 74.38

7. $22\frac{1}{2}$% of $135.23

8. $6\frac{1}{4}$% of $24.87

9. 6.25% of 630

10. 4.7% of $77.85

11. .25% of 6,432

12. $25\frac{1}{5}$% of $372.42

13. $\frac{1}{4}$% of 375

14. $\frac{4}{5}$% of 462

15. .6% of 32.16

16. $35\frac{3}{5}\%$ of $247.63   **17.** $47\frac{3}{20}\%$ of $473.65   **18.** $8\frac{3}{4}\%$ of $675.80

19. 65% of $762.38   **20.** 15.25% of 85.63

APPLICATION PROBLEMS

1. A dress selling for $37.50 was reduced by 25%. What is the amount of reduction?

What is the new price?

If there is a 5% sales tax, how much will a buyer have to pay for the dress?

2. The Browns bought a house for $28,575 and made a down payment of 20%. What is the amount of the down payment?

3. Because of a heavy snowfall, 30% of the students were absent. If the total number of students in the school is 1,250, how many students were absent?

4. The total number of students in a school is 2,340. If 45% of the students are girls, how many students are boys?

5. The Brown family income is $9,780 a year. They plan to use the following budget: food, 25%; shelter, 20%; clothing, 15%; all other expenses, 40%. How much will they spend for each item?

food: _____

shelter: _____

clothing: _____

other: _____

Unit 63. Finding What Percent One Number Is of Another Number

You know (Unit 58) that the word *percent* can be read as "hundredths," or as "out of 100." Thus, 40% means $\frac{40}{100}$ or 40 out of 100. You also know (Unit 40) that when two numbers are compared by division, the indicated division is called a *ratio*.

Therefore, any percent can be expressed as a ratio, and any ratio can be expressed as a percent.

EXAMPLE 1. Using the colon (:), write 40% as a ratio in lowest terms.

Solution: $40\% = \frac{40}{100} = \frac{4}{10} = \frac{2}{5}$ (Recall that any fraction or any ratio can be reduced to lowest terms without changing its value.) The fraction $\frac{2}{5}$ is the same as the ratio $2:5$.

Answer: $40\% = 2:5$

EXAMPLE 2. Express "30 out of 70" as a percent (to the nearest whole percent).

Solution: "30 out of 70" is $\frac{30}{70} = \frac{3}{7}$.

$$
\begin{array}{r}
.4\overset{3}{\cancel{2}} = .43 \\
7\overline{)3.00} \\
\underline{2\ 8} \\
20 \\
\underline{14} \\
6 \leftarrow
\end{array}
$$
remainder is larger than half the divisor

Answer: "30 out of 70" is 43%

Many word problems that deal with percents can be solved by writing the given information as a ratio. This ratio, which is a fraction, can then be changed to a percent.

EXAMPLE 3. In a class of 25 students, 5 are absent. Find the percent of students absent.

Solution: Write a fraction showing the ratio of the number of students absent to the total number of students.

$$\frac{\text{number of students absent}}{\text{total number of students}} = \frac{5}{25}$$

If you have difficulty setting up the fraction, you can use the $\frac{IS}{OF}$ method. The facts in this problem can be stated as: "5 is what percent of 25?"

$$\frac{IS}{OF} = \frac{5}{25}$$

Change the fraction to a percent.

$$\frac{5 \rightarrow 20}{25 \rightarrow 100}$$
(Think: "25 into 100 goes 4, and $4 \times 5 = 20$.")

Answer: 20%

EXAMPLE 4. What percent of 1776 is 373? (Answer to the nearest whole percent.)

Solution: "373 is what % of 1776?"

$$\frac{IS}{OF} = \frac{373}{1776}$$

$$
\begin{array}{r}
.21 = .21 \\
1776\overline{)373.00} \\
\underline{355\ 2} \\
17\ 80 \\
\underline{17\ 76} \\
4 \leftarrow
\end{array}
$$
remainder is less than half the divisor

Answer: 21%

EXERCISES

In 1 to 6, write the indicated ratio as a fraction. Then change the fraction to the nearest whole percent.

1. 28 out of 32
2. 30 out of 54
3. 12 out of 60

184

4. 32 out of 58   **5.** 50 out of 125   **6.** 64 out of 96

In 7 to 15, solve to the nearest whole percent.

7. 32 is what % of 64?   **8.** 49 is what % of 70?   **9.** 35 is what % of 120?

10. 43 is what % of 78?   **11.** 68 is what % of 134?   **12.** 123 is what % of 436?

13. · 215 is what % of 430?   **14.** 75 is what % of 240?   **15.** 235 is what % of 638?

APPLICATION PROBLEMS

1. Tom had $165 and spent $89.10. What percent of his money did he spend?

2. John earned $8,500 last year. If he saved $1,275, what percent of his income did he save?

3. There are 18 girls and 27 boys in class. What percent of the class is boys?

4. A coat regularly selling for $175 was reduced to $140. What is the percent of the reduction?

_____

5. The Wilsons obtained a $13,535 mortgage on their house. If the first year's interest is $947.45, what percent of the mortgage is this interest?

_____

Unit 64. Finding a Number When a Percent of It Is Known

You can find a number when you know a percent of it and the actual number that the percent represents.

EXAMPLE 1. If a 30% reduction in price is equal to $15.00, find the original price.

Solution:

Method 1: One way to solve the problem is to find out how much 1% is equal to, and then multiply this amount by 100.

30% of the original price is 15

1% of the original price is $\frac{1}{30}$ th of 15 = $\frac{15}{30}$ = .50

100% of the original price is 100 × .50 = 50.00

Check: If $50 is the correct answer, then 30% of $50 should equal the given reduction of $15.

$$\begin{array}{r} \$50 \\ \times\ .30 \\ \hline \$15.00 \end{array} \quad \checkmark$$

Method 2: Another method, and a much simpler one, is to divide the reduction in dollars by the reduction percent. The reduction is $15 and the reduction percent is 30%. Therefore, divide: $15 ÷ 30%.

$$\frac{\$15}{30\%} = \frac{15}{.30} \qquad \begin{array}{r} 50. = \$50.00 \\ .30\overline{)15.00} \\ \underline{15\ 0} \end{array}$$

This method is easily remembered if you use the $\frac{IS}{OF}$ fraction. The facts of this problem are: ("$15 is 30% of)what price?" $\frac{IS}{OF} = \frac{\$15}{30\%} = \frac{15}{.30}$

Perform the indicated division, as shown above.

Answer: The original price is $50.00

EXAMPLE 2. $87\frac{1}{2}$% of what number is 56?

Solution: Using Method 2, divide the number by the percent $\left(87\frac{1}{2}\% = 87.5\% = .875\right)$.

$$\begin{array}{r} 64. \\ .875\overline{)56.000.} \\ \underline{52\ 50} \\ 3\ 500 \\ \underline{3\ 500} \end{array}$$

By the $\frac{IS}{OF}$ fraction: "56 is $87\frac{1}{2}$% of what number?"

$$\frac{IS}{OF} = \frac{56}{87\frac{1}{2}\%} = \frac{56}{.875}$$

Perform the indicated division, as shown above.

Check: Does $87\frac{1}{2}$% of 64 = 56?

$$\begin{array}{r} 64 \\ \times .87 \\ \hline 448 \\ 512 \\ \hline 5568 \\ +32 \\ \hline 56.00 \end{array} \quad \frac{1}{2} \times \frac{64}{1} = 32 \quad \checkmark$$

Answer: 64

answer by dividing $\frac{7}{8}$ into 56.

Note that Method 2 is really the same method you used back in Unit 38 to find a number when you knew a *fractional* part of it. In Example 2, if you know that $87\frac{1}{2}\%$ is the same as $\frac{7}{8}$, you can find the

$$56 \div \frac{7}{8} = \frac{\overset{8}{\cancel{56}}}{1} \times \frac{8}{\cancel{7}} = 64$$

EXERCISES

In 1 to 10, find the unknown number.

Sample solutions

a. (45% of) what number (is 90?)   *200*

$$\frac{IS}{OF} = \frac{90}{45\%} = \frac{90}{.45}$$

$$.45\overline{)90.00.}\;\;^{200}$$

b. ($\frac{1}{5}\%$ of) what number (is $4.75?)   *$2,375*

$$\frac{IS}{OF} = \frac{4.75}{\frac{1}{5}\%} = \frac{4.75}{.2\%} = \frac{4.75}{.002}$$

$$.002\overline{)4.750.}\;\;^{2,375}$$
$$\underline{46}$$
$$15$$
$$\underline{14}$$
$$10$$
$$\underline{10}$$

1. 16% of what number is $48?

2. 65% of what number is 260?

3. 31% of what number is 279?

4. $3\frac{1}{4}\%$ of what number is $65.50?

5. 2.5% of what number is $5.65?

6. $33\frac{1}{3}\%$ of what number is 78?

7. 42% of what number is $24.36?   **8.** 35% of what number is $65.20?

9. $5\frac{1}{2}$% of what number is $23?   **10.** $.3\frac{1}{5}$% of what number is $.65?

APPLICATION PROBLEMS

1. John bought a radio at a sale where all prices were reduced by 30%. If the amount of the reduction was $45.75, what was the original price of the radio?

What was the new price?

2. How much money must be invested at 8% to earn $1,000 per year?

3. If 55% of the students in a school are boys, and there are 858 boys, find the total number of students.

4. A television set was reduced by $32.48. If this represents a reduction of 35%, find the original price.

5. The depreciation (loss of value) of a car is 25%, which is $735. Find the original cost of the car.

Unit 65. Finding the Percent of Decrease or Increase

To find the percent of decrease or increase, set up a ratio with the *amount of decrease or increase* as the numerator and the *original number* as the denominator.

EXAMPLE 1. A coat that was selling for $50.00 is reduced to $37.50. What is the percent of the reduction?

Solution: Since you have to find the reduction

percent, you first find the reduction *in dollars* by subtracting the new price from the original price.

$$\$50.00 \longleftarrow \text{original price}$$
$$-37.50 \longleftarrow \text{new price}$$
$$\overline{\$12.50} \longleftarrow \text{reduction}$$

The amount of reduction is $12.50. Now you find what percent $12.50 is of the original price, $50.00. Write a fraction with $12.50 as the numerator and $50 as the denominator. Then, change the fraction to a percent.

$$\frac{12.50}{50} \longrightarrow \frac{25}{100}$$ (Think: "50 into 100 goes 2, and 2 × 12.50 = 25.")

Using the $\dfrac{\text{IS}}{\text{OF}}$ fraction: "$12.50 is what % of $50?"

$$\frac{\text{IS}}{\text{OF}} = \frac{12.50}{50} = \frac{25}{100}$$

Answer: The reduction is 25%

EXAMPLE 2. If a salary is increased from $120 to $138, what is the percent of increase?

Solution: Find the amount of increase.

$$\$138.00$$
$$-120.00$$
$$\overline{\$\ 18.00}$$

Write a fraction with the increase as the numerator and the original salary as the denominator.

$$\frac{18}{120} = 120\overline{)18.00} \quad .15 = 15\%$$
$$\underline{12\ 0}$$
$$6\ 00$$
$$\underline{6\ 00}$$

Using the $\dfrac{\text{IS}}{\text{OF}}$ fraction: "$18 is what % of $120?"

$$\frac{\text{IS}}{\text{OF}} = \frac{18}{120}$$

Perform the indicated division, as shown above.

Answer: The increase is 15%.

Remember: When figuring percents of increase or decrease, the *original amount* is always the denominator.

EXERCISES

Answer all exercises to the nearest whole percent. In 1 to 6, find the percent of decrease if:

1. $235 is decreased to $185.

2. $325 is decreased to $128.

3. 327 is decreased to 295.

4. $387 is decreased to $234.

5. 436 is decreased to 228.

6. 425 is decreased to 319.

In 7 to 12, find the percent of increase if:

7. 100 is increased to 125.   **8.** $115 is increased to $147.   **9.** 135 is increased to 165.

10. 153 is increased to 232.   **11.** $243 is increased to $298.   **12.** $327 is increased to $415.

APPLICATION PROBLEMS

1. Tom earned $8,650 last year, and this year his salary will be $9,750. What is the percent of this salary increase?

2. The price of steak went up from $1.29 a pound to $1.47 a pound. Find the percent of increase.

3. A school had a student enrollment of 1,628 last year. This year the enrollment is 1,865. Find the percent of increase.

4. Tom weighed 235 pounds. After dieting for six months, his weight was 185 pounds. What percent of his weight did he lose?

5. A retailer sold $23,475 worth of merchandise last month. This month his sales were only $20,560. What is the percent of decrease in sales?

Review of Part XIII (Units 58 to 65)

In 1 to 10, change each percent to a decimal.

1. 25%   **2.** 5%   **3.** 12.5%   **4.** 250%

5. $\dfrac{1}{4}\%$ **6.** $.5\%$ **7.** $\dfrac{3}{4}\%$ **8.** $\dfrac{4}{5}\%$

9. $6\dfrac{1}{2}\%$ **10.** $15\dfrac{3}{4}\%$

In 11 to 20, change each decimal to a percent.

11. $.35$ **12.** $.05$ **13.** $.135$ **14.** $.075$ **15.** $.9$

16. $.005$ **17.** 3.75 **18.** $.5$ **19.** $.30$ **20.** $.105$

In 21 to 23, round off to the nearest penny.

21. Find 35% of \$245.85.   **22.** What is 8% of \$353.50?   **23.** $5\dfrac{1}{2}\%$ of \$568.85 =

In 24 to 30, round off each answer to the nearest whole number.

24. 35 is what percent of 125?

25. Write 28 out of 153 as a ratio. Change the ratio to a percent.

26. Find what percent 47 is of 265.

27. 35% of a number is 75. Find the number.

28. 15% of what amount is $125?

29. $5\frac{1}{2}$% of the cost is $82. Find the cost.

30. $\frac{3}{4}$% of what number is 8.35?

In 31 to 34, find the percent of increase or decrease. Round off to the nearest whole percent.

31. The expenses increased from $165 to $210.

32. The enrollment of 235 pupils decreased to 175 pupils.

33. Arnold's bank balance of $568 decreased to $365.

34. The 472 tons of paper increased to 595 tons.

Part XIV. Measures

INTRODUCTION: UNDERSTANDING MEASUREMENTS

As early man changed from a hunter to a farmer, he needed to measure lengths: the lengths of fields, the lengths of building materials, the lengths of cloth, etc. The first units of length were based on the human body. The *cubit* was the length of a man's forearm from his elbow to the tip of his middle finger. The cubit was divided into *palms* (the width of the hand), and the palms were divided into *digits* (the width of a finger). The *mile* was a thousand paces, and the *foot* was based on the actual length of someone's foot.

Of course, since people are of different size, there was considerable difference between these units of length. To avoid confusion, lengths and other measures were made *standard* (alike and unchanging). Today, the National Bureau of Standards in Washington, D.C., determines the units that you see on rulers and yardsticks. The basic measure of length in the United States is the *yard*. The *inch*, the *foot*, and the *mile* are all based on the yard. Every time you measure something with a ruler or a tape measure, you are comparing it with these *standard units*.

Unit 66. Measure of Length

The distance between the ends of something, or the distance between two separate objects, is called the *measure of length*. When you measure the length of something, you find the *distance* between its two ends by *measuring in a straight line in one direction only*.

If you know that a certain fence is "fifty feet long," you know only the *distance* from one end to the other. You know nothing about how high it is.

Such expressions as "a six-inch piece of wood" and "a ten-foot length of pipe" tell you only the *distance* between the ends. You know nothing about the other measurements such as the width of the wood or the diameter of the pipe.

At times the expression "measure of length" is awkward to use because such measurements as "width" and "height" and "altitude" and "breadth" are all really measures of length. Consequently, the expression *linear measure* is used in place of "measure of length" where confusion is possible.

Remember: Measure of length and linear measure both mean straight-line distance.

UNITS OF LINEAR MEASURE

The basic units of linear measure are the *inch*, the *foot*, the *yard*, and the *mile*. These units are described in the following table:

Table IV: *Units of Linear Measure*

Unit	Abbreviation	Description
Inch	in.	There are 12 in. in 1 ft. There are 36 in. in 1 yd.
Foot	ft.	One ft. contains 12 in. There are 3 ft. in 1 yd. There are 5,280 ft. in 1 mi.
Yard	yd.	One yd. contains 3 ft. One yd. contains 36 in. There are 1,760 yd. in 1 mi.
Mile	mi.	One mi. contains 5,280 ft. One mi. contains 1,760 yd.

CHANGING A SMALLER UNIT TO A LARGER UNIT

EXAMPLE 1. Change 72 inches to feet.

Solution: Since it takes 12 inches to make 1 foot, see how many times 12 is contained in 72.

$$\begin{array}{r} 6 \\ 12\overline{)72} \\ 72 \\ \hline \end{array}$$

Since there are 6 12-inch units in 72 inches, there are 6 feet.

Answer: 72 in. = 6 ft.

EXAMPLE 2. How many miles are there in a distance of 4,400 yards?

Solution: Since it takes 1,760 yards to make 1 mile, see how many times 1,760 is contained in 4,400.

$$\begin{array}{r} 2.5 \\ 1{,}760\overline{)4{,}400.0} \\ 3\ 520 \\ \hline 880\ 0 \\ 880\ 0 \\ \hline \end{array}$$

Answer: 4,400 yd. = 2.5 mi. or $2\frac{1}{2}$ mi.

These two examples illustrate the following rule, which we will call the *Unit Change Rule 1:*

Unit Change Rule 1: To change a smaller unit to a larger unit, determine how many smaller units are contained in 1 unit of the larger unit. Then **divide** the given number of smaller units by this number.

This rule is very important, as it will be used over and over again. We will use *Rule 1* whenever we change any smaller unit to any larger unit. As you will learn, this rule is used with measures of area, volume, liquid, time, and counting.

CHANGING A LARGER UNIT TO A SMALLER UNIT

EXAMPLE 3. Change 7 yards to (*a*) feet and (*b*) inches.

Solution: (*a*) One yard contains 3 feet. Thus, 7 yards contains 7 × 3 feet = 21 feet. (*b*) One yard contains 36 inches. Thus, 7 yards contains 7 × 36 inches = 252 inches.

Answer: (*a*) 7 yd. = 21 ft. (*b*) 7 yd. = 252 in.

This example illustrates the following rule, which we will call the *Unit Change Rule 2:*

Unit Change Rule 2: To change a larger unit to a smaller unit, determine how many smaller units are contained in 1 unit of the larger unit. Then **multiply** the given number of larger units by this number.

As with *Rule 1*, this rule will be used over and over again. We will use *Rule 2* whenever we change any larger unit to any smaller unit.

Remember: In both of the Unit Change Rules, find how many smaller units are contained in one unit of the larger unit. Then:
1. **To change a smaller unit to a larger unit,** *divide* by the number you found.
2. **To change a larger unit to a smaller unit,** *multiply* by the number you found.

Remember:

1 mi. = 1,760 yd. = 5,280 ft.
1 yd. = 3 ft. = 36 in.
1 ft. = 12 in.

EXERCISES

In 1 to 10, change each given length to *inches*. When necessary, use mixed numbers or mixed decimals to express your answers.

1. 17 ft.   **2.** 14 ft.   **3.** $4\frac{1}{2}$ ft.   **4.** 6.25 ft.

5. 6 ft. 11 in.   **6.** 4 yd.   **7.** 3 yd. 2 ft.   **8.** $4\frac{1}{2}$ yd.

9. 3.4 yd.   **10.** 5 yd. 2 ft.

In 11 to 20, change each given length to *feet*. When necessary, use mixed numbers or mixed decimals to express your answers.

11. 25 yd.   **12.** $15\frac{3}{5}$ yd.   **13.** 18.7 yd.   **14.** 87 in.

15. 102 in.   **16.** 8 yd. 25 in.   **17.** 12 yd. 34 in.   **18.** 137 in.

19. $17\frac{2}{3}$ yd.   **20.** $\frac{5}{6}$ yd.

In 21 to 30, change each given length to *yards*. When necessary, use mixed numbers or mixed decimals to express your answers.

21. 35 ft.   **22.** 247 in.   **23.** 3.7 mi.   **24.** 147 ft.

25. $75\frac{1}{3}$ ft.   **26.** 325 in.   **27.** $2\frac{1}{2}$ mi.   **28.** 448 in.

29. $73\frac{1}{2}$ ft.   **30.** 375 in.

APPLICATION PROBLEMS

1. Tom is $5\frac{1}{2}$ feet tall. Express his height in inches.

2. Jane bought 163 feet of ribbon. How many yards did she buy? (Express your answer as a mixed number.)

3. To the nearest tenth, how many miles high is a plane flying if its altitude is 32,063 feet?

4. A manufacturer bought 254 yards of material. If he uses 2 feet of material to make a flag, how many flags can he make?

5. How many feet high will a stack of 7-inch boxes be if the stack contains 237 boxes? (Express your answer as a mixed number or a mixed decimal.)

Unit 67. Measure of Length: Perimeters

Words to know

The shape or outline of something forms a **figure**. Common figures include the *triangle*, the *quadrilateral*, the *rectangle*, and the *square*.

A **triangle** is a closed figure that has *three straight sides*.

A **quadrilateral** is a closed figure that has *four straight sides*.

A **rectangle** is a special kind of quadrilateral: It has four sides, but the four angles are all 90-degree angles, or *right angles*. Also, as shown, the opposite sides are equal in length.

A **square** is a special kind of rectangle. It has four sides and four 90-degree angles, but all four sides are the *same length*.

The distance completely round any figure is found by adding together the lengths of all the sides. This measure of length is called the **perimeter**.

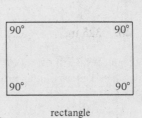

triangle   quadrilateral   rectangle   square

Many problems deal with the perimeters of figures such as **triangles**, **quadrilaterals**, **rectangles**, and **squares**. To determine the perimeter of such a figure, find the length of each side of the figure and then add all the lengths together. Be sure to add *all* of the lengths.

EXAMPLE 1. Find the perimeter of each of the following figures:

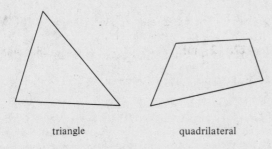

a.

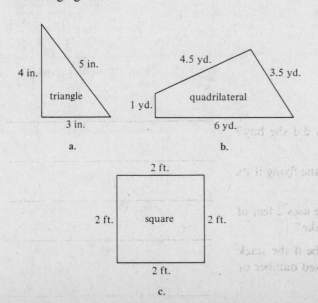

c.

Solution:

a. 3 in. + 4 in. + 5 in. = 12 in.

    Answer: The perimeter of the triangle is 12 inches.

b. 1 yd. + 4.5 yd. + 3.5 yd. + 6 yd. = 15.0 yd.

    Answer: The perimeter of the quadrilateral is 15 yards.

c. Every square has *four equal sides*. Therefore, you can find the perimeter by multiplying the length of the given side by 4:

$$2 \text{ ft.} \times 4 = 8 \text{ ft.}$$

If you prefer, you can add the lengths of the four equal sides:

$$2 \text{ ft.} + 2 \text{ ft.} + 2 \text{ ft.} + 2 \text{ ft.} = 8 \text{ ft.}$$

    Answer: The perimeter of the square is 8 feet.

EXAMPLE 2. Find the perimeter of a rectangle whose length is 8 feet and whose width is 6 feet.

Solution: A *rectangle* is a very important geometric figure. Remember the following facts:

1. A rectangle has *four* sides and *four* right angles.
2. The *opposite sides* of a rectangle are always the *same length*.

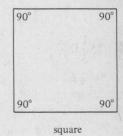

197

Using these facts, you can draw a picture of the rectangle whose dimensions are 8 feet × 6 feet. (*Note:* A notation such as "8 feet × 6 feet" is often used to describe rectangles. It is read, "8 feet long by 6 feet wide.")

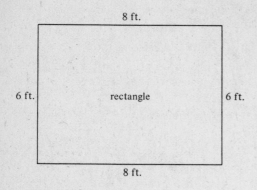

8 ft.

6 ft.   rectangle   6 ft.

8 ft.

From the figure, the perimeter is:

$$6 \text{ ft.} + 8 \text{ ft.} + 6 \text{ ft.} + 8 \text{ ft.} = 28 \text{ ft.}$$

Answer: The perimeter of the rectangle is 28 feet.

EXAMPLE 3. Find the perimeter of a triangle whose sides are 4 feet 6 inches, 5 feet 1 inch, and 6 feet 8 inches. Express the answer in *feet*.

Solution: Before adding the three lengths, change the inches to fractions of a foot. Since there are 12 inches in a foot: 6 inches $= \dfrac{6}{12}$ foot, 1 inch $= \dfrac{1}{12}$ foot, and 8 inches $= \dfrac{8}{12}$ foot. Thus,

$$4 \text{ ft. } 6 \text{ in.} = 4\frac{6}{12} \text{ ft.}$$

$$5 \text{ ft. } 1 \text{ in.} = 5\frac{1}{12} \text{ ft.}$$

$$6 \text{ ft. } 8 \text{ in.} = 6\frac{8}{12} \text{ ft.}$$

Add the lengths and simplify the sum.

$$4\frac{6}{12}$$
$$5\frac{1}{12}$$
$$6\frac{8}{12}$$
$$\overline{15\frac{15}{12}}$$

$$\frac{15}{12} = 12\overline{)15} \quad \begin{array}{r} 1\frac{3}{12} \\ \underline{12} \\ 3 \end{array}$$

$$15 + 1\frac{3}{12} = 16\frac{3}{12} = 16\frac{1}{4}$$

Answer: The perimeter of the triangle is $16\frac{1}{4}$ feet.

EXAMPLE 4. Find the perimeter of a triangle whose sides measure 18 inches, $2\frac{1}{2}$ feet, and 1 yard.

Solution: 18 in. $= \dfrac{18}{12}$ ft. $= 1\frac{1}{2}$ ft. and 1 yd. $=$ 3 ft.

Add the three lengths.

$$1\frac{1}{2}$$
$$2\frac{1}{2}$$
$$3$$
$$\overline{6\frac{2}{2}} = 7$$

Answer: The perimeter of the triangle is 7 feet.

EXERCISES

In 1 to 6, find the perimeter of each triangle if the sides measure:

1. 4 ft., 8 ft., and 6 ft.

2. 13 in., 13 in., and 7 in.

3. $5\frac{3}{4}$ ft., $11\frac{7}{8}$ ft., and $15\frac{1}{3}$ ft.

4. 23.8 in., 15.5 in., and 18.9 in.

5. 7 yd., 9 ft., and 5 yd.

6. 30 in., $3\frac{1}{4}$ ft., and $5\frac{1}{2}$ ft.

In 7 to 10, find the perimeter of each quadrilateral if the sides measure:

7. 15 yd., 12 yd., 8 yd., and 27 yd.

8. 12.6 in., 5.3 in., 13.7 in., and 15.9 in.

9. 15 ft., 27 ft., 15 yd., and 18 ft.

10. 25 in., 16 in., 12.7 in., and 21.5 in.

In 11 to 19, find the perimeter of each rectangle, given the length and the width.

11. 3 ft. by 7 ft.

12. $5\frac{1}{2}$ in. $\times$ $12\frac{1}{4}$ in.

13. 7.5 in. $\times$ 4.2 in.

14. 25 ft. by 137 ft.

15. 5 in. by $3\frac{1}{2}$ in.

16. 12.6 ft. $\times$ 14.8 ft.

17. $5\frac{1}{2}$ ft. $\times$ 8.3 ft.   **18.** 9.6 ft. by $3\frac{1}{4}$ ft.   **19.** 18 in. $\times$ 5 ft.

In 20 to 22, find the perimeter of each square, given the length of one side.

20. $3\frac{1}{3}$ in.   **21.** 225 in.   **22.** .09 ft.

APPLICATION PROBLEMS

1. Mr. Gordon plans to build a rectangular fence around his home. If the property measures 39 feet 6 inches by 105 feet 6 inches, how many feet of fencing will he need? $\left(\textit{Hint:} \text{ 6 inches is } \frac{1}{2} \text{ foot.}\right)$

2. Mrs. Doheny wants to sew ribbon around her bedspread, which measures $4\frac{5}{8}$ feet by $8\frac{3}{4}$ feet. To the nearest whole yard, how many yards of ribbon must she buy?

At 30¢ per yard, how much will the ribbon cost?

3. In a yacht race, the distance from the starting point to the first marker buoy is 6.8 miles. From the first buoy to the second marker buoy, the distance is 10.3 miles. From the second buoy back to the starting point is 7.4 miles. How long is the triangular race course, to the nearest tenth of a mile?

4. A baseball "diamond" is really a square whose sides are 90 feet in length. If a player hits three home runs, how far will he run around the bases?

5. How many times must Ben run around a rectangular schoolyard that measures 367 feet by 293 feet in order to run a mile? (*Hint:* 1 mi. = 5,280 ft.)

Unit 68. Measure of Area

Words to know

The units of linear measure are the *inch*, the *foot*, the *yard*, and the *mile*. All linear measures, such as distances or perimeters, are obtained by measuring in *one direction only*. Measures of length are said to be *one-dimensional*.

The units of *square measure* include the *square inch*, the *square foot*, the *square yard*, the *acre*, and the *square mile*. The number of square units in a given figure is the **area** of that figure. As you will learn, measures of area are obtained by measuring in *two directions*. Measures of area are said to be *two-dimensional*.

Measures of **area** are quite common in everyday life. A tile man figures out how many *square feet* of tile he needs to make a bathroom floor. A dress designer calculates how many *square yards* of material are needed to make a certain dress. A farmer measures the size of his farm in *acres*.

Remember: When you find the *measure of area* of a figure, you find out how many times a standard unit of *square measure* **is contained in that figure.**

UNITS OF SQUARE MEASURE

The basic units of square measure are the *square inch*, the *square foot*, the *square yard*, the *acre*, and the *square mile*. These units are described in the following table:

Table V: *Units of Square Measure*

Unit	Abbreviation	Description
square inch	sq. in.	There are 144 sq. in. in 1 sq. ft.
square foot	sq. ft.	One sq. ft. contains 144 sq. in. There are 9 sq. ft. in 1 sq. yd.
square yard	sq. yd.	One sq. yd. contains 9 sq. ft. There are 4,840 sq. yd. in 1 A.
acre	A.	One A. contains 43,560 sq. ft. One A. contains 4,840 sq. yd. There are 640 A. in 1 sq. mi.
square mile	sq. mi.	One sq. mi. contains 640 A.

It is easy to picture a square inch. Just think of a square whose sides are 1 inch in length. (Recall that a square has four equal sides.) Similarly, a square foot may be thought of as a square whose sides are 1 foot in length.

Note in the figure at the right that a square with a side of 1 foot contains 144 squares that each have a side of 1 inch. This is why 1 square foot contains 144 square inches.

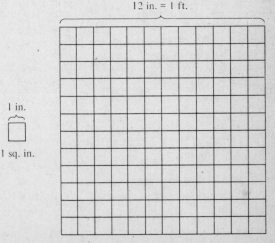

12 in. = 1 ft.

1 in.

1 sq. in.

1 sq. ft. = 144 sq. in.

Note in the following figure that a square with a side of 1 yard contains 9 squares that each have a side of 1 foot. This is why 1 square yard contains 9 square feet.

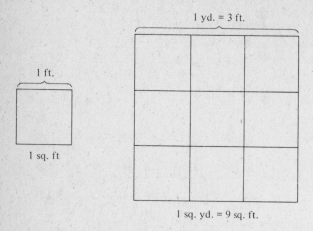

1 yd. = 3 ft.

1 ft.

1 sq. ft

1 sq. yd. = 9 sq. ft.

When dealing with acres, keep in mind that an acre is already a unit of square measure. There is no such unit as a "square acre."

Remember:

1 sq. mi. = 640 A.
1 A. = 4,840 sq. yd. = 43,560 sq. ft.
1 sq. yd. = 9 sq. ft.
1 sq. ft. = 144 sq. in.

To change a smaller unit of square measure to a larger unit, follow *Unit Change Rule 1*, which you learned in Unit 66: First, determine how many smaller units are contained in 1 unit of the larger unit. Then *divide* the given number of smaller units by this number.

EXAMPLE 1. Change 720 square inches to square feet.

Solution: Since it takes 144 square inches to make 1 square foot, find how many times 144 is contained in 720.

$$\begin{array}{r} 5 \\ 144\overline{)720} \\ \underline{720} \end{array}$$

Since there are 5 144-square-inch units in 720 square inches, there are 5 square feet.

Answer: 720 sq. in. = 5 sq. ft.

EXAMPLE 2. Change 75.6 square feet to square yards.

Solution: Since it takes 9 square feet to make 1 square yard, divide 75.6 by 9.

$$\begin{array}{r} 8.4 \\ 9\overline{)75.6} \\ \underline{72} \\ 3\ 6 \\ \underline{3\ 6} \end{array}$$

Answer: 75.6 sq. ft. = 8.4 sq. yd.

EXAMPLE 3. Change 1,600 acres to square miles.

Solution: There are 640 acres in 1 square mile. Therefore, divide 1,600 by 640.

$$\begin{array}{r} 2.5 \\ 640\overline{)1600} \\ \underline{128} \\ 32\ 0 \\ \underline{32\ 0} \end{array}$$

Answer: 1,600 A. = 2.5 sq. mi. or $2\frac{1}{2}$ sq. mi.

To change a larger unit of square measure to a smaller unit, follow *Unit Change Rule 2*, which you learned in Unit 66: First, determine how many smaller units are contained in 1 unit of the larger unit. Then *multiply* the given number of larger units by this number.

EXAMPLE 4. Change 100 square feet to square inches.

Solution: Since 1 square foot contains 144 square inches, multiply 100 by 144. (Multiply by 100 mentally.)

$$144 \times 100 = 144(00) = 14,400$$

Answer: 100 sq. ft. = 14,400 sq. in.

EXAMPLE 5. Change $7\frac{2}{3}$ square yards to square feet.

Solution: Since 1 square yard contains 9 square feet, multiply $7\frac{2}{3}$ by 9.

$$7\frac{2}{3} \times 9 = \frac{23}{3} \times \frac{\cancel{9}^{3}}{1} = 69$$

Answer: $7\frac{2}{3}$ sq. yd. = 69 sq. ft.

EXAMPLE 6. Change 2.37 square miles to acres. Round off to the nearest acre.

Solution: Since 1 square mile contains 640 acres, multiply 2.37 by 640. Then round off to the nearest whole number. The multiplication is shown at the right.

$$
\begin{array}{r}
2.37 \\
\times 640 \\
\hline
94\,80 \\
1422 \\
\hline
1516.\cancel{80} \\
+1 \\
\hline
1517 \\
\end{array}
$$

Answer: 2.37 sq. mi. = 1,517 A., to the nearest acre.

EXERCISES

In 1 to 10, change the given area to *square inches*. (Round off to the nearest whole number.)

1. 16 sq. ft.

2. $4\frac{1}{2}$ sq. ft.

3. 18.75 sq. ft.

4. 18 sq. ft.

5. $\frac{4}{5}$ sq. yd.

6. $6\frac{4}{5}$ sq. ft.

7. .5 sq. yd.

8. 60 sq. ft.

9. 6.9 sq. yd.

10. $18\frac{2}{3}$ sq. yd.

In 11 to 20, change the given area to *square feet*. (Round off to the nearest tenth.)

11. 367 sq. in.

12. 37 sq. yd.

13. $12\frac{1}{2}$ sq. yd.

14. 2,465 sq. in.

15. 37.25 sq. yd.   **16.** 3,216 sq. in.   **17.** .75 sq. yd.   **18.** 187 sq. yd.

19. 864 sq. in.   **20.** $\frac{1}{4}$ A.

In 21 to 32, change the given area to *square yards*. (Round off to the nearest tenth.)

21. 567 sq. ft.   **22.** 247.30 sq. ft.   **23.** 5,184 sq. in.   **24.** 6,804 sq. in.

25. 40.5 sq. ft.   **26.** 207 sq. ft.   **27.** $3\frac{1}{2}$ sq. mi.   **28.** .7 sq. mi.

29. $2\frac{1}{5}$ sq. mi.   **30.** 178 sq. ft.   **31.** $\frac{3}{4}$ A.   **32.** $2\frac{1}{2}$ A.

APPLICATION PROBLEMS

1. A kitchen has 123 square feet of floor space. Assuming no waste, how many square yards of linoleum are needed to cover the floor? (Figure to the nearest square yard.)

2. A table top contains 3,024 square inches. How many square feet of Formica will be needed to cover it?

3. How many square yards are contained in a field that has 5.25 acres?

4. How much will 216 square feet of linoleum cost at $2.25 a square yard?

5. How much will it cost to shingle a roof with an area of 21,600 square inches? The cost of the shingles is $.32 per square foot.

_____

Unit 69. Measuring Area

Words to know

A **formula** is a rule for figuring out something. In a formula, the rule is written with _letters_ instead of words. In Unit 67, we found the perimeter of a square by multiplying the length of one side by 4. As a formula, this rule is written as follows:

$$P = 4 \times s$$

In this formula, _P_ means the _perimeter_ of a square and _s_ means the length of one _side_.

When you find the measure of area of a figure, you find how many times a standard unit of _square measure_ is contained by that figure.

A given unit of square measure is the area contained by a square with a side whose length is the given linear measure. For example, one square inch means a surface that is 1 inch by 1 inch. Here is a square whose side is 1 inch:

1 in.
1 in. ☐ 1 in.
1 in.

And here is a square whose side is 5 inches:

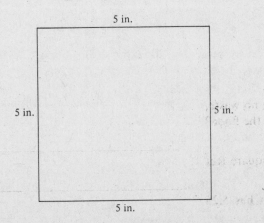

When you divide the 5-inch square into 1-inch squares, you see that the 5-inch square contains 25 1-inch squares:

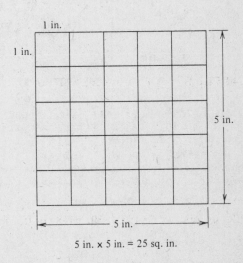

5 in. x 5 in. = 25 sq. in.

If you have a _rectangle_ whose length is 6 inches and whose width is 4 inches, you will obtain an area of 24 square inches:

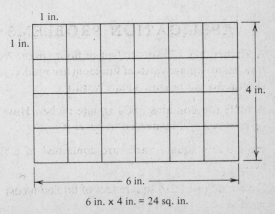

6 in. x 4 in. = 24 sq. in.

These examples illustrate the following rule:

Rule: The area of any *rectangle* is found by multiplying the length (in units of linear measure) by the width (in the same units of linear measure). The product is the area, in units of square measure.

Since a square is a rectangle whose length and width are the same, this rule is true for all squares and for all rectangles. The rule is usually written as a **formula** in which A means *area* of the rectangle, l means *length* of the rectangle, and w means *width* of the rectangle:

$$A = l \times w$$

EXAMPLE 1. A rectangular kitchen measures 9 feet by 12 feet. How many square feet of tiles are needed to cover the surface of the floor?

Solution: From the problem, $l = 12$ feet and $w = 9$ feet.

$$A = l \times w$$
$$A = 12 \text{ ft.} \times 9 \text{ ft.}$$
$$A = 108 \text{ sq. ft.}$$

Answer: 108 square feet of tiles are needed.

EXAMPLE 2. Find the area of a rectangular room that measures 8 feet 4 inches $\times$ $10\frac{1}{2}$ feet.

Solution: Whenever you calculate with units of measure, you *must* change all units to the same measure. Therefore, change 8 feet 4 inches to *feet*. Since there are 12 inches in 1 foot, 4 inches are $\frac{4}{12}$ of a foot.

$$8 \text{ ft. } 4 \text{ in.} = 8\frac{4}{12} \text{ ft.} = 8\frac{1}{3} \text{ ft.}$$

Now, use the formula to solve for the area. Replace l with $10\frac{1}{2}$ feet and w with $8\frac{1}{3}$ feet.

$$A = l \times w$$
$$A = 10\frac{1}{2} \text{ ft.} \times 8\frac{1}{3} \text{ ft.}$$
$$A = \frac{\overset{7}{\cancel{21}}}{2} \text{ ft.} \times \frac{25}{\underset{1}{\cancel{3}}} \text{ ft.}$$

$$A = \frac{175}{2} \text{ sq. ft.}$$

$$A = 87\frac{1}{2} \text{ sq. ft.}$$

Answer: Area of the room is $87\frac{1}{2}$ square feet.

EXAMPLE 3. How many acres are contained in a rectangular field that is 653.4 feet by 200 feet?

Solution: Find the area in square feet. Then, change it to acres (1 acre = 43,560 square feet). From the problem, $l = 653.4$ feet and $w = 200$ feet.

$$A = l \times w$$
$$A = 653.4 \text{ ft.} \times 200 \text{ ft.}$$

$$\begin{array}{r} 653.4 \\ \times\ 200 \\ \hline 130,680.0 \end{array}$$

$$A = 130,680 \text{ sq. ft.}$$

Since one acre contains 43,560 square feet, divide 130,680 by 43,560.

$$\begin{array}{r} 3 \text{ acres} \\ 4,356\cancel{0}\overline{)13\ 068\cancel{0}} \\ \underline{13\ 068} \end{array}$$

Answer: The field contains 3 acres.

Remember: A linear measure times a linear measure gives a square measure.

in. $\times$ in. = sq. in.
ft. $\times$ ft. = sq. ft.
yd. $\times$ yd. = sq. yd.
mi. $\times$ mi. = sq. mi.

In the preceding unit, we said that measures of area are *two-dimensional*. Now that you know how to calculate areas, you can see why: In order to obtain a measure of area, you must obtain *two* linear measures, or dimensions, the length and the width. These two linear measures are then multiplied to obtain the area measure.

EXERCISES

In 1 to 12, the given linear measures represent the lengths and widths of rectangles. Find the area of each rectangle. Be sure to include a unit of square measure with each answer.

1. 12 mi. × 22 mi.

2. $2\frac{1}{2}$ in. × $8\frac{1}{4}$ in.

3. 23 ft. × $35\frac{1}{5}$ ft.

4. $17\frac{1}{3}$ in. × $17\frac{1}{3}$ in.

5. 15.6 yd. × 27 yd.

6. 36.25 ft. × 68.71 ft.

7. $12\frac{1}{2}$ mi. by 34.4 mi.

8. 67.3 yd. by 123.5 yd.

9. 18 in. by 19 ft.

10. 9 in. × $5\frac{1}{2}$ ft.

11. 37.7 ft. × 85.2 ft.

12. 6 in. × $27\frac{1}{2}$ ft.

APPLICATION PROBLEMS

1. Find the cost of cementing a driveway 8 feet wide by 46 feet long at a cost of $1.25 per square foot.

2. A floor measures 18 feet long by 26 feet. How much will it cost to carpet the floor if the carpeting costs $7.95 a square yard?

3. How many square yards are contained in a rectangular field measuring 235 feet by 347 feet?

4. How much will the material cost to make a bedspread measuring 6 feet by 9 feet if the material sells for $3.85 a square yard?

5. Find the value of a rectangular field 648 yards by 897 yards at $875 per acre. (Find the area to the nearest whole acre.)

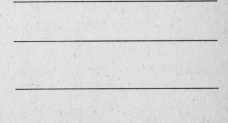

Unit 70. Measure of Volume

Words to know

The units of square measure include the *square inch*, the *square foot*, and the *square yard*. Area measures are obtained by making *two linear measures*, length and width, and then multiplying these two measures. Measures of area are said to be *two-dimensional*.

The units of *volume measure* include the *cubic inch*, the *cubic foot*, and the *cubic yard*. Measures of **volume** are obtained by making *three linear measures*, length, width, and height, and then multiplying these three measures. Measures of volume are said to be *three-dimensional*.

To measure the **volume** means to measure the capacity or contents of a three-dimensional figure. Such three-dimensional figures as boxes or cartons are called *solids*. We call the three linear measures of a solid the *length*, the *width*, and the *height*. (Words such as *altitude*, *breadth*, and *depth* may also be used.)

A *cube* is a solid that is made up of six squares, all coming together at right angles. A *cubic inch* is a cube that is 1 inch long, 1 inch wide, and 1 inch deep. The dimensions of such a cube are written " 1 inch × 1 inch × 1 inch." A cubic inch is shown at the right.

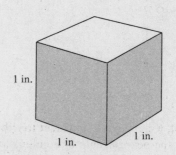

The standard units of volume are the *cubic inch*, the *cubic foot*, and the *cubic yard*. These units are described in the following table:

Table VI: *Units of Volume Measure*

Unit	Abbreviation	Description
cubic inch	cu. in.	There are 1,728 cu. in. in a cu. ft.
cubic foot	cu. ft.	One cu. ft. = 12 in. × 12 in. × 12 in. = 1,728 cu. in. There are 27 cu. ft. in 1 cu. yd.
cubic yard	cu. yd.	One cu. yd. = 3 ft. × 3 ft. × 3 ft. = 27 cu. ft.

Remember:

1 cu. yd. = 27 cu. ft.
1 cu. ft. = 1,728 cu. in.

To change larger units of volume to smaller units, follow *Unit Change Rule 1*, which you learned in Unit 66. To change smaller units of volume to larger units, follow *Unit Change Rule 2*, which you learned in Unit 66.

EXAMPLE 1. Change 10 cubic feet to cubic inches.

Solution: Since 1 cubic foot = 1,728 cubic inches, multiply 10 by 1,728. (Multiply by 10 mentally.)

$$1,728 \times 10 = 1728(0) = 17,280$$

Answer: 10 cu. ft. = 17,280 cu. in.

EXAMPLE 2. Change 7,776 cubic inches to cubic feet.

Solution: Since there are 1,728 cubic inches in 1 cubic foot, divide 7,776 by 1,728.

$$
\begin{array}{r}
4.5 \\
1,728\overline{)7,776.0} \\
6\ 912 \\
\hline
864\ 0 \\
864\ 0 \\
\hline
\end{array}
$$

Answer: 7,776 cu. in. = 4.5 cu. ft. or $4\frac{1}{2}$ cu. ft.

EXAMPLE 3. How many cubic feet are contained in $\frac{1}{10}$ of a cubic yard?

Solution: Since 1 cubic yard = 27 cubic feet, multiply $\frac{1}{10}$ by 27. You can multiply by the common fraction $\frac{1}{10}$ or by the decimal fraction .1.

By fraction: $\frac{1}{10} \times \frac{27}{1} = \frac{27}{10} = 2.7$ (Divide by 10 mentally.)

By decimal:
$$\begin{array}{r} 27 \\ \times\ .1 \\ \hline 2.7 \end{array}$$

Answer: $\frac{1}{10}$ cu. yd. = 2.7 cu. ft.

EXAMPLE 4. Change 643 cubic feet to cubic yards. Round off to the nearest *tenth* of a cubic yard.

Solution: Since there are 27 cubic feet in a cubic yard, divide 643 by 27.

$$\begin{array}{r} 23.8 = 23.8 \\ 27\overline{)643.0} \\ 54 \\ \hline 103 \\ 81 \\ \hline 22\ 0 \\ 21\ 6 \\ \hline 4 \end{array}$$

Answer: 643 cu. ft. = 23.8 cu. yd.

Other standard units of volume include measures of *liquid volume*, which you will study in Unit 72, and certain special measures that are used in different professions. For example, one *board foot* is defined as 144 cubic inches. (A board foot is a piece of board that is 1 foot long by 1 foot wide by 1 inch thick.) One *cord* is defined as 128 cubic feet. (A cord is a unit of chopped wood equal to a pile 4 ft. × 4 ft. × 8 ft.) One *bushel* is defined as 2,150.42 cubic inches. (A bushel is equal in volume to a round bucket 8 in. deep, with a diameter of $18\frac{1}{2}$ in.)

EXERCISES

In 1 to 10, change the given volume to *cubic inches*. When necessary, round off to the nearest whole number.

1. 8 cu. ft.

2. 25 cu. ft.

3. 15 cu. yd.

4. $\frac{3}{4}$ cu. yd.

5. 12.7 cu. yd.

6. $3\frac{1}{2}$ cu. ft.

7. 9.25 cu. ft.

8. $7\frac{4}{5}$ cu. yd.

9. .63 cu. yd.   **10.** $\frac{1}{4}$ cu. yd.

In 11 to 20, change the given volume to *cubic feet*. When necessary, round off to the nearest whole number.

11. 5,184 cu. in.   **12.** 25 cu. yd.   **13.** 7.5 cu. yd.   **14.** 3,888 cu. in.

15. 29,376 cu. in.   **16.** $8\frac{3}{4}$ cu. yd.   **17.** $\frac{1}{2}$ cu. yd.   **18.** $4\frac{1}{5}$ cu. yd.

19. .8 cu. yd.   **20.** $5\frac{2}{5}$ cu. yd.

In 21 to 30, change the given volume to *cubic yards*. When necessary, round off to the nearest whole number.

21. 135 cu. ft.   **22.** 11,664 cu. in.   **23.** 688.5 cu. ft.   **24.** $37\frac{1}{2}$ cu. ft.

25. 69,984 cu. in.   26. 2,538 cu. ft.   27. 233,280 cu. in.   28. 472 cu. ft.

29. 93,312 cu. in.   30. 351 cu. ft.

APPLICATION PROBLEMS

1. A certain metal weighs .41 pound per cubic inch. Find the weight of 3 cubic feet of this metal.

2. A truck holds 4 cubic yards of sand. If a cubic foot of sand costs 25¢, what is the cost of a truckful of sand?

3. How much will 5 cubic yards of topsoil cost at $.15 per cubic foot?

4. What is the weight of a cubic inch of a metal alloy if a cubic foot weighs 345.6 pounds?

5. How much will 405 cubic feet of cement cost at $12.50 a cubic yard?

Unit 71. Measuring Volume

Words to know

A very important three-dimensional figure is the **rectangular solid**. This is a solid made up of rectangles or squares. In a rectangular solid, all the surfaces meet at right angles. Everyday examples of such solids include books, shoe boxes, boards, suitcases, and classrooms.

To find the volume of a **rectangular solid**, you must know all three dimensions: length, width, and height.

Rule: To find the volume of a rectangular solid, **multiply the length by the width. Then multiply this product by the height.** All three dimensions must be in the same units of linear measure. The final product is the volume, in units of cubic measure.

This rule is usually written as a *formula* in which V means the *volume*, l means *length*, w means *width*, and h means *height*:

$$V = l \times w \times h$$

EXAMPLE. How much water will you need to fill a rectangular fish tank that measures 1 foot × 2 feet × 3 feet? Leave a space of 1 inch at the top so that the water will not overflow.

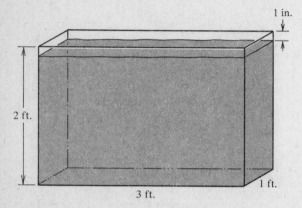

2 ft.

3 ft.   1 ft.

1 in.

Solution: First, find the volume of the tank, ignoring the empty space at the top. The volume of the tank is the space enclosed inside the tank, which is found by the formula $V = l \times w \times h$. From the problem, $l = 3$ feet, $w = 1$ foot, and $h = 2$ feet.

$$V = l \times w \times h$$
$$V = 3 \text{ ft.} \times 1 \text{ ft.} \times 2 \text{ ft.}$$
$$V = 6 \text{ cu. ft.}$$

The fish tank holds 6 cubic feet of water, if filled to the top. Since you must leave 1 inch of space at the top of the tank, calculate the volume of this empty

space. For the space at the top, $l = 3$ feet, $w = 1$ foot, and $h = 1$ inch, which is $\frac{1}{12}$ of a foot.

$$V = l \times w \times h$$
$$V = \overset{1}{\cancel{3}} \text{ ft.} \times 1 \text{ ft.} \times \frac{1}{\underset{4}{\cancel{12}}} \text{ ft.}$$
$$= \frac{1}{4} \text{ cu. ft.}$$
$$V = \frac{1}{4} \text{ cu. ft.}$$

The amount of water needed is the volume of the entire tank less the volume of the space at the top: 6 cubic feet $-\frac{1}{4}$ cubic foot.

$$5\frac{4}{4} \text{ cu. ft.}$$
$$-\frac{1}{4} \text{ cu. ft.}$$
$$\overline{}$$
$$5\frac{3}{4} \text{ cu. ft.}$$

Answer: $5\frac{3}{4}$ cubic feet of water are needed.

Remember: A linear measure times a linear measure times a linear measure gives a cubic measure.

in. × in. × in. = cu. in.
ft. × ft. × ft. = cu. ft.
yd. × yd. × yd. = cu. yd.

EXERCISES

In 1 to 8, find the volume of each of the rectangular solids.

1. 12 ft. × 3 ft. × 4 ft.

2. 8 in. × 10 in. × 4 in.

3. $6\frac{1}{2}$ ft. × $3\frac{1}{4}$ ft. × $4\frac{5}{8}$ ft.

4. 36 in. × $5\frac{1}{2}$ ft. × 40 in.   **5.** $2\frac{1}{2}$ ft. × $5\frac{1}{3}$ ft. × 56 in.   **6.** 3 ft. × 28 in. × 5 ft.

7. 14.7 yd. × $15\frac{1}{5}$ yd. × 8 yd.   **8.** $12\frac{3}{4}$ ft. × $14\frac{2}{3}$ ft. × $16\frac{4}{5}$ ft.

APPLICATION PROBLEMS

1. To prepare for the foundation of a building, a contractor must dig an excavation that is 126 feet by 48 feet by 96 feet. How many cubic yards of dirt will he have to remove?

2. What is the capacity of a truck if the inside measurements are 36 feet by 12 feet by 9 feet?

3. If an aluminum alloy weighs $\frac{1}{10}$ pound per cubic inch, how much will an aluminum bar measuring 3 feet by 9 inches by 8 inches weigh?

4. How many cubic inches of gold are contained in a bar of gold measuring $11\frac{1}{2}$ inches by $5\frac{1}{5}$ inches by $3\frac{3}{4}$ inches?

5. How many cartons, 3 feet by 2 feet by 6 inches, can be stored in a space measuring 15 feet by 9 feet by 24 feet? (Assume that there is no waste space.)

Review of Part XIV (Units 66 to 71)

In 1 to 4, round off all answers to the nearest *tenth*.

1. Change to feet:

   a. 136 in.   *b.* $8\frac{1}{2}$ yd.   *c.* 12 yd. 28 in.   *d.* 15.75 yd.

2. Change to yards:

   a. 43 ft.   *b.* 463 in.   *c.* $83\frac{1}{2}$ ft.   *d.* $3\frac{1}{4}$ mi.

3. Change to square feet:

   a. 872 sq. in.   *b.* $34\frac{1}{2}$ sq. yd.   *c.* half an acre   *d.* $\frac{1}{10}$ sq. mi.

4. Change to square yards:

   a. 1,460 sq. ft.   *b.* 3,625 sq. in.   *c.* 3.8 acres   *d.* .5 sq. mi.

5. Find the perimeter of each of the following figures:

a. A square whose side measures $1\frac{7}{8}$ inches.

b. A rectangle whose length is 12 ft. and whose width is 6 ft.

c. A triangle with sides that measure $2\frac{1}{2}$ ft., 20 in., and $\frac{1}{2}$ yd.

d. A rectangle whose dimensions are $8\frac{1}{2}$ in. $\times$ $3\frac{3}{4}$ in.

6. Find the area of each of the following figures. Round off answers to the nearest whole units.

a. A rectangle 24 in. $\times$ 35 in.

b. A square whose side is $9\frac{1}{2}$ ft.

c. A rectangular field $\frac{1}{2}$ mile wide by $1\frac{1}{2}$ miles long. Answer in acres.

d. A rectangle that measures 28 inches by .75 feet.

7. Find the volume of each of the following solids. Round off your answers to the nearest whole units.

   a. A rectangular solid 18 in. × 15 in. × 6 in.

   b. A cube whose side measures $3\frac{1}{2}$ in. (*Hint:* In a cube, the length, width, and height are all the same length.)

   c. A rectangular solid 9 in. × 3 ft. × 8 ft.

   d. A wooden crate 10 in. by $\frac{1}{2}$ yd. by 2 ft.

Part XV. More Measures

Unit 72. Measure of Liquids

To measure amounts of liquids, you use *liquid measures*, which are based on cubic measures.

The basic unit in measuring liquids is the *gallon*, which is defined as 231 cubic inches. The gallon is divided into 4 *quarts*, the quart is divided into 2 *pints*, and the pint is divided into 16 *ounces*.

Table VII: *Units of Liquid Measure*

1 gallon (gal.) = 4 quarts (qt.)
1 quart (qt.) = 2 pints (pt.)
1 pint (pt.) = 16 ounces (oz.)

Using the information in the table, you should be able to change measures of liquids just as you have changed measures of length, measures of area, and measures of volume. Use *Unit Change Rule 1* (from Unit 66) when you change a smaller unit to a larger unit. Use *Unit Change Rule 2* (also from Unit 66) when you change a larger unit to a smaller unit. You have used these same rules in Units 68 and 70.

EXAMPLE 1. (*a*) Change 32 pints to ounces. (*b*) Change 32 ounces to pints.

Solution:

(*a*) Since there are 16 ounces in 1 pint, multiply 32 by 16.

$$\begin{array}{r} 32 \\ \times 16 \\ \hline 192 \\ 32 \\ \hline 512 \end{array}$$

Answer: 32 pt. = 512 oz.

(*b*) Since 1 pint contains 16 ounces, divide 32 by 16.

$$32 \div 16 = 2$$

Answer: 32 oz. = 2 pt.

EXAMPLE 2. (*a*) Change $3\frac{1}{2}$ pints to quarts. (*b*) Change $3\frac{1}{2}$ quarts to pints.

Solution:

(*a*) Since there are 2 pints in 1 quart, divide $3\frac{1}{2}$ by 2.

$$3\frac{1}{2} \div 2 = \frac{7}{2} \div \frac{2}{1} = \frac{7}{2} \times \frac{1}{2} = \frac{7}{4} = 1\frac{3}{4}$$

Answer: $3\frac{1}{2}$ pt. = $1\frac{3}{4}$ qt.

(*b*) Since 1 quart contains 2 pints, multiply $3\frac{1}{2}$ by 2.

$$3\frac{1}{2} \times 2 = \frac{7}{2} \times \frac{2}{1} = 7$$

Answer: $3\frac{1}{2}$ qt. = 7 pt.

EXAMPLE 3. (*a*) Change 8.2 gallons to quarts. (*b*) Change 8.2 quarts to gallons.

Solution:

(*a*) Since there are 4 quarts in 1 gallon, multiply 8.2 by 4.

$$\begin{array}{r} 8.2 \\ \times\ 4 \\ \hline 32.8 \end{array}$$

$$\begin{array}{r} 2.05 \\ 4\overline{\smash{)}8.20} \\ \underline{8} \\ 20 \\ \underline{20} \end{array}$$

Answer: 8.2 gal. = 32.8 qt.

(*b*) Since 1 gallon contains 4 quarts, divide 8.2 by 4.   *Answer:* 8.2 qt. = 2.05 gal.

EXERCISES

In 1 to 10, change the given liquid measure to *ounces*.

1. 12 pt.   **2.** $8\frac{1}{2}$ pt.   **3.** 4 qt.   **4.** 12.5 pt.   **5.** $3\frac{1}{2}$ gal.

6. 4.25 qt.   **7.** 28 pt.   **8.** 15.8 qt.   **9.** 6 gal.   **10.** 8.3 gal.

In 11 to 15, change the given liquid measure to *pints*.

11. 15 qt.   **12.** 192 oz.   **13.** 23 gal.   **14.** 15.25 gal.   **15.** $29\frac{3}{4}$ qt.

In 16 to 20, change the given liquid measure to *quarts*.

16. 28 gal.   **17.** 27 pt.   **18.** $12\frac{3}{4}$ pt.   **19.** 13.75 gal.   **20.** $14\frac{2}{3}$ gal.

In 21 to 25, change the given liquid measure to *gallons*.

21. 267 pt.   **22.** 78 qt.   **23.** 640 oz.   **24.** 328 qt.   **25.** 75 pt.

APPLICATION PROBLEMS

1. How much will a drum containing 63 gallons of oil cost at $.45 per quart?

2. A family uses 3 quarts of milk each day. How many gallons of milk will the family use in 1 year (365 days)?

3. If a can contains 14 ounces of orange juice, how many gallons of juice does a case of 48 cans contain?

4. How much will 175 quarts of paint cost at $6.55 a gallon?

5. How many ounces of water should be added to 6 ounces of frozen concentrated lemon juice to make $1\frac{1}{2}$ gallons of lemonade?

Unit 73. Measure of Weight

To measure weight, you measure how heavy an object is. The basic unit of weight is the *pound*, which is divided into 16 *ounces*. (The ounce used to measure weight is not the same ounce used to measure liquids.) The ordinary ton, defined as 2,000 pounds, is often called a *short ton*. Iron ore and coal are measured by the *long ton*, which is defined as 2,240 pounds.

Using the information in Table VIII, you should be able to change measures of weight just as you have changed measures of length, area, volume, and liquids. Compare the solutions in the following

Table VIII: *Units of Weight Measure*

1 pound (lb.) = 16 ounces (oz.)
1 short ton (s.t. or T.) = 2,000 pounds (lb.)
1 long ton (l.t.) = 2,240 pounds (lb.)

example to the *Unit Change Rules* you learned in Unit 66 and to what you have learned in Units 68, 70, and 72.

EXAMPLE 1. State the rules for changing (1)

pounds to ounces, (2) ounces to pounds, (3) short tons to pounds, (4) pounds to short tons, (5) long tons to pounds, and (6) pounds to long tons.

Solution:

(1) Pounds to ounces: Multiply the number of pounds by 16.

(2) Ounces to pounds: Divide the number of ounces by 16.

(3) Short tons to pounds: Multiply the number of short tons by 2,000.

(4) Pounds to short tons: Divide the number of pounds by 2,000.

(5) Long tons to pounds: Multiply the number of long tons by 2,240.

(6) Pounds to long tons: Divide the number of pounds by 2,240.

EXAMPLE 2. Change $3\frac{1}{2}$ pounds to ounces.

Solution: Since there are 16 ounces in 1 pound, multiply the number of pounds, $3\frac{1}{2}$, by 16.

$$\frac{1}{2} \times \frac{16}{1} = 8$$

$$\begin{array}{r} 16 \\ \times\, 3 \\ \hline 48 \\ +\, 8 \\ \hline 56 \end{array}$$

Answer: $3\frac{1}{2}$ lb. = 56 oz.

EXAMPLE 3. How many pounds of iron ore are contained in 10 long tons?

Solution: 1 long ton contains 2,240 pounds. Therefore, multiply 2,240 by 10 (multiply mentally).

$$2{,}240 \times 10$$
$$= 2240.\underset{\frown}{(0)}. = 22{,}400$$

Answer: 10 long tons contain 22,400 pounds.

EXERCISES

In 1 to 5, change the given weight to *ounces*.

1. 5 lb.   **2.** $8\frac{1}{2}$ lb.   **3.** 9.7 lb.   **4.** $\frac{3}{4}$ lb.   **5.** 37 lb.

In 6 to 10, change the given weight to *pounds*.

6. 368 oz.   **7.** 7.75 s.t.   **8.** $12\frac{1}{2}$ l.t.   **9.** $\frac{4}{5}$ l.t.   **10.** .8 s.t.

In 11 to 15, change the given weight to *short tons*. When necessary, round off to the nearest hundredth.

11. 25,000 lb.   **12.** 17,850 lb.   **13.** 5,678 lb.   **14.** 14.25 l.t.   **15.** 23,167 lb.

In 16 to 20, change the given weight to *long tons*. When necessary, round off to the nearest hundredth.

16. 34,649 lb.   **17.** $12\frac{1}{2}$ s.t.   **18.** 27,325 lb.   **19.** 6.15 s.t.   **20.** 37,878 lb.

APPLICATION PROBLEMS

1. How much would 12 ounces of meat cost at $1.89 a pound?

2. If coal sells at $.14 a pound, how much would 3.6 l.t. cost?

3. How many 50-pound bags of potatoes can be obtained from a short ton of potatoes?

4. How many 8-ounce packages of candy can be obtained from 63 pounds of candy?

5. How much would 8 ounces of candy cost at $2.37 per pound?

Unit 74. Measure of Time

Measuring time means measuring the duration of time in a given period or between two separate events.

A basic unit for measuring time is the time it takes for the earth to travel once completely around the sun. This measure is the *year*, which is divided into *months* and *weeks*. Another basic time unit is the time it takes for the earth to turn completely around once. This measure is the *day*, which is divided into *hours*, *minutes*, and *seconds*.

Table IX: *Units of Time Measure*

1 minute (min.) = 60 seconds (sec.)
1 hour (hr.) = 60 minutes (min.)
1 day (da.) = 24 hours (hr.)
1 week (wk.) = 7 days (da.)
1 month (mo.) = 30 days (da.)
1 year (yr.) = 365 days (da.)
          = 52 weeks (wk.)
          = 12 months (mo.)

Using the information in the table, you should be able to change measures of time just as you have changed measures of length, area, volume, liquids, and weights. If you have difficulty in understanding the following examples, review the examples in Units 66, 68, 70, 72, and 73.

EXAMPLE 1. State the rule for changing (1) days to years, (2) days to hours, (3) days to seconds.

Solution:
(1) Days to years: Divide the number of days by 365.
(2) Days to hours: Multiply the number of days by 24.
(3) Days to seconds: Multiply the number of days by 24 to get hours; then multiply the number of hours by 60 to get minutes; finally, multiply the number of minutes by 60 to get seconds.

EXAMPLE 2. Change 3 days to hours.

Solution: Since 1 day is 24 hours, 3 days are 3 × 24 hours.

$$\begin{array}{r} 24 \\ \times\ 3 \\ \hline 72 \end{array}$$

Answer: 3 da. = 72 hr.

EXAMPLE 3. What fraction of a day is 144 minutes?

Solution: First, change 1 day to minutes: 24 hours in a day × 60 minutes in an hour.

$$\begin{array}{r} 24 \\ \times\ 60 \\ \hline 1,440 \end{array}$$

Now, 144 minutes is what fraction of 1,440 minutes?

$$\frac{\text{IS}}{\text{OF}} = \frac{\overset{1}{\cancel{144}}}{\underset{10}{\cancel{1440}}} = \frac{1}{10}$$

Answer: 144 min. is $\frac{1}{10}$ of a da.

EXERCISES

In 1 to 5, change the given time to *months*.

1. 8 yr. **2.** $\frac{3}{4}$ yr. **3.** $5\frac{1}{4}$ yr. **4.** 7.5 yr. **5.** $6\frac{1}{3}$ yr.

In 6 to 10, change the given time to *days*. When necessary, round off to the nearest whole number.

6. 6 yr. **7.** 26 wk. **8.** $3\frac{4}{5}$ yr. **9.** $13\frac{1}{2}$ wk. **10.** .75 yr.

In 11 to 15, change the given time to *years*. When necessary, round off to the nearest hundredth.

11. 73 mo.　　**12.** 2,555 da.　　**13.** 628 wk.　　**14.** 735 wk.　　**15.** 115 mo.

In 16 to 20, change the given time to *hours*.

16. 5 da.　　**17.** $3\frac{5}{8}$ da.　　**18.** 4 wk.　　**19.** 240 min.　　**20.** $3\frac{3}{7}$ wk.

APPLICATION PROBLEMS

1. Tom's father works 40 hours a week at $3.75 per hour. How much does he earn in a year? (He is paid for 52 weeks each year.)

2. The total cost of a car is $3,875, to be paid for over 3 years. If the down payment is $600, how much will each of the monthly payments be?

3. The Browns have a 25-year mortgage on their house for $23,500. How much will each of the monthly payments be?

4. The Wilsons use 1,875 gallons of fuel oil each year for heating and hot water. If the fuel costs $.21 per gallon, what is the average cost per month?

5. John is paid $485 bimonthly (twice a month). What is his yearly salary?

Unit 75. Measure of Counting

Articles are sometimes sold in counting units such as the dozen, the gross, and the score.

The basic unit of the counting measure is the *unit*, which means 1 article. Standard units include the *dozen*, which is 12 units; the *gross*, which is 12 dozen units; and the *score*, which is 20 units.

Table X: *Units of Counting Measure*

1 dozen (doz.) = 12 units
1 gross (gr.) = 12 dozen = 144 units
1 score = 20 units

You change measures of counting by applying the same *Unit Change Rules* you have used for changing measures of length, area, volume, liquids, weight, and time. (See Units 66, 68, 70, 72, 73, and 74.)

EXAMPLE 1. State the rule for changing (1) dozens to units, (2) units to dozens, (3) gross to dozens, (4) gross to units, (5) units to gross.

Solution:

(1) Dozens to units: Multiply the number of dozens by 12.

(2) Units to dozens: Divide the number of units by 12.

(3) Gross to dozens: Multiply the number of gross by 12.

(4) Gross to units: Multiply the number of gross by 144.

(5) Units to gross: Divide the number of units by 144.

EXAMPLE 2. Change $6\frac{1}{2}$ gross to dozens.

Solution: 1 gross contains 12 dozens. Therefore, multiply the number of gross, $6\frac{1}{2}$, by 12.

$$
\begin{array}{r}
12 \\
\times \, 6 \\
\hline
72 \\
+ \, 6 \\
\hline
78
\end{array}
\qquad \frac{1}{2} \times \frac{12}{1} = 6
$$

Answer: $6\frac{1}{2}$ gr. = 78 doz.

EXAMPLE 3. Which is the larger quantity, 10 dozen or 6 score?

Solution: 10 dozen = $10 \times 12 = 120$ and 6 score = $6 \times 20 = 120$.

Answer: The quantities are the same.

EXERCISES

In 1 to 5, express the given quantity in terms of units.

1. 8 doz.   **2.** $9\frac{3}{4}$ doz.   **3.** 3.5 gr.   **4.** $13\frac{5}{6}$ doz.   **5.** 5.25 gr.

In 6 to 10, change the given quantity to dozens. Express remainders as common fractions.

6. 253 units   **7.** $12\frac{1}{4}$ gr.   **8.** $8\frac{2}{3}$ gr.   **9.** 628 units   **10.** 5.75 gr.

In 11 to 15, express the given quantity in terms of gross. (Round off to the nearest tenth.)

11. 865 units   **12.** 427 doz.   **13.** $629\frac{1}{2}$ doz.   **14.** 1,627 units   **15.** 329 doz.

In 16 to 20, change the given times to *scores*. Express the remainders as *units*.

Sample solution

Change 87 years to scores.

1 score = 20 years

$$20\overline{)87} \quad \leftarrow \text{score}$$
80
7 ← years   *4 score and 7 years*

16. 50 yr.   **17.** 75 yr.   **18.** 138 yr.   **19.** 15 yr.   **20.** 45 yr.

APPLICATION PROBLEMS

1. If shirts sell at $60 a dozen, how much would 4 shirts cost?

2. Safety pins are packed 32 pins to a box. How many pins will there be in $3\frac{1}{2}$ gross of boxes?

3. Socks sell at $8 a dozen. How much will 8 pairs of socks cost?

4. Pencils sell at $.60 a dozen. How much will 7,920 pencils cost?

5. Oranges sell at 6 for $.49. How much will $3\frac{1}{2}$ dozen cost?

Unit 76. Adding and Subtracting Measures That Have Mixed Units

Words to know

In everyday life, we often deal with measured quantities that are expressed in "mixed units." For example, "The movie ran for 2 hours and 15 minutes," and "The roast weighs 5 pounds 6 ounces," and "He is 6 feet $2\frac{1}{2}$ inches tall." Such measures, which combine two or more different units, are known as **mixed units**.

When you must add or subtract **mixed units**, be sure to arrange the like units one under the other, and then add or subtract each column separately. Whenever possible, simplify the answer.

EXAMPLE 1. Add: 5 ft. 6 in. + 2 ft. 4 in. + 6 ft. 5 in.

Solution: Arrange the columns with feet under feet and inches under inches. Add each column separately.

$$
\begin{array}{rr}
5\,\text{ft.} & 6\,\text{in.} \\
2\,\text{ft.} & 4\,\text{in.} \\
+\,6\,\text{ft.} & 5\,\text{in.} \\
\hline
13\,\text{ft.} & 15\,\text{in.}
\end{array}
$$

Since 15 inches is 3 inches more than 1 foot, change 15 inches to 1 foot 3 inches.

$$
\begin{array}{rr}
13\,\text{ft.} & \cancel{15\,\text{in.}} \\
+\,1\,\text{ft.} & 3\,\text{in.} \\
\hline
14\,\text{ft.} & 3\,\text{in.}
\end{array}
$$

Answer: 14 ft. 3 in.

EXAMPLE 2. Add: 1 hr. 40 min. 30 sec. + 32 min. 50 sec. + 2 hr.

Solution:

$$
\begin{array}{rrr}
1\,\text{hr.} & 40\,\text{min.} & 30\,\text{sec.} \\
 & 32\,\text{min.} & 50\,\text{sec.} \\
2\,\text{hr.} & & \\
\hline
3\,\text{hr.} & \cancel{72\,\text{min.}} & \cancel{80\,\text{sec.}} \\
1\,\text{hr.} & 12\,\text{min.} & \\
 & 1\,\text{min.} & 20\,\text{sec.} \\
\hline
4\,\text{hr.} & 13\,\text{min.} & 20\,\text{sec.}
\end{array}
$$

To simplify, change 72 min. to 1 hr. 12 min. and change 80 sec. to 1 min. 20 sec.

Answer: 4 hr. 13 min. 20 sec.

EXAMPLE 3. Subtract 5 pounds 8 ounces from 8 pounds 6 ounces.

Solution: Set up the problem:

$$
\begin{array}{rr}
8\,\text{lb.} & 6\,\text{oz.} \\
-\,5\,\text{lb.} & 8\,\text{oz.} \\
\hline
\end{array}
$$

Since 8 ounces is larger than 6 ounces, you cannot subtract. Therefore, rewrite 8 pounds 6 ounces as 7 pounds 22 ounces. This is similar to ordinary borrowing when subtracting dollars and cents. Here, you borrow 1 pound (16 ounces) from the 8 pounds, which leaves 7 pounds; you add the borrowed 16 ounces (1 pound) to the 6 ounces and get 22 ounces. This step can usually be done mentally. Your problem should look like this:

$$
\begin{array}{rr}
7 & 22 \\
\cancel{8}\,\text{lb.} & \cancel{6}\,\text{oz.} \\
-\,5\,\text{lb.} & 8\,\text{oz.} \\
\hline
\end{array}
$$

Now, subtract as usual.

$$
\begin{array}{rr}
7\,\text{lb.} & 22\,\text{oz.} \\
-\,5\,\text{lb.} & 8\,\text{oz.} \\
\hline
2\,\text{lb.} & 14\,\text{oz.}
\end{array}
$$

Answer: 2 lb. 14 oz.

EXAMPLE 4. A room measures 9 feet 3 inches long by 6 feet 10 inches wide. By how much does the length exceed the width?

Solution: Find the excess by subtracting the width from the length.

$$
\begin{array}{rrl}
8 & 15 & \\
\cancel{9}\,\text{ft.} & \cancel{3}\,\text{in.} & \text{(Borrow 1 ft.,} \\
-\,6\,\text{ft.} & 10\,\text{in.} & \text{which is 12 in.)} \\
\hline
2\,\text{ft.} & 5\,\text{in.} &
\end{array}
$$

Answer: 2 ft. 5 in.

EXERCISES

In 1 to 6, add. Simplify your answer.

1.   6 ft.   8 in.
     12 ft. 10 in.
      8 ft.   6 in.

2. 5 yd. 2 ft.   9 in.
   7 yd. 2 ft.   8 in.
   8 yd.   10 in.

3. 12 lb. 12 oz.
    6 lb.   8 oz.
   14 lb. 10 oz.

4.   8 hr. 42 min.
     9 hr. 50 min.
   12 hr. 35 min.

5. 12 yd. 2 ft. 8 in.
    9 yd. 2 ft. 9 in.
    7 yd. 2 ft. 5 in.

6. 5 yr. 10 mo. 25 da.
   7 yr. 8 mo. 21 da.
   3 yr. 6 mo. 15 da.

In 7 to 12, subtract the lower quantity from the upper quantity. Simplify your answer.

7. 8 ft. 10 in.
   4 ft. 6 in.

8. 12 yd. 1 ft.
    8 yd. 2 ft.

9. 9 gal. 2 qt.
   7 gal. 3 qt.

10.   8 lb.   5 oz.   **11.**   18 yd. 1 ft. 6 in.   **12.**   12 lb. 14 oz.
        3 lb. 12 oz.   7 yd. 2 ft. 8 in.   5 lb. 15 oz.

APPLICATION PROBLEMS

1. John has a part-time job and worked the following hours last week: 5 hours 25 minutes; 4 hours 50 minutes; 6 hours 30 minutes; 3 hours 15 minutes; 5 hours 40 minutes. How many hours and minutes did John work?

2. Nancy bought the following amounts of cold cuts: 1 pound 8 ounces of ham, 12 ounces of salami, 1 pound 10 ounces of bologna, and 10 ounces of spiced ham. What is the total weight of all the cold cuts?

3. A clerk sold 3 yards 25 inches of material from a bolt that had 28 yards 15 inches. How much material is left on the bolt?

4. Three pieces of board were cut from a 23-foot board. The lengths of the cut-off pieces were 3 feet 8 inches, 4 feet 10 inches, and 6 feet 8 inches. What is the length of the remaining board?

5. From a 50-pound sack of potatoes, a grocer sold the following weights: 5 pounds 12 ounces, 3 pounds 14 ounces, and 4 pounds, 8 ounces. How many pounds of potatoes are left in the sack?

Unit 77. Multiplying and Dividing Measures That Have Mixed Units

MULTIPLYING MIXED UNITS

To multiply mixed units, you must treat each different unit as a separate problem. Then, combine and simplify the separate products to get your final answer.

EXAMPLE 1. Multiply: 3 lb. 2 oz. × 4

Solution: Multiply the pounds by 4; multiply the ounces by 4.

$$\begin{array}{r} 3 \text{ lb. } 2 \text{ oz.} \\ \times\, 4 \\ \hline 12 \text{ lb. } 8 \text{ oz.} \end{array}$$

Answer: 12 lb. 8 oz.

EXAMPLE 2. Multiply: 4 ft. 8 in. × 7

Solution:

$$\begin{array}{r} 4 \text{ ft.} \quad 8 \text{ in.} \\ \times\, 7 \\ \hline 28 \text{ ft.} \cancel{56 \text{ in.}} \quad (56 \text{ in.} = 4 \text{ ft. 8 in.}) \\ +\, 4 \text{ ft.} \quad 8 \text{ in.} \\ \hline 32 \text{ ft.} \quad 8 \text{ in.} \end{array}$$

Answer: 32 ft. 8 in.

DIVIDING MIXED UNITS

When the divisor goes *evenly* into all units, you simply perform the indicated divisions.

EXAMPLE 3. Divide: 15 ft. 10 in. ÷ 5

Solution:

$$\begin{array}{r} 3 \text{ ft.} \quad 2 \text{ in.} \\ 5\,\overline{)15 \text{ ft.} \quad 10 \text{ in.}} \\ \underline{15} \quad \underline{10} \end{array}$$

Answer: 3 ft. 2 in.

When the divisor does not go evenly into the larger units, you must change the remainder to the next smaller units. You then combine the remainder with the given dividend of smaller units.

EXAMPLE 4. Divide: 13 ft. 4 in. ÷ 5

Solution:

$$\begin{array}{r} 2 \text{ ft.} \\ 5\,\overline{)13 \text{ ft.} \quad 4 \text{ in.}} \\ \underline{10} \\ 3 \text{ ft.} \quad \longleftarrow \text{ remainder} \end{array}$$

Change the remainder of 3 feet to 36 inches. Then combine 36 inches with the given dividend of 4 inches (36 inches + 4 inches = 40 inches). Your problem should look like this:

$$\begin{array}{r} 2 \text{ ft.} \\ 5\,\overline{)13 \text{ ft.} \quad 4 \text{ in.}} \\ \underline{10} \\ 3 \text{ ft.} + 4 \text{ in.} = 40 \text{ in.} \end{array}$$

Now, divide 5 into 40 in.

$$\begin{array}{r} 2 \text{ ft.} \quad 8 \text{ in.} \leftarrow \\ 5\,\overline{)13 \text{ ft.} \quad 4 \text{ in.}} \\ \underline{10} \qquad \boxed{8 \text{ in.}} \\ 3 \text{ ft.} + 4 \text{ in.} = \overline{)40 \text{ in.}} \\ \underline{40} \end{array}$$

Answer: 2 ft. 8 in.

EXAMPLE 5. Divide: 15 hours 10 minutes by 13.

Solution:

$$\begin{array}{r} 1 \text{ hr.} \quad 10 \text{ min.} \\ 13\,\overline{)15 \text{ hr.} \quad 10 \text{ min.}} \\ \underline{13} \\ 2 \text{ hr.} \qquad \boxed{10 \text{ min.}} \\ + 10 \text{ min.} = \overline{)130 \text{ min.}} \\ \underline{130} \end{array}$$

Answer: 1 hr. 10 min.

EXERCISES

In 1 to 6, multiply and simplify.

1. $\begin{array}{r} 2 \text{ ft. } 8 \text{ in.} \\ \times\, 4 \\ \hline \end{array}$

2. $\begin{array}{r} 5 \text{ lb. } 12 \text{ oz.} \\ \times\, 6 \\ \hline \end{array}$

3. $\begin{array}{r} 6 \text{ yd. } 2 \text{ ft. } 8 \text{ in.} \\ \times\, 7 \\ \hline \end{array}$

4. 8 gal. 3 qt. 1 pt.
×6
_____

5. 5 yd. 2 ft. 6 in.
×8
_____

6. 5 da. 7 hr.
×5
_____

In 7 to 12, divide and simplify. When necessary, express the smaller quantity of the quotient as a mixed number.

7. 4⟌8 ft. 12 in.

8. 4⟌5 yd. 1 ft.

9. 7⟌28 lb. 14 oz.

10. 5⟌16 wk. 3 da.

11. 6⟌14 lb. 4 oz.

12. 6⟌18 da. 18 hr.

APPLICATION PROBLEMS

1. If a can holds 1 quart 12 ounces, how much do 8 of these cans hold?

2. A dressmaker uses 4 yards 2 feet 8 inches of material to make a dress. How much material will she need to make 8 dresses?

3. A cake weighs 3 pounds 2 ounces. How much will half of the cake weigh?

4. Tom worked 42 hours and 45 minutes last week. What is the average number of hours and minutes per day for the 5-day week?

5. A can of juice holds 1 pint 4 ounces. How much juice will 12 of these cans hold?

Review of Part XV (Units 72 to 77)

In 1 to 4, round off your answers to the nearest *whole unit*.

1. Change:

a. $15\frac{3}{4}$ gal. to qt.   b. 57 pt. to qt.   c. 88 oz. to pt.

d. 12.75 gal. to pt.   e. $3\frac{1}{2}$ pt. to oz.   f. 84.65 qt. to gal.

g. 100 oz. to qt.   h. half a gallon to ounces

2. Change:

a. 23 lb. to oz.   b. 640 oz. to lb.   c. 18 lb. 5 oz. to oz.

d. 84.6 oz. to lb.   *e.* 10,000 lb. to short tons   *f.* 5,600 lb. to short tons

g. half a long ton to pounds   *h.* $\frac{1}{100}$ short ton to ounces

3. Change:

    a. 2 days to minutes   *b.* 1 week to hours   *c.* 6,000 seconds to hours

    d. $\frac{1}{10}$ day to minutes

4. Change:

    a. 10 gross to dozens   *b.* 120 dozens to gross   *c.* 240 units to scores

    d. 240 units to dozens

In 5 to 7, add and simplify.

5. 12 yd. 2 ft. 10 in.
   6 yd. 1 ft. 8 in.
 16 yd. 2 ft. 9 in.
———————————

6. 15 lb. 12 oz.
 19 lb. 15 oz.
 23 lb. 7 oz.
——————

7.   8 yr. 9 mo. 23 da.
 12 yr. 11 mo. 16 da.
 19 yr. 7 mo. 28 da.
———————————————

In 8 to 10, subtract and simplify.

8.   23 ft. 7 in.
−13 ft. 11 in.
——————————

9. 18 gal. 2 qt.
−5 gal. 3 qt.
——————————

10. 21 yd. 1 ft. 7 in.
−12 yd. 2 ft. 9 in.
——————————————

In 11 to 13, multiply and simplify.

11. 21 lb. 13 oz.
      × 5
——————————

12. 15 yd. 2 ft. 8 in.
        × 7
——————————————

13. 12 gal. 3 qt. 1 pt.
                        × 9
———————————————

In 14 to 16, divide and simplify.

14. 5⟌18 gal. 3 qt.   **15.** 3⟌16 lb. 5 oz.   **16.** 6⟌28 yd. 2 ft. 6 in.

Part XVI. The Metric System

Unit 78. The Metric System

Words to know

The units of measure that you have studied—miles, yards, feet, inches, acres, gallons, pints, ounces—belong to the **English system**. The English system is used only in America, Burma, and a dozen other smaller nations including Liberia, Sierra Leone, and Trinidad.

All other countries use the **metric system**, which is named after the basic unit of length, the **meter**. The meter is defined as one ten-millionth of the distance from the North Pole to the Equator. It is equal to about 39.37 inches. The basic unit of liquid measure is the **liter**, and the basic unit of weight is the **gram**.

As long ago as 1799, the metric system was adopted by France. Today, the metric system is used by scientists all over the world (including scientists in America). Many businessmen and statesmen feel that it will eventually replace the English system entirely.

The difficulty with the *English system* is that you have to *memorize* many different facts: the number of feet in a mile, the number of square feet in an acre, the number of cubic inches in a cubic foot. And, even when you know the relations between the different units, it is still necessary to perform inconvenient multiplications and divisions to change miles to feet or square feet to acres.

The *metric system*, however, is much easier to use because *all standard units of measurement increase in powers of 10.* Study the following examples:

In units of length:

    10 meters   = 1 decameter
    10 decameters = 1 hectometer
    10 hectometers = 1 kilometer

In units of capacity (liquid measure):

    10 liters   = 1 decaliter
    10 decaliters = 1 hectoliter
    10 hectoliters = 1 kiloliter

In units of weight:

    10 grams   = 1 decagram
    10 decagrams   = 1 hectogram
    10 hectograms = 1 kilogram

Once you know the names of the units (meter, gram, liter), you use the *same prefixes* over and over:

> *deca* means *ten* (10)
> *hecto* means *hundred* (100)
> *kilo* means *thousand* (1,000)

Thus, a kilometer is 1,000 meters; a hectogram is 100 grams; a decameter is 10 meters.

Further, in the metric system, *all standard units of measurement decrease in powers of 10.* Study the following examples:

In units of length:

1 decimeter $= \frac{1}{10}$ of a meter

1 centimeter $= \frac{1}{10}$ of a decimeter,

  or $\frac{1}{100}$ of a meter

1 millimeter $= \frac{1}{10}$ of a centimeter,

  or $\frac{1}{1,000}$ of a meter

In units of capacity:

1 deciliter $= \frac{1}{10}$ of a liter

1 centiliter $= \frac{1}{10}$ of a deciliter,

  or $\frac{1}{100}$ of a liter

1 milliliter $= \frac{1}{10}$ of a centiliter,

  or $\frac{1}{1,000}$ of a liter

In units of weight:

1 decigram $= \frac{1}{10}$ of a gram

1 centigram $= \frac{1}{10}$ of a decigram,

  or $\frac{1}{100}$ of a gram

1 milligram $= \frac{1}{10}$ of a centigram,

  or $\frac{1}{1,000}$ of a gram

Notice that you use the *same prefixes* over and over:

deci means ***tenth*** $\left(\frac{1}{10}\right)$

centi means ***hundredth*** $\left(\frac{1}{100}\right)$

milli means ***thousandth*** $\left(\frac{1}{1,000}\right)$

Thus, a millimeter is $\frac{1}{1,000}$ of a meter; a centigram is $\frac{1}{100}$ of a gram; a decimeter is $\frac{1}{10}$ of a meter.

Table XI shows the most commonly used metric units. Refer to this table when converting from one metric unit to another metric unit.

Note: For a more complete table of metric units, see Table XX on page 353.

Table XI: *Common Metric Units*

MEASURES OF LENGTH

1 millimeter (mm) $= \frac{1}{1,000}$ meter (m)

1 centimeter (cm) $= \frac{1}{100}$ meter (m) = 10 millimeters (mm)

1 meter = 1,000 millimeters (mm) = 100 centimeters (cm)

1 kilometer (km) = 1,000 meters (m)

MEASURES OF CAPACITY

1 milliliter (ml) $= \frac{1}{1,000}$ liter (l)

1 liter (l) = 1,000 milliliters (ml)

1 kiloliter (kl) = 1,000 liters (l)

MEASURES OF WEIGHT

1 milligram (mg) $= \frac{1}{1,000}$ gram (g)

1 gram (g) = 1,000 milligrams (mg)

1 kilogram (kg) = 1,000 grams (g)

CHANGING A SMALLER UNIT TO A LARGER UNIT

To change a smaller unit of measure to a larger unit, follow *Unit Change Rule 1*, which you first learned in Unit 66: Determine how many smaller units are contained in 1 unit of the larger unit. Then *divide* the given number of smaller units by this number.

EXAMPLE 1. Change 15,000 meters to kilometers.

Solution: From Table XI, 1 kilometer equals 1,000 meters. Divide the given number of meters by 1,000.

$$15,000 \div 1,000 = 15.000. = 15$$

Answer: 15,000 m = 15 km

EXAMPLE 2. How many grams are there in 460 milligrams?

Solution: From Table XI, 1 gram = 1,000 milligrams. Divide the given number of milligrams by 1,000.

$$460 \div 1,000 = .460. = .46$$

Answer: There are .46 g in 460 mg

EXAMPLE 3. Change 875 liters to kiloliters.

Solution: From Table XI, 1 kiloliter = 1,000 liters. Divide the given number of liters by 1,000.

$$875 \div 1,000 = .875. = .875$$

Answer: 875 l = .875 kl

Note how much easier it is to divide by powers of 10 than by such numbers as 36 and 5,280, which you must use in the English system.

CHANGING A LARGER UNIT TO A SMALLER UNIT

To change a larger unit to a smaller unit, use *Unit Change Rule 2*: Determine how many smaller units are contained in 1 unit of the larger unit. Then *multiply* the given number of larger units by this number.

EXAMPLE 4. Change 8 meters to centimeters.

Solution: From Table XI, 1 meter = 100 centimeters. Multiply the given number of meters by 100.

$$8 \times 100 = 8.00. = 800$$

Answer: 8 m = 800 cm

EXAMPLE 5. Change 3.47 liters to milliliters.

Solution: From Table XI, 1 liter = 1,000 milliliters. Multiply the given number of liters by 1,000.

$$3.47 \times 1,000 = 3.47(0). = 3,470$$

Answer: 3.47 l = 3,470 ml

EXAMPLE 6. Change .007 kilogram to milligrams.

Solution: From Table XI, 1 kilogram = 1,000 grams. Multiply the given number of kilograms by 1,000.

$$.007 \times 1,000 = .007. = 7$$

Thus, .007 kg = 7 g. However, we must find the number of milligrams. From Table XI, 1 gram = 1,000 milligrams. Therefore, we multiply the number of grams by 1,000.

$$7 \times 1,000 = 7.000. = 7,000$$

Answer: .007 kg = 7,000 mg

EXERCISES

Refer to Table XI when solving these exercises. In 1 to 18, you should be able to perform most of the multiplications and divisions *mentally*, by moving the decimal point.

Change:

1. 250 cm to meters
2. 2,500 m to kilometers
3. .68 m to millimeters
4. 20 km to meters
5. 675 ml to liters
6. 5,000 l to kiloliters

7. 3.8 kl to liters   **8.** .75 l to milliliters   **9.** 850 g to kilograms

10. 8,500 mg to grams   **11.** 12.2 kg to grams   **12.** .8 g to milligrams

13. .022 m to centimeters   **14.** 7.1 mm to centimeters   **15.** .07 kl to liters

16. 5 ml to liters   **17.** 25.2 mg to grams   **18.** 50,000 mg to grams

In 19 to 24, change each fraction to a decimal. Then change the units as indicated.

Change:

19. $2\frac{2}{10}$ km to meters   **20.** $99\frac{44}{100}$ mm to centimeters   **21.** $2\frac{1}{4}$ l to milliliters

22. $80\frac{4}{5}$ l to kiloliters   **23.** $7\frac{7}{8}$ kg to grams   **24.** $1,416\frac{2}{5}$ mg to grams

In 25 to 30, the exercises will require two steps.

Sample solution _____

Change 50,000 mm to kilometers.

1. mm to m : 50,000 mm = 50.000. = 50 m

2. m to km : 50 m = .050. = .05 km

Change:

25. .05 km to millimeters

26. .3 km to centimeters

27. 400,000 mm to kilometers

28. .01 kl to milliliters

29. $\frac{1}{2}$ kg to milligrams

30. 10,000,000 mg to kilograms

APPLICATION PROBLEMS

1. An aspirin tablet weighs 5 grams. If a box holds 24 tablets, how many *milligrams* of aspirin are in one box?

2. For a chemistry experiment, Dave needs a piece of rubber tubing 8 centimeters in length. He has three pieces to choose from: one is .08 mm, another is 8 mm, and the third is 80 mm. Which should he use?

3. The cost of 50 centimeters of wire is 29¢. How much will 25 meters of this wire cost?

4. A chemical sells at $20 per kilogram. How much will 100 grams cost?

5. How many 100-milliliter vials can be filled with 3 liters of liquid?

Unit 79. Equivalent Measures in the Metric System and the English System

An imported ham weighs 6.8 kilograms. How many pounds does it weigh? A foreign car has a gas tank that holds 45 liters. How many gallons will it hold? Which is longer, a 1-mile race or a 1,500-meter race?

As the metric system becomes increasingly popular in the United States, it is often necessary to change measurements in that system to equivalent measure-ments in the English system.

Table XII shows common English-metric and metric-English equivalents. Note, under Measures of Capacity, that the liquid quart and the dry quart have different metric equivalents. (The dry quart is used for measuring farm products such as berries.)

Table XII: *Equivalent Measures in the Metric System and the English System*

MEASURES OF LENGTH

Metric to English	English to Metric
1 meter = 39.37 inches = 3.28 feet = 1.09 yards 1 centimeter = .39 inch 1 millimeter = .04 inch 1 kilometer = .62 mile	1 inch = 25.4 millimeters = 2.54 centimeters = .03 meter 1 foot = .30 meter 1 yard = .91 meter 1 mile = 1.61 kilometers

MEASURES OF CAPACITY

Metric to English	English to Metric
1 liter = 1.06 liquid quarts = .91 dry quart	1 liquid quart = .95 liter 1 dry quart = 1.10 liters

MEASURES OF WEIGHT

Metric to English	English to Metric
1 gram = .04 ounce 1 kilogram = 2.20 pounds 1 metric ton = 2,204.62 pounds	1 ounce = 28.35 grams 1 pound = .45 kilogram 1 short ton = .91 metric ton

METRIC TO ENGLISH

To change measurements *from the metric system* to equivalent measurements in the English system, find the number of English units contained in *one metric unit*. Then multiply the given number of metric units by this value.

To avoid confusion, remember this first step: To change *from the metric*, find the number of units in *one metric unit*.

EXAMPLE 1. How many yards are there in 123 meters? (Answer to the nearest yard.)

Solution: From Table XII, 1 meter = 1.09 yards. Multiply the given number of meters by 1.09.

$$\begin{array}{r} 123 \\ \times 1.09 \\ \hline 11\ 07 \\ 123\ 0 \\ \hline 134.\cancel{(07)} \end{array}$$

Answer: 123 m = 134 yd.

EXAMPLE 2. Change 6.8 kilograms to pounds. (Answer to the nearest tenth of a pound.)

Solution: From Table XII, 1 kilogram = 2.20 pounds. Multiply the given number of kilograms by 2.20.

$$\begin{array}{r} 6.8 \\ \times 2.20 \\ \hline 1\ 360 \\ 13\ 6 \\ \hline 14.9\cancel{(60)} = 15.0 \end{array}$$

Answer: 6.8 kg = 15.0 lb., to the nearest tenth.

EXAMPLE 3. Change 45 liters to gallons. (Answer to the nearest tenth of a gallon.)

Solution: From Table XII, 1 liter = 1.06 quarts. Multiply the given number of liters by 1.06.

$$\begin{array}{r} 1.06 \\ \times\ 45 \\ \hline 5\ 30 \\ 42\ 4 \\ \hline 47.70 = 47.7\ qt. \end{array}$$

Since 1 gallon = 4 quarts, divide the answer in quarts by 4 to get gallons.

$$\begin{array}{r} 3 \\ 11.9\!\!\!\not{2} = 11.9 \\ 4\overline{)47.70} \\ 4 \\ \hline 7 \\ 4 \\ \hline 3\ 7 \\ 3\ 6 \\ \hline 10 \\ 8 \\ \hline 2 \end{array}$$ ← remainder equals half the divisor.

Answer: 45 l = 11.9 gal., to the nearest tenth.

EXAMPLE 4. Change 1,500 meters to miles. (Answer to the nearest tenth of a mile.)

Solution: From Table XII, 1 meter = 3.28 feet. Multiply the given number of meters by 3.28.

$$\begin{array}{r} 3.28 \\ \times\ 1,500 \\ \hline 1\ 640\ 00 \\ 3\ 28 \\ \hline 4,920.00 = 4,920\ ft. \end{array}$$

Since 1 mile = 5,280 feet, divide the answer in feet by 5,280 to get miles.

$$\begin{array}{r} .9 = .9 \\ 5,280\overline{)4,920.0} \\ 4\ 752\ 0 \\ \hline 168\ 0 \end{array}$$ ← remainder is less than half the divisor

Answer: 1,500 m = .9 mi., to the nearest tenth.

ENGLISH TO METRIC

To change *from the English system* to the metric system, follow the procedure used in changing metric units to English units. However, find the number of metric units in *one English unit.* Then multiply the given number of English units by this number.

To avoid confusion, remember this first step: To change *from the English,* find the number of units in *one English unit.*

EXAMPLE 5. How many meters are there in 1,000 yards? (Answer to the nearest yard.)

Solution: From Table XII, 1 yard = .91 meter. Multiply the given number of yards by .91.

$$.91 \times 1,000 = .910. = 910$$

Answer: 1,000 yd. = 910 m

EXAMPLE 6. Change 25 gallons to liters.

Solution: Since there are 4 quarts in 1 gallon, 25 gallons = 25 × 4 = 100 quarts. From Table XII, 1 quart = .95 liter. Multiply the number of quarts by .95.

$$.95 \times 100 = .95. = 95$$

Answer: 25 gal. = 95 l

Remember:
1. **To change *from the metric system,* find the equivalent value for *one metric unit.* Then multiply the given number of metric units by this value.**
2. **To change *from the English system,* find the equivalent value for *one English unit.* Then multiply the given number of English units by this value.**

EXERCISES

Refer to Table XII when solving these exercises. In 1 to 15, when necessary, round off each answer to the *nearest whole unit.*

Change:

1. 10 m to feet

2. 10 m to yards

3. 100 km to miles

4. 100 l to liquid quarts   **5.** 500 g to ounces   **6.** 10 in. to millimeters

7. 100 mi. to kilometers   **8.** 60 lb. to kilograms   **9.** 20 dry qt. to liters

10. 1,000 in. to meters   **11.** $2\frac{7}{10}$ kg to pounds   **12.** .08 m to inches

13. 10 metric tons to pounds   **14.** 2.87 mi. to kilometers   **15.** 1.72 in. to millimeters

In 16 to 20, the exercises will require two steps. When necessary, round off each answer to the *nearest whole unit*.

Change:

16. 4,000 g to pounds   **17.** 100 cm to feet   **18.** 5,000 mm to feet

19. 200 oz. to kilograms

20. .5 mi. to meters

In 21 to 24, round off to the required decimal place.

Change:

21. 21.6 cm to inches (nearest *tenth*)

22. 16.4 in. to centimeters (nearest *tenth*)

23. .076 kg to pounds (nearest *hundredth*)

24. .001 metric ton to pounds (nearest *tenth*)

APPLICATION PROBLEMS

1. What is the width in inches of an 8-mm film? (Round off to the nearest *hundredth*.)

2. An imported can of coffee weighs 750 grams. How many ounces does the can of coffee weigh? (Round off to the nearest *tenth*.)

3. How many liters are there in 3 quarts of milk? (Round off to the nearest *tenth*.)

4. John high-jumped 2.5 meters. How high was his jump in feet? (Round off to the nearest *tenth*.)

5. A picture measures 8 cm × 12 cm. To the nearest hundredth, what are the measurements in inches?

Review of Part XVI (Units 78 and 79)

1. Change:

   a. 250 cm to m   *b.* 500 cm to mm   *c.* 1,500 km to m   *d.* 10,000 mm to km

2. Change:

   a. 10 l to ml   *b.* 750 ml to l   *c.* .2 kl to l   *d.* .5 kl to ml

3. Change:

   a. 1,500 gm to kg   *b.* .08 kg to g   *c.* 2.8 g to kg   *d.* .05 kg to mg

In 4 and 5, round off your answers to the nearest *tenth* of a unit when necessary.

4. Change:

    a. 10 m to in.   *b.* 200 cm to in.   *c.* 50 mi. to km   *d.* 100 m to yd.

5. Change:

    a. 5 kg to lb.   *b.* 200 g to oz.   *c.* 60 dry quarts to liters   *d.* 10 short tons to metric tons

6. Find, to the nearest whole unit:

    a. the number of grams in 26 pounds   *b.* the number of feet in half a kilometer

Part XVII. Income

Unit 80. Figuring Wage Income

Words to know

In many businesses and industries, workers are paid on an hourly basis for a 35- or 40-hour week. The pay for time worked beyond the regular weekly hours is usually figured at one and one-half times the regular hourly rate. The regular weekly salary, based on the 35- or 40-hour week, is known as **straight time pay**. The extra pay, based on extra hours at "time-and-a-half," is called **overtime pay**.

EXAMPLE. Harry Smith is paid $2.85 an hour for a 40-hour week plus time-and-a-half for overtime. Last week he worked 45 hours. How much did he earn?

Solution: First, compute the straight time pay at $2.85 per hour for a regular 40-hour week.

$$\begin{array}{r} \$2.85 \\ \times\ 40 \\ \hline \$114.00 \end{array} \longleftarrow \text{straight time pay}$$

Next, compute how much Smith earns per hour at time-and-a-half.

$$2.85 \times 1\frac{1}{2} = \frac{2.85}{1} \times \frac{3}{2} = \frac{8.55}{2}$$

$$= \$4.27\frac{1}{2} \longleftarrow \text{overtime pay per hour}$$

Since Smith worked 45 hours, his overtime is 45 − 40 = 5 hours. Compute the overtime pay at 4.27\frac{1}{2}$ per hour for 5 hours.

$$\begin{array}{r} \$4.27 \\ \times\ 5 \\ \hline 21.35 \end{array} \quad \begin{array}{l} \frac{1}{2} \times 5 = 2\frac{1}{2} \end{array}$$

$$+ 2\frac{1}{2} \longleftarrow$$

$$21.37\frac{1}{2} = \$21.38 \longleftarrow \text{overtime pay}$$

Smith's paycheck would carry a notation like this: (*Note:* The symbol @ means "each." Thus, "40 hr. @ 2.85" means 40 hours at $2.85 for each hour.)

$$40 \text{ hr. @ } 2.85 = 114.00$$

$$5 \text{ hr. @ } 4.27\frac{1}{2} = \ \ 21.38$$

Total earnings = $135.38

Answer: $135.38

Note: It is common bookkeeping practice to add a penny whenever a computation yields a fraction that

246

is one-half a penny or more. If this procedure were followed in the preceding example, the hourly overtime pay would have been figured at $4.28 per hour. Thus, the overtime pay for 5 hours would have been $21.40, giving a total earnings of $135.40.

APPLICATION PROBLEMS

1. Alan Carter is paid $3.10 an hour for a 35-hour week, plus time-and-a-half for overtime. Find his total earnings for last week, when he worked 43 hours.

2. Dorothy McIntire earns $3.25 an hour for a 40-hour week, plus time-and-a-half for overtime. Last week she worked the following hours:

Mon.	Tue.	Wed.	Thu.	Fri.
$8\frac{1}{2}$	$9\frac{1}{2}$	8	9	9

Find her total earnings for the week.

3. The payroll record of the Acme Window Washing Company is shown below. Based on a 40-hour week, with time-and-a-half for overtime, enter the following information for each employee: total regular hours, total overtime hours, and total earnings. As a sample solution, this information has been computed for James Bell, as shown on the following page.

PAYROLL RECORD

Acme Window Washing Company

No.	Name	Time Record					Hour Rate	Total Hours		Total Earnings
		M	T	W	Th	F		Regular	Over-time	
1	James Bell	8	7	9	10	8	$3.18	40	2	136.74
2	Juan Diaz	8	6	9	9	8	$3.20			
3	Sam Siegel	8	$9\frac{1}{2}$	9	9	9	$2.95			
4	Louis DeMato	7	9	8	10	10	$3.05			
5	Joseph Davis	$8\frac{1}{2}$	9	$7\frac{1}{2}$	9	8	$3.15			
6	Donald Westler	9	8	7	$8\frac{1}{2}$	$9\frac{1}{2}$	$3.40			
7	Manuel Ortiz	$8\frac{1}{2}$	$9\frac{1}{2}$	$8\frac{1}{2}$	8	9	$3.35			
8	Jerry Schultz	9	8	10	$8\frac{1}{2}$	$9\frac{1}{2}$	$3.25			

Bell: $8 + 7 + 9 + 10 + 8 = 42 = 40$ reg. $+ 2$ overtime

reg. pay $= \$3.18 \times 40 = 127.20$

overtime $= \frac{3}{2} \times \$3.18 \times 2 = 9.54$

$$
\begin{array}{r}
127.20 \\
+ 9.54 \\
\hline
136.74
\end{array}
$$

(Space for calculations.)

Unit 81. Piece-Work Wages

Words to know

In some industries, workers are not paid by the hour. Instead, they receive a certain amount of money for each article or unit that they complete or produce. These articles or units are called **pieces**, and the employee is said to be working on a **piece-work basis**. The amount he receives for each piece is called the **rate per piece**.

To find the wages earned by a worker on a **piece-work basis**, multiply the total number of **pieces** by the **rate per piece**.

EXAMPLE. For the week ending July 5, John Ward completed the following numbers of pieces: Mon. 47, Tue. 51, Wed. 50, Thu. 49, Fri. 48. The rate per piece is 65¢. Find his total wages.

Solution: Add the units completed daily: 47 + 51 + 50 + 49 + 48 = 245, the total number of units completed. Multiply this total by the rate per piece, $.65.

$$
\begin{array}{r}
245 \\
\times\,.65 \\
\hline
12\ 25 \\
147\ 0 \\
\hline
159.25
\end{array}
$$

Answer: Total wages for the week are $159.25.

APPLICATION PROBLEMS

1. From the following piece-work record, find the total number of pieces completed and the total earnings for each employee. As a sample solution, this information has been computed for C. Adams.

Name	Number of Pieces					Total Pieces	Rate per Piece	Total Earnings
	M	T	W	Th	F			
Adams, C.	32	34	30	29	35	160	$.75	120.00
Allan, B.	34	32	35	30	34		.82	
Agnew, G.	29	32	30	34	34		.85	
Berg, M.	32	33	34	30	32		.78	
Bernstein, D.	34	35	32	34	32		.84	
Burger, W.	33	34	32	35	34		.76	
Bursten, M.	30	34	32	35	33		.84	
Calder, G.	34	32	35	34	32		.80	
Curtis, L.	32	34	35	30	33		.85	
Chisholm, D.	33	35	34	32	34		.86	

Adams: 32+34+30+29+35 = 160 *pieces*

160 × .75 = 120.00

2. From the following piece-work record, find the total number of dozens completed and the total earnings for each employee. As a sample solution, this information has been computed for M. Gold.

Name	Number of Dozens					Total Dozens	Rate per Dozen	Total Earnings
	M	T	W	Th	F			
Gold, M.	10	$11\frac{1}{2}$	12	$13\frac{1}{4}$	$12\frac{1}{2}$	$59\frac{1}{4}$	$2.53	149.90
Green, S.	11	$13\frac{1}{4}$	$10\frac{3}{4}$	12	$12\frac{1}{2}$		$2.84	
Gonzales, M.	12	$11\frac{3}{4}$	$12\frac{1}{2}$	13	$10\frac{1}{4}$		$2.76	
Gomez, D.	10	$12\frac{1}{2}$	$13\frac{1}{4}$	$11\frac{3}{4}$	14		$2.68	
Goodman, L.	$13\frac{1}{2}$	$12\frac{1}{4}$	$11\frac{3}{4}$	13	$10\frac{1}{2}$		$2.97	
Gould, I.	12	$13\frac{3}{4}$	$11\frac{3}{4}$	$12\frac{1}{2}$	13		$2.85	
Hart, D.	$11\frac{3}{4}$	$12\frac{1}{2}$	14	$13\frac{3}{4}$	12		$2.74	
Hunt, E.	12	$13\frac{3}{4}$	$14\frac{1}{4}$	$12\frac{3}{4}$	$13\frac{1}{4}$		$2.93	
Huntley, B.	$13\frac{1}{2}$	$12\frac{3}{4}$	$11\frac{1}{4}$	12	14		$2.87	
Jones, D.	12	$13\frac{3}{4}$	12	$11\frac{3}{4}$	13		$2.88	

$$Gold: 10+11\frac{2}{4}+12+13\frac{1}{4}+12\frac{2}{4}=58\frac{5}{4}=59\frac{1}{4}=59.25 \, doz.$$

$$59.25 \times 2.53 = 149.9025 = \$149.90$$

Unit 82. Earning Commissions

Words to know

In some businesses, a salesman is paid a **commission** instead of a fixed salary. The commission usually is a percent of the dollar value of his sales. This percent is called the **rate of commission.**

When a salesman is paid a commission only, he is said to work on a **straight commission** basis.

To find the amount of **commission** a salesman has earned, multiply the **rate of commission** by the total sales. Since the rate of commission is a percent, change the given percent to a decimal before multiplying.

EXAMPLE. Charles Wilkins receives a commission of 10% on his sales. During July his sales came to $9,350. Find the amount of his commission.

Solution: Multiply the rate of commission, 10%, by the total sales, $9,350.

$$9350 \times 10\% = 9350 \times .10$$
$$= 935.0. = 935$$

Answer: His commission for July is $935.

APPLICATION PROBLEMS

1. A real estate salesman earns a commission of 12%. If he sold a house for $28,600 and another house for $34,750, how much commission did he earn on the two houses?

2. A car salesman earns a commission of 8%. He sold cars for $3,265, $3,482, and $2,985. What is his total commission for the three cars?

3. From the following sales record, find the amount of commission earned by each salesman. As a sample solution, the commission for L. Baker has been computed.

Name	Weekly Sales	Rate of Commission	Amount of Commission
Baker, L.	$1,872	15%	
Bates, D.	$2,320	12%	
Bean, C.	$1,968	15%	
Beam, A.	$2,475	13%	
Calb, W.	$2,298	12%	
Donald, R.	$2,463	12%	
Deeds, M.	$2,578	13%	
Dubrow, S.	$2,648	15%	
Dubler, F.	$2,329	14%	
Engle, R.	$2,468	13%	

Baker: 15% = .15

1,872 × .15 = 280.80

Unit 83. Earning Salary Plus Commission

Words to know

In many instances, a salesman receives a weekly salary, called a **base salary**, in addition to his commission. At times, his commission may be a percent of his sales above a fixed amount, known as a **quota**.

EXAMPLE. A salesman is paid $45 a week plus a commission of 5% on sales above a quota of $750. Last week his sales were $2,700. What were his total earnings for the week?

Solution: Subtract the quota, $750, from his total sales, $2,700, to find the part of his sales he gets a commission on. This part is known as his *net sales* or his *commission sales*.

$$
\begin{array}{r}
2,700 \\
-750 \\
\hline
1,950
\end{array}
$$

To find the commission, multiply the net sales,

$1,950, by the rate of commission, 5%.

$$
\begin{array}{r}
1,950 \\
\times .05 \\
\hline
97.50
\end{array}
$$

Add the base salary, $45.00, to the commission, $97.50, to compute the total earnings.

$$
\begin{array}{r}
97.50 \\
+45.00 \\
\hline
142.50
\end{array}
$$

Answer: His total earnings were $142.50.

APPLICATION PROBLEMS

1. A salesman earns $75 a week plus a commission of 8% on sales over $1,000. Last week, his sales were $2,627.50. Find his total earnings for the week.

2. A salesman earns $60 a week, plus a commission of 5% on all sales. What was his total salary last week if his sales were $2,162.75?

3. From the given record, find the net sales and the total earnings for each salesman. The quota for each salesman is $500. As a sample solution, this information has been computed for G. Evans.

Name	Weekly Salary	Weekly Sales	Net Sales	Commission	Total Earnings
Evans, G.	$64	$1,830.50	*1,330.50*	8%	*170.44*
Farley, B.	$63	$2,415.75		5%	
Farraro, V.	$60	$1,985.60		7%	
Farber, G.	$65	$2,317.48		6%	
Farbstein, D.	$62	$2,248.75		7%	
Ferguson, M.	$64	$2,178.45		8%	
Fenway, B.	$63	$2,268.50		5%	
Garden, D.	$65	$2,375.35		6%	
Gary, E.	$64	$2,347.62		7%	
Gutman, B.	$65	$2,238.45		6%	

Evans:

```
  1,830.50          1,330.50          106.44
 - 500.00           X .08           + 64.00
  --------          --------          ------
  1,330.50          106.4400          170.44
```

Review of Part XVII (Units 80 to 83)

1. From the information given, find for each employee the total regular hours worked, the total overtime hours worked, and the total earnings. The regular work week is 40 hours.

| Name | Time Recorded | | | | | Hourly Rate | Total Hours | | Total Earnings |
	M	T	W	Th	F		Regular	Overtime	
Adams, J.	7	$9\frac{1}{2}$	10	$8\frac{3}{4}$	9	$3.75			
Baum, H.	$9\frac{1}{2}$	10	$8\frac{1}{2}$	$9\frac{3}{4}$	10	$4.10			
Beame, S.	$8\frac{3}{4}$	$9\frac{1}{2}$	10	$9\frac{3}{4}$	$9\frac{1}{2}$	$3.85			
Curtis, G.	10	$9\frac{1}{2}$	$8\frac{3}{4}$	$9\frac{1}{2}$	9	$3.95			

2. From the given piece-work record, find for each employee the total number of dozens completed and the total earnings.

| Name | Number of Dozens | | | | | Total Dozens | Rate per Dozen | Total Earnings |
	M	T	W	Th	F			
Dell, F.	$12\frac{2}{3}$	13	$14\frac{1}{2}$	$12\frac{3}{4}$	$11\frac{1}{4}$		$2.95	
Dean, J.	13	$12\frac{1}{4}$	$10\frac{1}{2}$	14	$11\frac{3}{4}$		$2.80	
Earl, F.	14	$13\frac{3}{4}$	$11\frac{2}{3}$	$12\frac{1}{2}$	13		$2.85	
Eisen, G.	$12\frac{1}{2}$	$14\frac{1}{4}$	$13\frac{2}{3}$	$11\frac{3}{4}$	14		$2.90	

3. From the given sales record, find the commission earned by each salesman.

Name	Weekly Sales	Commission Rate	Commission
Farmer, L.	$1,972	15%	
Fuller, M.	$1,853	14%	
Gould, L.	$2,127	12%	
Hart, B.	$2,324	13%	

Part XVIII. Personal Finances

Unit 84. Income Budgets

Paying bills is a necessary part of everyday living. Many people "pay as they go," paying bills when they have the money and putting off payments when they are short of cash. In addition to causing worry, this practice usually costs money in extra finance charges, and often results in a poor credit rating.

Many home economists feel that the best way to handle personal finances is to treat your annual income as one big sum and to decide how to spend it by making an **income budget**.

To make an income budget, go back through your records and receipts and find out how much you spent last year for such items as food, clothing, housing, doctors, and operating expenses. (Operating expenses include home repairs, car maintenance, vacations, recreation, etc.) Then, estimate what your income will be for the entire year to come. Once you get all this information, you can figure out *in advance* how much you can afford to pay for the various expenses.

The chart below shows how the Wilson family plans to spend its estimated annual income of $8,500. (The figure of $8,500 is Mr. Wilson's "take-home pay" from which all taxes have already been deducted.)

Wilson Family Income Budget (Total Income: $8,500)

Food	Clothing	Housing	Operating	Medical	Savings
$2,125	$1,105	$1,700	$1,785	$765	$1,020

Note that the sum of all the expenses is the total income of $8,500.

Mr. Wilson wants to know what *percent* of his total income will be spent on each item. To find the percent of each expenditure, *divide the expenditure by the total income.*

EXAMPLE. What percent of Wilson's total income will be spent on food?

Solution: Divide the expenditure, $2,125, by $8,500.

$$
\begin{array}{r}
.25 = 25\% \\
8,500\overline{\smash{\big)}2,125.00} \\
\underline{1\ 700\ 0} \\
425\ 00 \\
\underline{425\ 00}
\end{array}
$$

Answer: 25% of the total income will be spent on food.

Note: Recall that finding what percent one number

is of another number can be calculated with the $\dfrac{\text{IS}}{\text{OF}}$ fraction. In the preceding example, the facts may be expressed as: ("$2,125 is) what %(of $8,500?")

$$\dfrac{\text{IS}}{\text{OF}} = \dfrac{2,125}{8,500}$$

Change the fraction to a percent by dividing the denominator into the numerator. This division is shown in the example.

The next chart is the Wilson family's budget with all percents figured out. Note that the sum of the percents must be 100%. (Recall that 100% means *all* of something, or the *total amount* of something.)

Wilson Family Income Budget (Total Income: $8,500)

Food	Clothing	Housing	Operating	Medical	Savings
$2,125	$1,105	$1,700	$1,785	$765	$1,020
25%	13%	20%	21%	9%	12%

APPLICATION PROBLEMS

1. If Mr. Wilson gets a raise, his estimated annual income will be $9,200. Using the same percentages as in the above chart, find the amount available for each expenditure. (The sum of the expenditures should be $9,200.)

Food_____   Clothing_____   Housing_____

Operating_____   Medical_____   Savings_____

2. The Watts family's estimated income is $8,750. The budget allowances for the year are:
   Food: $2,175; Clothing: $1,135; Housing: $1,800;
   Operating: $1,810; Medical & Drug: $850; Savings: $980
   Find the percent of income budgeted for each item.

Food_____   Clothing_____   Housing_____

Operating_____   Medical_____   Savings_____

Unit 85. Deductions From Wages

The law requires that all employers deduct two different taxes from the wages of each employee.

One tax is the *Federal Income Withholding Tax*, commonly called the *Income tax*. The amount deducted depends on the amount of the employee's wages and on the number of exemptions he claims. He usually claims one exemption for himself, one for his wife, and one for each dependent. Table XIII on the next page shows a portion of the table, supplied by the government, that tells an employer how much Income tax to withhold.

Table XIII: *Income Tax Withholding Table*

If the payroll period is weekly

And the wages are—		And the number of exemptions claimed is—			
		0	1	2	3
At least	But less than	The amount of income tax withheld shall be—			
90	92	14.10	11.00	8.30	5.70
92	94	14.50	11.40	8.70	6.10
94	96	14.90	11.90	9.00	6.40
96	98	15.30	12.30	9.40	6.80
98	100	15.70	12.70	9.80	7.20
100	102	16.50	13.40	10.40	7.80
102	107	17.50	14.50	11.50	8.70
107	112	18.60	15.50	12.50	9.60
112	117	19.60	16.60	13.60	10.50
117	122	20.70	17.60	14.60	11.60

EXAMPLE 1. Henry Sykes earns $120 per week and claims 2 exemptions. Compute the amount to be withheld from his weekly salary for the Income tax.

Solution: In Table XIII, Sykes' income of $120 falls into the "at least 117 but less than 122" group. Move across this row until you come to the column labeled "2" (for the 2 exemptions). The amount on the table reads 14.60.

Answer: $14.60 is withheld each week for the Income tax.

The other tax is the *Federal Insurance Contributions Act* (F.I.C.A.) tax, commonly known as the *Social Security tax*. This tax varies from year to year. At one time, the tax was 5.2% of the first $7,800 earned in a calendar year. (A calendar year is a year beginning on January 1.) No tax was withheld for any salary earned by an employee in excess of $7,800.

Table XIV shows a portion of the table, supplied by the government, that tells an employer how much to withhold for the Social Security tax.

Table XIV: *Social Security Tax Withholding Table—5.2%*

Weekly Wages		Social Security Tax to be Withheld	Weekly Wages		Social Security Tax to be Withheld
At Least	But Less Than		At Least	But Less Than	
113.95	114.14	5.93	117.41	117.60	6.11
114.14	114.33	5.94	117.60	117.79	6.12
114.33	114.52	5.95	117.79	118.00	6.13
114.52	114.72	5.96	118.00	118.18	6.14
114.72	114.91	5.97	118.18	118.37	6.15
114.91	115.10	5.98	118.37	118.56	6.16
115.10	115.29	5.99	118.56	118.75	6.17
115.29	115.49	6.00	118.75	118.95	6.18
115.49	115.68	6.01	118.95	119.14	6.19
115.68	115.87	6.02	119.14	119.33	6.20
115.87	116.06	6.03	119.33	119.52	6.21
116.06	116.25	6.04	119.52	119.72	6.22
116.25	116.45	6.05	119.72	119.91	6.23
116.45	116.64	6.06	119.91	120.10	6.24
116.64	116.83	6.07	120.10	120.29	6.25
116.83	117.02	6.08	120.29	120.49	6.26
117.02	117.22	6.09	120.49	120.68	6.27
117.22	117.41	6.10	120.68	120.87	6.28

EXAMPLE 2. Compute the amount of Social Security tax to be withheld from Henry Sykes' weekly salary. Sykes earns $120 per week.

Solution: In Table XIV, Sykes' salary of $120 falls into the "at least 119.91 but less than 120.10" group. The entry in the column to the right reads 6.24.

Answer: $6.24 is withheld each week.

In addition to the Income tax and the Social Security tax, other deductions may be made from an employee's weekly salary: state and city income taxes, union dues, health insurance plan, pension plan, etc. The salary that an employee gets after all deductions have been made is called the *net pay* or the *take-home pay*.

APPLICATION PROBLEMS

1. Using Table XIII and Table XIV, find the Income tax, the F.I.C.A. tax, the total deductions, and the net wages for each of the employees listed in the following table. As a sample solution, this information has been computed for J. Abrams.

   When this has been done, add the columns and enter the sums in the *Totals* boxes at the bottom of the table. Use the *Totals* sums to check your work: The Income tax sum plus the F.I.C.A. sum should equal the Total Deductions sum; the Total Wages sum minus the Total Deductions sum should equal the total Net Wages.

Name	Exemptions	Total Wages	Income Tax	F.I.C.A. Tax	Total Deductions	Net Wages
Abrams, J.	3	$120.00	*11.60*	*6.24*	*17.84*	*102.16*
Addison, F.	1	$114.00				
Agnew, P.	0	$115.75				
Brunillo, J.	3	$118.50				
Bates, F.	2	$116.65				
Curtis, A.	1	$117.85				
DeMato, J.	3	$118.60				
Delgado, G.	0	$119.50				
Delio, J.	1	$114.00				
Furman, M.	2	$115.40				
Finkelstein, C.	3	$120.50				
Totals						

$$\begin{array}{r} \textit{Abrams: } 11.60 \\ +\ 6.24 \\ \hline 17.84 \end{array} \qquad \begin{array}{r} 120.00 \\ -17.84 \\ \hline 102.16 \end{array}$$

2. Using Table XIII and Table XIV, find the Income tax and the F.I.C.A. tax for each of the following employees. As a sample solution, this information has been computed for J. Baker.

Name	Exemptions	Weekly Wages	Income Tax	F.I.C.A. Tax
Baker, J.	2	$119.50	14.60	6.21
Bates, M.	0	$115.00		
Cohen, J.	3	$114.75		
Colon, M.	1	$116.20		
Danzig, A.	3	$118.60		
Dean, W.	3	$120.50		
Dunbar, V.	0	$117.40		
Engle, L.	3	$115.80		
Fernandez, J.	1	$119.90		
Gold, N.	2	$120.00		

Unit 86. The Checking Account: Deposit Slips

Edward J. Martin, a salesman, has a **checking account** at the Newtown National Bank. When he receives payments for his salary and his commissions, he deposits the checks and cash in the bank. Then, when he has a bill to pay, he writes a check for the amount he owes and sends the check by mail.

By using his checking account, Mr. Martin does not have to spend time going from store to store and standing in line in order to pay his bills. Also, he does not have to worry about carrying large amounts of money with him. Finally, his canceled checks are proof that his bills have been paid.

The bank gives Mr. Martin a supply of **deposit slips**, which he fills out whenever he deposits cash or checks. One day, Mr. Martin had the following items to deposit:

4 $20 bills
2 $10 bills
4 $1 bills
7 quarters
a salary check for $86.53
commission checks for $23.65, $19.67, $37.15, $25.00

Here is how he filled out his deposit slip:

		DOLLARS	CENTS
Cash _____		105	75
Checks _____	1	86	53
list separately	2	23	65
	3	19	67
	4	37	15
	5	25	—
	6		
	7		
	8		
TOTAL		297	75

NEWTOWN NATIONAL BANK
NEWTOWN, N.Y.
DATE _____ Dec. 29 ___ 19 —

EDWARD J. MARTIN

ADDRESS .... 106 West Washington St.
.... Newtown, N.Y. ....

CHECK COUNT

First, Mr. Martin counted all of his bills and coins and entered the sum of $105.75 after " Cash."

4 $20 bills =	80.00
2 $10 bills =	20.00
4 $1 bills =	4.00
7 quarters =	1.75
	105.75

Next, he listed each of his checks separately. Then, he added together all of his deposits and entered this sum, $297.75, after "Total." Notice that he also filled in the date and his address.

After the bank teller received the deposit slip and counted the cash and the checks, he returned a carbon copy of the deposit slip to Mr. Martin. This **customer's receipt**, which the teller dated, is proof that the bank received the deposit.

EXERCISES

Below is a record of deposits made to the account of Edward J. Martin, 106 West Washington Street, Newtown, New York, for the current year. Prepare the deposit slips for these transactions. Use the blank deposit slips on pages 264 and 265.

	Date	Cash	Checks			
			1	2	3	4
1.	Jan. 5	115.60	38.25	19.63	31.75	
2.	Jan. 20	120.75	25.85	20.15		
3.	Feb. 5	125.80	37.50	21.20	32.60	27.80
4.	Feb. 20	120.75	35.65	19.70	31.10	
5.	Mar. 5	117.80	30.15	20.75		

1.

NEWTOWN NATIONAL BANK
NEWTOWN, N.Y.
DATE_____ 19____

EDWARD J. MARTIN

ADDRESS...

....

Cash _____
Checks _____ 1
list separately
CHECK COUNT

	DOLLARS	CENTS
1		
2		
3		
4		
5		
6		
7		
8		
TOTAL		

2.

NEWTOWN NATIONAL BANK
NEWTOWN, N.Y.
DATE_____ 19____

EDWARD J. MARTIN

ADDRESS...

....

Cash _____
Checks _____ 1
list separately
CHECK COUNT

	DOLLARS	CENTS
1		
2		
3		
4		
5		
6		
7		
8		
TOTAL		

3.

NEWTOWN NATIONAL BANK
NEWTOWN, N.Y.
DATE_____ 19____

EDWARD J. MARTIN

ADDRESS...

....

Cash _____
Checks _____ 1
list separately
CHECK COUNT

	DOLLARS	CENTS
1		
2		
3		
4		
5		
6		
7		
8		
TOTAL		

4.

	DOLLARS	CENTS
NEWTOWN NATIONAL BANK		
NEWTOWN, N.Y.		
DATE_____ 19_____		
EDWARD J. MARTIN		
ADDRESS............................		
....		

Cash _____
Checks _____ 1
list separately 2
3
4
5
6
7
8
CHECK COUNT TOTAL

5.

	DOLLARS	CENTS
NEWTOWN NATIONAL BANK		
NEWTOWN, N.Y.		
DATE_____ 19_____		
EDWARD J. MARTIN		
ADDRESS............................		
....		

Cash _____
Checks _____ 1
list separately 2
3
4
5
6
7
8
CHECK COUNT TOTAL

APPLICATION PROBLEMS

1. On November 8 of this year, Sylvia Thompson of 814 Central Terrace, Tacoma, Washington, deposited the following items to her checking account: 125 pennies, 83 nickels, 25 dimes, 32 quarters, 25 $1 bills, 7 $5 bills, a check for $32.15, and a check for $21.17. Fill in her deposit slip.

	DOLLARS	CENTS
MERCHANT'S BANK		
TACOMA, WASH.		
DATE_____ 19_____		
SYLVIA THOMPSON		
ADDRESS............................		
....		

Cash _____
Checks _____ 1
list separately 2
3
4
5
6
7
8
CHECK COUNT TOTAL

2. Last July 5th, David Disney of 711 Columbus Avenue, Lexington, Kentucky, deposited checks to his account in the amounts of $40.50, $19.70, and $40.15. He also deposited 28 dimes, 100 quarters, and 5 $20 bills. Make out his deposit slip.

		DOLLARS	CENTS
Cash - - - - - - - - - -			
Checks - - - - - - - - 1			
list separately 2			
3			
4			
5			
6			
7			
8			
TOTAL			

THE MUNICIPAL BANK
LEXINGTON, KY.
DATE_____19____

DAVID DISNEY

ADDRESS...

....

CHECK COUNT

Unit 87. The Checking Account: Checks and Check Stubs

WRITING CHECKS

In addition to deposit slips, the Newtown National Bank gives Mr. Martin a supply of **checks**. These checks are in a checkbook; to the left of each check is the **check stub**. Whenever Mr. Martin writes a check, he is careful to fill out the check stub. The check stub is separated from the check itself by a perforated line. When the check is torn out, the stub remains behind as a record.

To pay his December bill at Jay's Department Store, Mr. Martin filled out the following check and check stub:

NO. 225	$ 73.85
DATE Dec. 30 19—	
TO Jay's Dep't Store	
FOR Sports Jacket, shoes,	
& Raincoat (bought 12/15)	

	DOLLARS	CENTS
BAL. BRO'T FOR'D	120	95
AMT. DEPOSITED	105	75
TOTAL	226	70
AMT. THIS CHECK	73	85
BAL. CAR'D FOR'D	152	85

NO. 225   **NEWTOWN NATIONAL BANK**

NEWTOWN, N.Y.   December 30 19—

Pay to the
order of ___ Jay's Department Store ___ $73 85/100

Seventy-three and 85/100 ————————————— Dollars

Edward J. Martin
106 W. Washington St.
Newtown, New York

Edward J. Martin

check stub   check

perforated
line

Check number: After "No." on both the stub and the check, Mr. Martin writes "225." The last check he wrote was check No. 224; the next check he will write is check No. 226.

Date: The correct date is always written on both the stub and the check.

To: With this check, Mr. Martin tells his bank to pay a certain amount to *Jay's Department Store.* He writes this name on the stub and on the check.

For: When Mr. Martin goes over his records in a month or two, he may have forgotten what he bought at Jay's Department Store. Therefore, he writes on the stub what the check pays for.

Face amount: The amount of the check (the face amount) is usually written on the stub as a decimal. It must be written on the check in two different places: Once in numbers and once in words and numbers. Amounts less than one dollar are written as a fraction, for example, $\frac{85}{100}$ or 85/100.

Sometimes such amounts are written as $\frac{85}{xx}$ or as 85/. When the face amount is an even number of dollars, "no cents" is written as $\frac{no}{100}$ or as $\frac{xx}{100}$. Never write an amount as a decimal on a check.

Signature: Mr. Martin signs his *legal signature* to the check. He signs it in *exactly* the way he signed it when he opened his checking account. The bank has a record of his legal signature. If the check were signed "Ed Martin" or "E. J. Martin,"

the bank might return it to him for a proper signature.

USING THE STUBS TO FIGURE BALANCE

Balance brought forward: As of the last check he wrote, Mr. Martin has $120.95 in his checking account. He knows this, because that is the last number on his *previous* check stub, the number that is the "balance carried forward." He brings this balance forward and enters it on the check stub as shown.

Amount deposited: Mr. Martin has deposited $105.75 in his checking account (see the deposit slip in the preceding unit). He indicates this amount on his check stub as shown.

Total: The sum of the balance brought forward and the amount deposited gives the total amount in Mr. Martin's checking account, $226.70.

Amount of this check: Under the total, Mr. Martin writes the face amount of the check, $73.85.

Balance carried forward: By subtracting the amount of the check from the total, Mr. Martin knows that he now has $152.85 in his checking account. This "balance carried forward" becomes the "balance brought forward" on the *next* check stub.

The main purpose of the check stubs is to tell you what your checking account balance is. If you write a check for more than the balance, the bank will refuse to honor your check, and will return it marked "Insufficient Funds."

APPLICATION PROBLEMS

1. Fill in the following checks and check stubs from the information provided. Use your own name for the legal signature. Check No. 26 has been filled in as a sample solution.

Check No. 26: Balance brought forward, $152.85; amount deposited, $85.16; face amount of check, $36.50: to Dr. S. Fontek for dental work; date, July 15.

NO. 26 $36.50		UNION NATIONAL BANK
DATE 7/15 19—	NO. 26	
TO Dr. S. Fontek		
FOR Dental work	CHICAGO, ILL. July 15 19—	

	DOLLARS	CENTS
BAL. BRO'T FOR'D	152	85
AMT. DEPOSITED	85	16
TOTAL	238	01
AMT. THIS CHECK	36	50
BAL. CAR'D FOR'D	201	51

Pay to the order of *Dr. S. Fontek* $36 $\frac{50}{100}$

Thirty-Six and $\frac{50}{100}$ ———————————— Dollars

J. J. Johnson

Check No. 27: Balance brought forward, $201.51 (note that this amount can be picked up from the balance carried forward on check stub 26); face amount of check, $63.71; to Ace Men's Shop for clothing; date, July 25.

NO. *27*	$	
DATE _____ 19—		
TO _____		
FOR _____		

	DOLLARS	CENTS
BAL. BRO'T FOR'D		
AMT. DEPOSITED		
TOTAL		
AMT. THIS CHECK		
BAL. CAR'D FOR'D		

NO. *27* UNION NATIONAL BANK

CHICAGO, ILL. _____ 19___

Pay to the order of _____ $ _____

_____ Dollars

Check No. 28: Balance brought forward: pick up the balance carried forward that appears on check stub 27; face amount of check, $23.53; to Consolidated Gas Co. for June gas bill; date, July 25.

NO. *28*	$	
DATE _____ 19—		
TO _____		
FOR _____		

	DOLLARS	CENTS
BAL. BRO'T FOR'D		
AMT. DEPOSITED		
TOTAL		
AMT. THIS CHECK		
BAL. CAR'D FOR'D		

NO. *28* UNION NATIONAL BANK

CHICAGO, ILL. _____ 19___

Pay to the order of _____ $ _____

_____ Dollars

Check No. 29: Balance brought forward: pick up the balance carried forward that appears on check stub 28; amount deposited, $125.60; face amount of check, $73.85; to Service Insurance Co. for life insurance premium; date, July 30.

NO. *29*	$	
DATE _____ 19—		
TO _____		
FOR _____		

	DOLLARS	CENTS
BAL. BRO'T FOR'D		
AMT. DEPOSITED		
TOTAL		
AMT. THIS CHECK		
BAL. CAR'D FOR'D		

NO. *29* UNION NATIONAL BANK

CHICAGO, ILL. _____ 19___

Pay to the order of _____ $ _____

_____ Dollars

Note: If you have properly filled in the check stubs, the balance carried forward on check stub 29 should be $166.02.

2. In the month of August, John Germaine made the deposits and wrote the checks indicated on the check stubs shown below. Complete the stub records of checks 107-112.

NO. *107*	$ *136.—*
DATE *Aug. 1* 19—	
TO *John Realty*	
FOR *Rent*	

	DOLLARS	CENTS
BAL. BRO'T FOR'D	325	60
AMT. DEPOSITED		
TOTAL		
AMT. THIS CHECK	136	—
BAL. CAR'D FOR'D		

NO. *108*	$ *53.65*
DATE *Aug. 3* 19—	
TO *Supermarket*	
FOR *Food*	

	DOLLARS	CENTS
BAL. BRO'T FOR'D		
AMT. DEPOSITED	116	70
TOTAL		
AMT. THIS CHECK	53	65
BAL. CAR'D FOR'D		

NO. *109*	$ *21.75*
DATE *Aug. 10* 19—	
TO *Dr. James*	
FOR *X-rays*	

	DOLLARS	CENTS
BAL. BRO'T FOR'D		
AMT. DEPOSITED		
TOTAL		
AMT. THIS CHECK	21	75
BAL. CAR'D FOR'D		

NO. *110*	$ *21.70*
DATE *Aug. 15* 19—	
TO *Dell pharmacy*	
FOR *Drugs*	

	DOLLARS	CENTS
BAL. BRO'T FOR'D		
AMT. DEPOSITED	115	45
TOTAL		
AMT. THIS CHECK	21	70
BAL. CAR'D FOR'D		

NO. *111*	$ *18.50*
DATE *Aug. 20* 19—	
TO *Telephone Co.*	
FOR *Tel. bill*	

	DOLLARS	CENTS
BAL. BRO'T FOR'D		
AMT. DEPOSITED		
TOTAL		
AMT. THIS CHECK	18	50
BAL. CAR'D FOR'D		

NO. *112*	$ *78.50*
DATE *Aug. 25* 19—	
TO *Ace Appliance Co.*	
FOR *T.V. set*	

	DOLLARS	CENTS
BAL. BRO'T FOR'D		
AMT. DEPOSITED		
TOTAL		
AMT. THIS CHECK	78	50
BAL. CAR'D FOR'D		

Note: If you have properly filled in the check stubs, the balance carried forward on check stub 112 should be $227.65.

Unit 88. The Checking Account: Reconciling the Bank Balance

Nancy Watts went to the First Federal Bank on January 3 and opened a checking account with a deposit of $250.00. She received a supply of checks and deposit slips. During the month of January, she wrote checks and made deposits.

On February 5, she received in the mail a **bank statement** showing all the transactions made during January. Included with the statement were a number of canceled checks. Here is the bank statement:

FIRST FEDERAL BANK
Philadelphia

ACCOUNT OF	ACCOUNT NUMBER
MS NANCY E WATTS	01197391
875 SOUTH 12TH ST	1004
PHILADELPHIA PA	

DEBITS (checks)	CREDITS (deposits)	DATE	BALANCE
BALANCE BROUGHT FORWARD ▶			000.00
	250.00	1 03	250.00
34.25		1 05	215.75
25.00		1 07	190.75
	158.73	1 07	349.48
40.20		1 17	309.28
45.50		1 17	263.78
25.00		1 21	238.78
	158.73	1 21	397.51
111.86		1 28	(285.65)
NO OF DEBITS 6	NO OF CREDITS 3	DATE RENDERED 1 31	

Looking at the last number in the right column, Nancy saw that her balance was $285.65. But when she looked at her last check stub, she saw that her balance was only $262.35.

NO. *12*	$
DATE	19—
TO	
FOR	

	DOLLARS	CENTS
BAL. BRO'T FOR'D	262	35
AMT. DEPOSITED		
TOTAL		
AMT. THIS CHECK		
BAL. CAR'D FOR'D		

To account for this difference, Nancy had to *reconcile* her checkbook with the bank statement. She got out all of her deposit slip receipts, her canceled checks from the bank, and her checkbook.

From her deposit slip receipts, Nancy knew she had made the following deposits:

Jan. 3	250.00	Jan. 21	158.73
Jan. 7	158.73	Feb. 4	158.73

She matched each deposit slip receipt against the deposits that appeared on the bank statement in the column labeled CREDITS and realized that her February 4 deposit was not included. She had deposited the $158.73 after January 31, the last date that the bank included in her monthly statement. (This last date appears in the bottom right corner of her statement as DATE RENDERED 1 31.)

Therefore, Nancy added the February 4 deposit to the bank balance shown on the statement.

    285.65   (bank balance on Jan. 31 statement)
   +158.73   (deposit made on Feb. 4)
   ───────
    444.38

The total, $444.38, was still not the same as her balance of $262.35 that was shown on her last check stub.

Nancy then matched each canceled check against the checks listed on the bank statement in the column labeled DEBITS, and found that they matched, one for one. Finally, she put her canceled checks into numerical order:

Check No.	Amount	To
1	34.25	Wanamaker's (bookcases & lamps)
2	25.00	"cash" (food, etc.)
3	40.20	Penn Discount (table & chairs)
4	45.50	Bond's (linen & blankets)
6	25.00	"cash"
7	111.86	Market St. Electronics (bal. due on TV)

Then she saw what had happened. According to her check stubs, she had written eleven checks, from No. 1 through No. 11. But checks No. 5, 8, 9, 10, and 11 were not included in the statement. These five checks had not reached the bank in time to be included in the January 31 statement. They were still **outstanding**.

From her check stubs, Nancy knew the amounts of the checks outstanding:

Check No.	Amount	To
5	20.00	Hospital fund (contribution)
8	34.23	Beck's Dept. Store (Christmas gifts)
9	9.80	Phila. Gas & Electric (utilities)
10	25.00	"cash"
11	93.00	Quaker Realty (Feb. rent)
	182.03	

Since these checks would be charged against her account, Nancy subtracted the total amount, $182.03, from the total of her balance shown on the January 31 statement and the deposit she made on February 4.

```
  285.65  (bank balance on Jan. 31 statement)
+ 158.73  (deposit made on Feb. 4)
  ------
  444.38
- 182.03  (total amount of all checks outstanding)
  ------
  262.35
```

Nancy's corrected balance was the same as that shown in her checkbook. Nancy had reconciled her checkbook with the bank statement, and knew that her checking account had a balance of $262.35, as shown on her last check stub.

On the back of Nancy's statement was a form that she could have used to reconcile her checkbook with the bank statement. Here is the form, correctly filled in:

				CHECK(S) OUTSTANDING	
				NO.	AMOUNT
1. ENTER FINAL BALANCE	285	65			
	158	73		5	20 00
2. ADD DEPOSITS NOT SHOWN ON THIS STATEMENT				8	34 23
				9	9 80
				10	25 00
3. TOTAL	444	38		11	93 00
4. SUBTRACT TOTAL "CHECKS OUTSTANDING"	182	03	◀	TOTAL	182 03
BALANCE	262	35			

EXERCISES

In each of these exercises, reconcile the checkbook balance with the bank statement balance. The corrected balance should be the same as the checkbook balance.

Sample solution

Bill Grady's bank statement, dated Oct. 4, shows a balance of $147.80. His checkbook balance is $115.92. Bill has three checks outstanding: No. 17, $15.65; No. 18, $10.75; No. 19, $5.48. He made no deposits after Oct. 4. Reconcile Bill's checkbook balance.

			CHECK(S) OUTSTANDING		
1. ENTER FINAL BALANCE	147	80	NO.	AMOUNT	
2. ADD DEPOSITS NOT SHOWN ON THIS STATEMENT			17	15	65
			18	10	75
			19	5	48
3. TOTAL	147	80			
4. SUBTRACT TOTAL "CHECKS OUTSTANDING"	31	88	TOTAL	31	88
BALANCE	115	92			

Note that Bill's corrected balance, $115.92, is the same as his checkbook balance.

---

1. Nancy Bennett's bank statement balance is $115.17, dated December 31. She made no deposits after this date, and has check No. 61 for $19.35 outstanding. Reconcile the checkbook balance of $95.82.

			CHECK(S) OUTSTANDING		
1. ENTER FINAL BALANCE			NO.	AMOUNT	
2. ADD DEPOSITS NOT SHOWN ON THIS STATEMENT					
3. TOTAL					
4. SUBTRACT TOTAL "CHECKS OUTSTANDING"			TOTAL		
BALANCE					

2. Mr. Dawes' Oct. 31 bank statement shows a balance of $237.85. He made no deposits after this date. His checks outstanding are: No. 52, $37.65; No. 54, $51.61. Reconcile his checkbook balance of $148.59.

				CHECK(S) OUTSTANDING	
1. ENTER FINAL BALANCE				NO.	AMOUNT
2. ADD DEPOSITS NOT SHOWN ON THIS STATEMENT					
3. TOTAL					
4. SUBTRACT TOTAL "CHECKS OUTSTANDING"				TOTAL	
BALANCE					

3. Henry Blake's April 30 bank statement shows a balance of $173.16. He has the following checks outstanding: No. 67, $43.83; No. 68, $35.05. Also, he deposited a check in the amount of $85.00 on May 1, after the bank sent out his statement. Reconcile his checkbook balance of $179.28.

				CHECK(S) OUTSTANDING	
1. ENTER FINAL BALANCE				NO.	AMOUNT
2. ADD DEPOSITS NOT SHOWN ON THIS STATEMENT					
3. TOTAL					
4. SUBTRACT TOTAL "CHECKS OUTSTANDING"				TOTAL	
BALANCE					

APPLICATION PROBLEMS

Many people have difficulty reconciling their checkbook balance because they make mistakes on their check stubs. The most common mistakes are in the arithmetic. However, there are many others:

1. Overlooking a check that is outstanding. (To correct this mistake, subtract the amount of the check from the checkbook balance.)
2. Failing to record a deposit on the check stub. (To correct this mistake, add the deposit to the checkbook balance.)
3. Recording the same deposit *twice* on the check stubs. (To correct this mistake, subtract the extra deposit from the checkbook balance.)
4. Overlooking bank service charges. (To correct this mistake, subtract all service charges from the checkbook balance.)

Use the forms below to reconcile the following accounts. Use the *checks outstanding* column for all adjustments that must be subtracted from the balance, such as service charges or a deposit that was recorded twice. Use the *deposits* column for all adjustments that must be added to the balance, such as a forgotten deposit or some other credit. Account No. 1 has been reconciled as a sample solution.

Note: Whenever an error has been made somewhere in the check stubs, the corrected balance will *not* be the same as the checkbook balance.

Account No.	Check-book Balance	Bank Statement Balance	Outstanding Checks	Other Adjustments	Corrected Balance
1.	245.49	365.39	23.50 20.75 75.65	Service charge of 3.15	242.34
2.	245.75	330.20	73.50 10.95	none	
3.	273.18	327.13	15.25 38.70	none	
4.	315.65	445.50	19.25 35.60	$75 deposit left off of check stubs	
5.	275.50	226.55	130.75	$180 late deposit not on bank statement	
6.	313.75	220.40	23.65 15.20 7.80	$140 late deposit not on bank statement	
7.	315.65	308.80	43.60 28.75 120.80	$100 deposit recorded twice on check stubs	
8.	497.85	197.85	none	$150 deposit recorded twice on check stubs	

1.

1. ENTER FINAL BALANCE	365	39
2. ADD DEPOSITS NOT SHOWN ON THIS STATEMENT		
3. TOTAL	365	39
4. SUBTRACT TOTAL "CHECKS OUTSTANDING"	123	05
BALANCE	242	34

CHECK(S) OUTSTANDING		
NO.	AMOUNT	
	23	50
	20	75
	75	65
svc. chge.	3	15
TOTAL	123	05

2.

1. ENTER FINAL BALANCE		
2. ADD DEPOSITS NOT SHOWN ON THIS STATEMENT		
3. TOTAL		
4. SUBTRACT TOTAL "CHECKS OUTSTANDING"		
BALANCE		

CHECK(S) OUTSTANDING		
NO.	AMOUNT	
TOTAL		

3.

1. ENTER FINAL BALANCE		
2. ADD DEPOSITS NOT SHOWN ON THIS STATEMENT		
3. TOTAL		
4. SUBTRACT TOTAL "CHECKS OUTSTANDING"		
BALANCE		

CHECK(S) OUTSTANDING		
NO.	AMOUNT	
TOTAL		

4.

1. ENTER FINAL BALANCE		
2. ADD DEPOSITS NOT SHOWN ON THIS STATEMENT		
3. TOTAL		
4. SUBTRACT TOTAL "CHECKS OUTSTANDING"		
BALANCE		

CHECK(S) OUTSTANDING		
NO.	AMOUNT	
TOTAL		

5.

1. ENTER FINAL BALANCE		
2. ADD DEPOSITS NOT SHOWN ON THIS STATEMENT		
3. TOTAL		
4. SUBTRACT TOTAL "CHECKS OUTSTANDING"		
BALANCE		

CHECK(S) OUTSTANDING		
NO.	AMOUNT	
TOTAL		

6.

1. ENTER FINAL BALANCE		
2. ADD DEPOSITS NOT SHOWN ON THIS STATEMENT		
3. TOTAL		
4. SUBTRACT TOTAL "CHECKS OUTSTANDING"		
BALANCE		

CHECK(S) OUTSTANDING		
NO.	AMOUNT	
TOTAL		

7.

1. ENTER FINAL BALANCE		
2. ADD DEPOSITS NOT SHOWN ON THIS STATEMENT		
3. TOTAL		
4. SUBTRACT TOTAL "CHECKS OUTSTANDING"		
BALANCE		

CHECK(S) OUTSTANDING		
NO.	AMOUNT	
TOTAL		

8.

1. ENTER FINAL BALANCE		
2. ADD DEPOSITS NOT SHOWN ON THIS STATEMENT		
3. TOTAL		
4. SUBTRACT TOTAL "CHECKS OUTSTANDING"		
BALANCE		

CHECK(S) OUTSTANDING	
NO.	AMOUNT
TOTAL	

Review of Part XVIII (Units 84 to 88)

1. Mr. Goldsboro estimated that his income would be $10,000 next year, after all taxes were withheld from his salary. Calculate the percent of his income that he will spend for each of the following budget expenses. (*Hint:* Since the net income is $10,000, you should be able to calculate the percents mentally, by moving the decimal point.)

   a. Food: $2,400_____ %

   b. Clothing: $1,500_____ %

   c. Housing: $2,100_____ %

   d. Operating: $1,930_____ %

   e. Medical: $950_____ %

   f. Savings: $1,120_____ %

2. Use Table XIII (page 260) and Table XIV (page 260) to calculate the Income tax and the F.I.C.A. tax that are withheld from each employee in the following table. Then find the total amount deducted and the net wages (take-home pay).

Name	Exemptions	Total Wages	Income Tax	F.I.C.A. Tax	Total Deductions	Total Wages
Reilly, C.	2	$117.50				
Sanford, F.	3	$120.00				
Thomas, J.	0	$115.00				
Unger, L.	2	$118.75				

3. Tina Trent had $85.50 in her checking account at the beginning of last month. During the month, she made deposits of $65.00, $62.50, and $67.20. Also, she wrote checks in the amounts of $18.75, $96.20, $25.00, $16.05, and $47.37. What is her new balance?

4. Arnold Smith received his bank statement, which showed a balance of $318.85. However, when Arnold looked at his checkbook stub, he found a checkbook balance of only $206.25. If Arnold has checks outstanding in the amounts of $40.50, $52.60, and $19.50, use the following form to reconcile the checkbook balance.

				CHECK(S) OUTSTANDING	
1. ENTER FINAL BALANCE				NO.	AMOUNT
2. ADD DEPOSITS NOT SHOWN ON THIS STATEMENT					
3. TOTAL					
4. SUBTRACT TOTAL "CHECKS OUTSTANDING"			◄	TOTAL	
BALANCE					

5. Mr. Bucknell's June 30 bank statement shows a balance of $267.89. He has checks outstanding in the amounts of $65.79, $23.60, $87.00, and $150.75. Also, he deposited a check in the amount of $150.00 on July 2, which is not included on the bank statement. How much does Mr. Bucknell have in the bank?

				CHECK(S) OUTSTANDING	
1. ENTER FINAL BALANCE				NO.	AMOUNT
2. ADD DEPOSITS NOT SHOWN ON THIS STATEMENT					
3. TOTAL					
4. SUBTRACT TOTAL "CHECKS OUTSTANDING"			◄	TOTAL	
BALANCE					

Part XIX. Insurance / Automobile Ownership

Unit 89. Property Insurance

Homeowners, apartment dwellers, and businessmen insure their property against loss or damage by fire, storms, theft, and other causes. The most common type of property insurance is **fire insurance**.

In return for an annual **premium** (yearly payment), the insurance company agrees to repay the insured person a percent of his financial losses caused by fire. These losses include indirect damage, such as damage caused by the water used to put out the fire and damage caused by smoke.

The annual premium rates are usually given in cents per $100 of insurance. The rates vary according to the type of building, its occupancy, and its location. A brick building used as a private home, located near a fire hydrant, would have a relatively low rate of fire insurance. A wooden building used for storing chemicals, located far away from any source of water, would have an extremely high rate.

Following is a portion of a table showing the annual premiums for $100 of fire insurance for various types of buildings. Each insurance company has different rates and various classifications for different types of buildings. In the opinion of the company that uses the following rates, a "Type A" building is safer to insure than a "Type D" building.

Table XV: *Annual Premium Per $100 of Fire Insurance*

Type of Building	A	B	C	D
Cost per $100	.35	.42	.46	.51

EXAMPLE 1. Find the premium for an $8,000 policy for a Type A building.

Solution: Calculate the number of 100's in 8,000. (Recall that, to divide by 100, you move the decimal point two places to the left.)

$$8000 \div 100 = 80.00. = 80$$

Multiply 80 (the number of 100's in 8,000) by .35 (the premium per $100 of a Type A building).

$$
\begin{array}{r}
80 \\
\times .35 \\
\hline
4\,00 \\
24\,0 \\
\hline
28.00
\end{array}
$$

Answer: The annual premium is $28.

EXAMPLE 2. John Doe's home, a Type A building, is insured for $25,000. Doe's commercial garage, a Type D building, is insured for 80% of its market value of $110,000. What is the total annual premium for the fire insurance on both buildings?

Solution:

Home: 25,000 ÷ 100 = 250; rate per $100 (Type A) is .35; 250 × .35 = 87.50

Garage: 80% of $110,000 = .80 × 110,000 = 88,000; 88,000 ÷ 100 = 880; rate per $100 (Type D) is .51; 880 × .51 = 448.80

Home + Garage:
$$
\begin{array}{r}
87.50 \\
+\,448.80 \\
\hline
536.30
\end{array}
$$

Answer: $536.30 is the total annual premium.

EXERCISES

Using Table XV, find the premium rate per $100 and calculate the annual premium for each fire insurance policy listed below. As a sample solution, this information has been computed for the first policy.

	Face Value	Type of Dwelling	Rate per $100	Number of $100's in Face Value	Annual Premium
1.	$12,500	A	.35	125	43.75
2.	$11,800	D			
3.	$10,500	B			
4.	$9,000	C			
5.	$13,900	D			
6.	$12,800	C			
7.	$11,500	B			
8.	$10,700	A			

1.
$$
\begin{array}{r}
125 \\
\times\ .35 \\
\hline
625 \\
375\ \ \\
\hline
43.75
\end{array}
$$

APPLICATION PROBLEMS

1. A manufacturer has equipment and machinery valued at $85,000. He plans to insure the equipment against loss by fire for $\frac{4}{5}$ of its value. If the annual premium rate is $.73 per $100, what will his

Unit 90. Life Insurance

Words to know

The **insurer** is the insurance company.

The **insured** is the person who is insured, sometimes called the *policyholder*.

The **policy** is the contract between the insurer and the insured.

The **premium** is the amount that the insured pays to the company. It is usually paid in advance, annually, semiannually, quarterly, or monthly.

The **beneficiary** is the person to whom the company pays the insurance on the death of the insured.

The **face value** is the amount of insurance that will be paid to the beneficiary.

Life insurance is an arrangement whereby the **insurer**, in return for a certain **premium**, agrees to pay to the **beneficiary** a fixed sum when the **insured** dies.

In a **straight life** policy (also called *ordinary life*), the insured pays premiums throughout his lifetime. The policy is payable at his death.

In a **limited payment life** policy, the insured pays premiums for a fixed period of time, such as 20 or 25 years. (Such policies are also called *20 payment life* or *25 payment life*.) At the end of the fixed period, the insured does not pay additional premiums. He remains insured for his entire life, the company paying his beneficiary when he dies.

In an **endowment** policy, the insured pays premiums for a fixed period, as in a limited payment life policy. However, after the period of 20 or 25 years has passed, the insurance company pays to the policyholder the full amount of the policy. If the insured dies before this time, the company pays to the beneficiary the full amount.

The following table shows annual rates for $1,000 of insurance under the three previous plans. These rates may differ somewhat from company to company and also may vary according to the health and occupation of the insured.

Table XVI: *Annual Premiums Per $1,000 of Life Insurance*

Age at Issue	Kind of Policy		
	Straight Life	20 Year Payment	20 Year Endowment
20	15.60	27.10	52.19
25	17.50	29.37	53.16
30	21.46	34.17	54.23
35	23.17	37.53	55.35
40	27.86	40.19	56.53
45	34.09	44.73	57.73
50	40.15	51.32	60.45

EXAMPLE. Find the annual premium for a straight life policy with a face value of $7,500, issued at age 25.

Solution: Multiply 7.5 (the number of 1,000's in $7,500) by $17.50 (the premium rate per $1,000 at age 25).

Answer: The annual premium is $131.25.

$$
\begin{array}{r}
17.50 \\
\times\,7.5 \\
\hline
8\ 750 \\
122\ 50 \\
\hline
131.250
\end{array}
$$

EXERCISES

Using Table XVI, find the annual premium per $1,000 of life insurance and calculate the annual premiums for each policy listed below. As a sample solution, this information has been computed for the first policy.

	Face Value	Type of Insurance	Age at Issue	Annual Premium per $1,000	Number of $1,000's in Face Value	Annual Premium
1.	$15,500	straight life	25	17.50	15.5	271.25
2.	$20,500	20 year endowment	35			
3.	$18,500	straight life	45			
4.	$23,500	20 year payment	30			
5.	$22,000	straight life	40			
6.	$24,500	20 year endowment	45			
7.	$26,500	20 year payment	30			
8.	$28,500	straight life	20			

1.
$$
\begin{array}{r}
17.50 \\
\times 15.5 \\
\hline
8750 \\
8750 \\
1750 \\
\hline
271.250
\end{array}
$$

APPLICATION PROBLEMS

1. Tom, age 20, wants to buy a 20 year payment life insurance policy with a face value of $28,500. Using Table XVI, find the annual premium.

_____

2. Tom (Problem 1) plans to pay the premium quarterly (4 times a year). How much will each quarterly premium be?

_____

3. Harry, age 35, plans to buy an additional straight life policy that has a face value of $17,500. Using Table XVI, find his semi-annual premium.

_____

Note: Most insurance companies make a small additional charge when the insured pays his premiums semiannually, quarterly, or monthly. The extra cost covers the clerical work of billing, collecting, and recording payments more than once each year.

Unit 91. Automobile Ownership: Annual Depreciation

Owning an automobile involves many expenses other than the initial cost of the car. Expenses include the license fees, insurance, gasoline and oil, tires, repairs, and general upkeep such as parking fees, tolls, seat covers, etc. Also, if the car was bought on the installment plan, there will be extra finance charges.

Many car owners overlook the fact that a major expense is the **depreciation** of the car. *Depreciation is the loss in value of a car (or any other article) through use and the passage of time.* The **total depreciation** of a car is the difference between the original cost and the amount received when the car is sold or traded in.

EXAMPLE 1. A person buys a car for $3,000 and five years later trades it in for $750. What is the total depreciation?

Solution: Subtract the trade-in value, $750, from the original cost, $3,000.

$$
\begin{array}{rl}
3000 & \text{original cost} \\
-750 & \text{trade-in value} \\
\hline
2250 & \text{depreciation}
\end{array}
$$

Answer: The total depreciation is $2,250.

Because the "life" of a car varies considerably, it is usual to calculate the amount of depreciation on an annual basis. To find the **average annual depreciation,** *divide the amount of total depreciation by the number of years of service.*

EXAMPLE 2. Find the average annual depreciation of the car in Example 1.

Solution: Divide the total depreciation, $2,250, by the number of years of service, 5.

$$
\begin{array}{r}
450 \\
5\overline{)2250} \\
20 \\
\hline
25 \\
25 \\
\hline
\end{array}
$$

Answer: The average annual depreciation is $450.

EXERCISES

Using the given facts about each of the following cars, find the total depreciation and the average annual depreciation. As a sample solution, this information has been computed for the first car.

	Original Cost of Car	Trade-in Value		Total Depreciation	Average Annual Depreciation
		At End of:	Amount		
1.	$3,430	5 yr.	$1,250	2,180	436
2.	$3,680	2 yr.	$2,400		
3.	$2,975	4 yr.	$1,300		
4.	$3,650	6 yr.	$875		
5.	$3,865	5 yr.	$1,375		
6.	$3,250	3 yr.	$1,575		
7.	$2,870	4 yr.	$1,250		
8.	$3,580	6 yr.	$825		

1.
```
    3,430              436
   -1,250          5)2,180
   ------            20
    2,180            --
                     18
                     15
                     --
                     30
                     30
                     --
```

APPLICATION PROBLEMS

1. Tom purchased a car for $3,750. Six years later, he was allowed $925 toward the purchase of a new car. Find the average annual depreciation.

_____

2. A car was purchased for $3,450 and was traded in 5 years later for $1,325. What is the average annual depreciation?

_____

Unit 92. Automobile Ownership: Annual Operating Cost

Words to know

For a car owner, the **annual operating cost** is the total of all the annual expenses, _including depreciation._

EXAMPLE 1. Mr. Davidson bought a car for $3,400, paying cash. His annual automobile insurance cost $175. During the first year, he paid $345 for gas and oil, $110 for repairs, and $125 for license fees, snow tires, and parking fees. If the average annual depreciation is $510, what is Mr. Davidson's annual operating cost?

Solution: To find the annual operating cost, add all the annual expenses, including the average annual depreciation.

$$
\begin{array}{ll}
510 & \text{(depreciation)} \\
175 & \text{(insurance)} \\
345 & \text{(gas and oil)} \\
110 & \text{(repairs)} \\
\underline{125} & \text{(license, tires, parking)} \\
1265 &
\end{array}
$$

Answer: The annual operating cost is $1,265.

EXAMPLE 2. What is the average _monthly_ operating cost of the car in Example 1?

Solution: To find the average monthly cost, divide the annual cost by 12.

$$
105.4\cancel{1} = 105.42
$$

$$
12\overline{)1,265.00}
$$

$$
\begin{array}{r}
\,1\ 2 \\
\hline
6\ 5 \\
6\ 0 \\
\hline
5\ 0 \\
4\ 8 \\
\hline
2\ 0 \\
1\ 2 \\
\hline
8 \longleftarrow
\end{array}
$$

larger than half of the divisor

Answer: The average monthly operating expense is $105.42.

EXAMPLE 3. Mr. Davidson drove his car for 15,000 miles during the year. Using the annual operating cost found in Exercise 1, find his average cost *per mile*. Calculate to the nearest tenth of a cent.

Solution: To find the cost per mile, divide the annual operating cost, $1,265, by the number of miles driven in a year, 15,000.

Answer: The average cost per mile is 8.4¢.

$$
\begin{array}{r}
.084 \\
15,000\overline{)1,265.000} \\
1\ 200 \\
\hline
65\ 000 \\
60\ 000 \\
\hline
5\ 000
\end{array}
$$

.084 = .084

= 8.4 ¢

less than half of the divisor ← 5 000

EXERCISES

Using the given facts about each of the following cars, find the annual operating cost, the average monthly cost, and the cost per mile, to the nearest tenth of a cent. As a sample solution, this information has been computed for the first car.

	Average Annual Depreciation	Other Annual Expenses	Miles Driven per Year	Annual Cost	Average Monthly Cost	Average Cost per Mile
1.	$650	$460	8,000 mi.	1,110	92.50	13.9¢
2.	$525	$520	10,000 mi.			
3.	$500	$610	15,000 mi.			
4.	$480	$725	17,000 mi.			
5.	$620	$565	12,000 mi.			
6.	$510	$735	17,500 mi.			
7.	$600	$863	20,000 mi.			
8.	$550	$748	18,000 mi.			

1.
$$
\begin{array}{r}
650 \\
+460 \\
\hline
1,110
\end{array}
$$

$$
\begin{array}{r}
92.50 \\
12\overline{)1,110.00} \\
108 \\
\hline
30 \\
24 \\
\hline
60 \\
60
\end{array}
$$

$$
\begin{array}{r}
.138\ ^9 \\
8,000\overline{)1,110.000} \\
8000 \\
\hline
31000 \\
24000 \\
\hline
70000 \\
64000 \\
\hline
6000
\end{array}
$$
= 13.9¢

APPLICATION PROBLEMS

1. John bought a car. His expenses for the year were: gasoline and oil, $465; repairs, $47; insurance, $185; other expenses, $23. The average annual depreciation is $655. Find the total annual operating expense.

2. Tom had the following annual operating expenses on his car: gasoline and oil, $375; repairs, $78; insurance, $210; other expenses, $43; depreciation, $600. Find his average monthly cost.

Review of Part XIX (Units 89 to 92)

1. Mr. Green wants to insure his household contents for $9,000. The annual premium rate is $.47 per $100 of insurance. Find the cost of the policy for 3 years.

2. How much would it cost to buy fire insurance for 3 years on a policy whose face value is $7,500 if the annual rate is $.39 per $100 of insurance?

3. A retailer wants to insure his inventory for 75% of its $63,000 value. Find his annual premium if the rate of insurance is $.85 per $100 of insurance.

4. Harry wants to buy a straight life insurance policy with a face value of $12,500. If the annual rate of the policy is $23.17 per $1,000 of insurance, what will the *quarterly* premium be?

5. How much will the *quarterly* premiums be on a 20-year endowment policy with the face value of $27,500 if the annual rate is $54.23 per $1,000 of insurance?

6. Nick bought a car for $3,875 and sold it four years later for $1,450. Find the average annual depreciation.

7. A car was bought for $3,375 and five years later it was sold for $1,235. Find the average *monthly* depreciation.

8. Tom bought a car for $3,580. His expenses for the year were: gasoline and oil, $635; repairs, $37; insurance, $215; estimated depreciation, 25% of the purchase price; all other expenses, $28. Find Tom's total annual operating cost.

9. Using the figures in the above problem, find the cost per mile, if Tom drove his car 15,000 miles that year. (Round off to the nearest tenth of a cent.)

10. Harry paid $3,675 for his car. His total annual expenses were $965 plus depreciation figured at 18% of the purchase price. Find his average *weekly* cost.

Unit 93. Sales Slips

When you buy something at a store, the clerk often makes out a **sales slip**, which is a record of your purchase. You are given a copy of the sales slip as proof that you paid for your purchase.

In many stores, the sales slip is simply the **cash register receipt**, which carries only the name of the store, the date, and the amount of the purchase. A cash register receipt, or "tape," is what you receive at the check-out counter in most supermarkets.

When the clerk prepares the sales slip, the following information should be included:

Name and address of store
Date
Name and address of the customer

Quantity of items purchased
Description of the items
Unit price of each item
Amount, sometimes called the *extension total*, which is the product of the number of items multiplied by the unit cost
Exchange policy, which tells whether or not the store will exchange merchandise and the terms of the exchange.

Following is a properly completed sales slip. Next to it is a cash register receipt for the same purchases. (Assume that there is no sales tax on the items purchased.)

NORTH SUPPLY CO.
914 River St., Dover, Del.

June 16, 19 —

SOLD TO __I. Gould__
ADDRESS __13 East St.__
__Dover, Del.__

QUAN.	DESCRIPTION	UNIT	AMOUNT
3	Shirts	4.75	14 25
2 pr.	Slacks	11.50	23 —
3 pr.	Socks	.95	2 85
			40 10

POSITIVELY NO EXCHANGES MADE UNLESS
THIS SLIP IS PRESENTED WITHIN 3 DAYS.

NORTH
SUPPLY CO.

JUN 16

4.75

4.75

4.75

11.50

11.50

.95

.95

.95

T   40.10

289

APPLICATION PROBLEMS

In 1 to 6, make out a sales slip for each purchase, using the given information. Use your city and state to complete the buyer's address. Assume that there is no sales tax. (Recall that the symbol @ means "each." Thus, "3 shirts, @ $4.95" means that the shirts cost $4.95 each.)

1. On August 3, Henry J. Perkins of 123 West 94th Street bought: 2 pr. pajamas @ $4.95; 1 bathrobe, $9.65; 1 pr. slippers, $2.95.

2. On February 3, David Henderson of 711 Main Street bought: 1 sports jacket, $37.50; 3 ties, @ $1.25; 3 sports shirts, @ $6.95; 1 tie clip, $2.85.

3. On December 11, Gloria Davis of 409 Jefferson Place bought: 1 lady's coat, $115.75; 3 skirts, @ $8.25; 3 blouses, @ $4.85.

4. On June 12, Terry Saunders of 954 Washington Street bought: 3 pr. jeans, @ $5.95; 2 pr. shoes, @ $12.85; 1 pr. sandals, $2.95; 1 pr. swim trunks, $15.95.

5. On October 12, Albert Goldstone of 79 Columbus Plaza bought: 2 pr. shoes, @ $14.95; 1 pr. sneakers, $5.85; 6 pr. socks, @ $.79.

6. On January 4, Wilma Watts of 10 Greenwich Avenue bought: 4 bed sheets, @ $7.95; 2 bed covers, @ $22.75; 6 pillow cases, at 3 for $4.95.

ALLAN DEPARTMENT STORE
76 LIBERTY PLACE, GOTHAM CITY

_____19_____

SOLD TO_____

ADDRESS_____

_____

QUAN.	DESCRIPTION	UNIT	AMOUNT

POSITIVELY NO EXCHANGES MADE UNLESS
THIS SLIP IS PRESENTED WITHIN 10 DAYS.

ALLAN DEPARTMENT STORE
76 LIBERTY PLACE, GOTHAM CITY

_____19_____

SOLD TO_____

ADDRESS_____

_____

QUAN.	DESCRIPTION	UNIT	AMOUNT

POSITIVELY NO EXCHANGES MADE UNLESS
THIS SLIP IS PRESENTED WITHIN 10 DAYS.

ALLAN DEPARTMENT STORE
76 LIBERTY PLACE, GOTHAM CITY

_____19_____

SOLD TO_____

ADDRESS_____

_____

QUAN.	DESCRIPTION	UNIT	AMOUNT

POSITIVELY NO EXCHANGES MADE UNLESS
THIS SLIP IS PRESENTED WITHIN 10 DAYS.

ALLAN DEPARTMENT STORE
76 LIBERTY PLACE, GOTHAM CITY

_____19_____

SOLD TO_____

ADDRESS_____

_____

QUAN.	DESCRIPTION	UNIT	AMOUNT

POSITIVELY NO EXCHANGES MADE UNLESS
THIS SLIP IS PRESENTED WITHIN 10 DAYS.

ALLAN DEPARTMENT STORE
76 LIBERTY PLACE, GOTHAM CITY

_____19_____

SOLD TO_____

ADDRESS_____

_____

QUAN.	DESCRIPTION	UNIT	AMOUNT

POSITIVELY NO EXCHANGES MADE UNLESS
THIS SLIP IS PRESENTED WITHIN 10 DAYS.

ALLAN DEPARTMENT STORE
76 LIBERTY PLACE, GOTHAM CITY

_____19_____

SOLD TO_____

ADDRESS_____

_____

QUAN.	DESCRIPTION	UNIT	AMOUNT

POSITIVELY NO EXCHANGES MADE UNLESS
THIS SLIP IS PRESENTED WITHIN 10 DAYS.

Unit 94. Sales Slips With Taxes

There are two types of taxes that may be added to the amount of a retail purchase. The most common one is the **sales tax**, which may be a combination of state and city taxes. The amount of the sales tax varies from city to city. It usually is collected on all retail sales except for special items such as prescription drugs and foods.

The second tax is the **Federal excise tax**, which applies only to certain selected items such as gasoline, alcoholic beverages, cigarettes, telephone bills, and air travel tickets. The items subject to the Federal excise tax vary from year to year. Because this tax is usually included in the unit price of a taxed item, it is seldom necessary for the retail buyer or seller to figure it out. For example, the price of a gallon of gasoline includes both the sales tax and the Federal excise tax.

The retailer collects the sales tax from the purchaser and sends this tax periodically to the proper agencies.

Following are sample sales slips with the sales tax added to the cost of the purchases.

If you have difficulty finding a percent of a given amount, review Unit 62.

	CHELSEA MEN'S SHOP				
	NEW YORK, N.Y.				
	Jun. 19, 19—				
SOLD TO	J. Cooper				
ADDRESS	119 State St.				
QUAN.	DESCRIPTION		UNIT	AMOUNT	
1	Overcoat			79	75
1	Jacket			22	95
				102	70
	Sales tax 7%			7	19
	Total			109	89

POSITIVELY NO EXCHANGES MADE UNLESS
THIS SLIP IS PRESENTED WITHIN 3 DAYS.

	CENTRAL HARDWARE CO.			
	LOS ANGELES, CAL.			
	Feb. 14 19—			
SOLD TO	R. J. Diaz			
ADDRESS	203 San Martino Blvd.			
QUAN.	DESCRIPTION	UNIT	AMOUNT	
2	Phillips Screwdriver	1.25	2	50
12	Fine Sandpaper	.15	1	80
1	# 302 Wrench		6	95
1	Flashlight		1	95
			13	20
	5% Sales Tax			66
			13	86

ALL SALES ARE FINAL.

APPLICATION PROBLEMS

In 1 to 6, make out a sales slip for each purchase, using the given information. Use your city and state to complete the buyer's address.

1. On March 4, Mrs. D. Riccardi of 100 Fifth Avenue bought: 1 silver teapot, $57.85; 1 silver tray, $38.95; 6 silver spoons, @ $3.75. Sales tax is 5%.

2. On August 30, Mary O'Brian of 211 Old River Road bought: 1 lady's coat, $215.75; 3 pr. shoes, @ $14.95. Sales tax is 7%.

3. On November 11, J. B. Torres of 68 Juarez Place bought: 1 lady's watch, $95.95; 2 pr. earrings, @ $4.85; 1 watch band, $7.95. Sales tax is $5\frac{1}{2}$%.

4. On September 15, Daniel McClosky of 403 Market Street bought: 1 man's overcoat, $185.50; 4 pr. slacks, @ $18.75; 1 suit, $95.50. The sales tax is 7%.

ALLAN DEPARTMENT STORE
76 LIBERTY PLACE, GOTHAM CITY

_____19____

SOLD TO_____

ADDRESS_____

_____

QUAN.	DESCRIPTION	UNIT	AMOUNT

POSITIVELY NO EXCHANGES MADE UNLESS
THIS SLIP IS PRESENTED WITHIN 10 DAYS.

ALLAN DEPARTMENT STORE
76 LIBERTY PLACE, GOTHAM CITY

_____19____

SOLD TO_____

ADDRESS_____

_____

QUAN.	DESCRIPTION	UNIT	AMOUNT

POSITIVELY NO EXCHANGES MADE UNLESS
THIS SLIP IS PRESENTED WITHIN 10 DAYS.

ALLAN DEPARTMENT STORE
76 LIBERTY PLACE, GOTHAM CITY

_____19____

SOLD TO_____

ADDRESS_____

_____

QUAN.	DESCRIPTION	UNIT	AMOUNT

POSITIVELY NO EXCHANGES MADE UNLESS
THIS SLIP IS PRESENTED WITHIN 10 DAYS.

ALLAN DEPARTMENT STORE
76 LIBERTY PLACE, GOTHAM CITY

_____19____

SOLD TO_____

ADDRESS_____

_____

QUAN.	DESCRIPTION	UNIT	AMOUNT

POSITIVELY NO EXCHANGES MADE UNLESS
THIS SLIP IS PRESENTED WITHIN 10 DAYS.

5. On May 1, Aaron Weiss of 182 Delaware Avenue bought: 1 toaster, $21.85; 1 broiler, $67.90; 1 blender, $45.85. Sales tax is 3%.

6. On June 26, Lillian Vance of 3 Adams Place bought: 1 gold bracelet, $258.00; 2 rings, @ $19.95. Sales tax is $5\frac{3}{4}$%.

ALLAN DEPARTMENT STORE			
76 LIBERTY PLACE, GOTHAM CITY			
_____19____			
SOLD TO_____			
ADDRESS_____			
_____			
QUAN.	DESCRIPTION	UNIT	AMOUNT
POSITIVELY NO EXCHANGES MADE UNLESS THIS SLIP IS PRESENTED WITHIN 10 DAYS.			

ALLAN DEPARTMENT STORE			
76 LIBERTY PLACE, GOTHAM CITY			
_____19____			
SOLD TO_____			
ADDRESS_____			
_____			
QUAN.	DESCRIPTION	UNIT	AMOUNT
POSITIVELY NO EXCHANGES MADE UNLESS THIS SLIP IS PRESENTED WITHIN 10 DAYS.			

Unit 95. Buying Fractional Quantities

There are times when you buy fractional parts of weights or measures that are priced per whole unit.

For example, what is the cost of $\frac{3}{4}$ of a yard of velvet at $3.75 a yard? What should you pay for $\frac{1}{4}$ of a pound of bacon priced at 84¢ a pound?

To find the cost of a fractional part, *multiply the*

fraction by the price per whole unit.

EXAMPLE 1. If you buy $\frac{3}{4}$ of a yard of gabardine at a price of \$4.25 per yard, what is the price you pay?

Solution: Multiply the fraction, $\frac{3}{4}$, by the cost per yard, \$4.25.

Multiply the fraction, $\frac{3}{32}$, by the cost per pound, \$4.80.

$$\frac{3}{\cancel{32}_{2}} \times \frac{\overset{.30}{\cancel{4.80}}}{1} = \frac{.90}{2} = .45$$

Answer: $1\frac{1}{2}$ oz. cost 45¢.

Common Fraction:

$$\frac{3}{4} \times \frac{4.25}{1} = \frac{12.75}{4}$$

$$= 3.19$$

Decimal Fraction:

$$\begin{array}{r} 4.25 \\ \times\ .75 \\ \hline 2125 \\ 2\ 975 \\ \hline 3.1875 = 3.19 \end{array}$$

Answer: The cost of $\frac{3}{4}$ of a yard is \$3.19.

EXAMPLE 2. A certain imported cheese costs \$4.80 per pound. How much should you pay for $1\frac{1}{2}$ ounces?

Solution: $1\frac{1}{2}$ ounces is $\frac{1\frac{1}{2}}{16}$ of a pound. Simplify the complex fraction.

$$\frac{1\frac{1}{2}}{16} = 1\frac{1}{2} \div 16 = \frac{3}{2} \div \frac{16}{1}$$

$$= \frac{3}{2} \times \frac{1}{16} = \frac{3}{32}$$

Alternate solution: Find the cost per ounce by dividing the price per pound, \$4.80, by the number of ounces in a pound, 16.

$$\begin{array}{r} .30 \\ 16\overline{)4.80} \\ \underline{4\ 80} \end{array}$$

Multiply the price per ounce, 30¢, by the number of ounces purchased, $1\frac{1}{2}$.

Common fraction:

$$1\frac{1}{2} \times \frac{.30}{1} = \frac{3}{\cancel{2}_{1}} \times \frac{\overset{.15}{\cancel{.30}}}{1} = .45$$

Decimal fraction:

$$\begin{array}{r} .30 \\ \times\ 1.5 \\ \hline 150 \\ 30 \\ \hline .450 = 45¢ \end{array}$$

Answer: $1\frac{1}{2}$ oz. cost 45¢.

EXERCISES

Turn to the chart on page 296. From the given information, find the cost of the fractional part of each item. (Round off all answers to the nearest penny.)

	Item	Price per Unit	Fractional Part	Cost of Fractional Part
1.	steak	$2.15 per lb.	$\frac{3}{4}$ lb.	
2.	coffee	$1.09 per lb.	$\frac{1}{4}$ lb.	
3.	sateen	$5.75 per yd.	$\frac{2}{3}$ yd.	
4.	grapes	$.89 per lb.	$\frac{3}{4}$ lb.	
5.	paint	$7.45 per gal.	$\frac{4}{5}$ gal.	
6.	eggs	$.83 per doz.	$\frac{3}{4}$ doz.	
7.	gasoline	$.46 per gal.	$\frac{2}{3}$ gal.	
8.	ham	$2.28 per lb.	$\frac{5}{8}$ lb.	

APPLICATION PROBLEMS

1. Mrs. Wilson bought 28 in. of velvet at $4.65 a yard. What fraction of a yard did she buy?

How much did she pay?

2. Jerry bought 12 oz. of ham at $2.28 a pound. What fraction of a pound did he buy?

How much did he pay?

3. Mrs. Bianca bought the following items:

   14 oz. of pork at 95¢ per pound
   12 oz. of veal cutlets at $1.15 per pound
   10 oz. of bacon at 79¢ per pound
   8 oranges at 63¢ per dozen

How much did she spend?

Unit 96. Finding the Unit Price

A Federal law requires most food stores to display the **unit price** of all food products. The unit price is the price of a standard unit of food, such as the price per gallon, the price per pound, or the price per dozen.

For example, if a certain sauce is priced at "35¢ for a 4-oz. can," the unit price of "$1.40 per pound" must also be displayed.

Small grocery stores, however, are not required to post the unit prices. In order to get the best value for your money, you should be able to figure out unit prices in order to compare the cost of comparable items.

In Unit 38, you learned how to find a number when a fractional part of it was known. In Unit 64, you learned how to find a number when a percent of it was known. You will use the same method to figure out unit pricing.

Rule: To find the unit price of a given fractional part, divide the cost of the fractional part by the fraction.

EXAMPLE 1. Which is the better value, Brand A bacon at 65¢ for $\frac{3}{4}$ of a pound or Brand B bacon at 80¢ a pound?

Solution: Find the cost per pound of Brand A bacon by dividing the cost of the fractional part, 65¢, by the fraction, $\frac{3}{4}$.

$$.65 \div \frac{3}{4} = \frac{.65}{1} \times \frac{4}{3}$$

$$= \frac{2.60}{3} = .86\frac{2}{3} = .87$$

Answer: Brand B at 80¢ a pound is a better value than Brand A at 87¢ a pound.

Note: The $\frac{IS}{OF}$ fraction can be used to solve unit-price problems. The facts about Brand A can be reworded as follows: "65¢ is $\frac{3}{4}$ of what price?"

$$\frac{IS}{OF} = \frac{.65}{\frac{3}{4}} = .65 \div \frac{3}{4}$$

Solve as above.

EXAMPLE 2. What is the price per pound of a 5-ounce jar of instant coffee selling at 59¢?

Solution: 5 ounces is $\frac{5}{16}$ of a pound. Therefore,

"59¢ is $\frac{5}{16}$ of what price?"

Answer: $1.88 per pound

$$\frac{IS}{OF} = \frac{.59}{\frac{5}{16}} = .59 \div \frac{5}{16}$$

$$= \frac{.59}{1} \times \frac{16}{5} = \frac{9.44}{5} = 1.88$$

EXERCISES

From the given information, find the unit price of each of the following items:

	Item	Fractional Weight or Measure	Cost of Fractional Unit	Price per Unit
1.	potato chips	12-oz. bag	53¢	____ per lb.
2.	butter	4-oz. stick	27¢	____ per lb.
3.	velvet	24 in.	$3.50	____ per yd.
4.	coffee	$\frac{3}{4}$ lb.	84¢	____ per lb.
5.	wine	$\frac{1}{5}$ gal.	$2.35	____ per gal.
6.	tomato juice	8-oz. can	63¢	____ per qt.
7.	cookies	10-oz. box	57¢	____ per lb.
8.	sardines	4-oz. can	49¢	____ per lb.

APPLICATION PROBLEMS

1. Mrs. Meyers bought 3 cucumbers for 31¢.
   a. What fraction of a dozen did she buy?

   b. What is the price per dozen?

_____

2. Mr. Dawes bought 5 ears of corn for 48¢.
   a. What fraction of a dozen did he buy?

   b. What is the price per dozen?

_____

3. Harry bought 5 oranges for 37¢.
   a. What fraction of a dozen did he buy?

   b. What is the price per dozen?

_____

4. Find the price *per dozen* for each of the following items:
   a. Socks at 3 for $2.15

   b. Underwear at 5 for $4.25

   c. Grapefruits at 3 for 47¢

   d. Handkerchiefs at 7 for $5.65

_____

Unit 97. Buying During Sales (Discounts)

The consumer can often save money by buying merchandise during special sales when stores sell goods at advertised **discounts** from regular prices. The expression " 10% discount " means that the original price has been reduced by 10%; at a " 50% discount sale " or a " half-off sale," the original price has been reduced by 50%; etc.

EXAMPLE 1. What is the sales price of a coat at a " 35% discount sale," if the coat regularly sells for $95.75?

Solution:

Step 1: Find the amount of discount by multiplying the original price, $95.75, by the discount percent, 35%.

$$
\begin{array}{r}
95.75 \\
\times\ .35 \\
\hline
4\ 78\ 75 \\
28\ 72\ 5 \\
\hline
33.51(25) = 33.51
\end{array}
$$

Step 2: Find the sales price by subtracting the amount of discount, $33.51, from the original price, $95.75.

$$
\begin{array}{r}
95.75 \\
-33.51 \\
\hline
62.24
\end{array}
$$

Answer: The sales price is $62.24.

EXAMPLE 2. At a "40% off sale," Dave buys a radio originally priced at $39.95. How much does he pay, if the sales tax is 7%?

Solution:

Step 1: Find the amount of discount by multiplying the original price, $39.95, by the discount percent, 40%.

$$
\begin{array}{r}
39.95 \\
\times .4 \\
\hline
15.980
\end{array}
$$

Step 2: Find the sales price by subtracting the

amount of discount, $15.98, from the original price, $39.95.

$$
\begin{array}{r}
39.95 \\
-15.98 \\
\hline
23.97
\end{array}
$$

Step 3: Find the sales tax by multiplying the percent of the tax, 7%, by the sales price, $23.97.

$$
\begin{array}{r}
23.97 \\
\times .07 \\
\hline
1.67(79) = 1.68
\end{array}
$$

Step 4: Find the cost by adding the sales tax, $1.68, to the sales price, $23.97.

$$
\begin{array}{r}
23.97 \\
+1.68 \\
\hline
25.65
\end{array}
$$

Answer: Dave pays $25.65 for the radio.

EXERCISES

From the given information, find the amount of discount and the new price of each of the following items. As a sample solution, this information has been computed for the first item.

	Original Price	Discount Percent	Amount of Discount	New Price
1.	$87.95	35%	30.78	57.17
2.	$235.80	$33\frac{1}{3}$%		
3.	$347.90	25%		
4.	$185.75	30%		
5.	$247.95	40%		
6.	$375.75	28%		
7.	$268.90	$33\frac{1}{3}$%		
8.	$368.45	33%		

1.

$$
\begin{array}{r}
87.95 \\
\times .35 \\
\hline
43975 \\
26385 \\
\hline
30.78(25) = 30.78
\end{array}
$$

$$
\begin{array}{r}
87.95 \\
-30.78 \\
\hline
57.17
\end{array}
$$

APPLICATION PROBLEMS

1. A freezer originally selling for $485.90 is on sale at a 35% discount. Find the amount of discount.

   _____

   Find the new price.

   _____

2. A color television set selling at a regular price of $525.75 is on sale at "30% off."
   Find the amount of discount.

   _____

   Find the new price.

   _____

Review of Part XX (Units 93 to 97)

1. What is the total cost of a stereo receiver that sells for $875.95 if the sales tax is 7%?

   _____

2. Find the total cost of four automobile tires selling for $26.75 each. Include a $5\frac{1}{2}$% sales tax.

   _____

3. During World War II, Mrs. Whyte bought a diamond ring for $565.00. What was the total amount she paid if the sales tax was 2%, and there was a 10% "luxury tax" on the cost of the ring?

   _____

4. Find how much each of the following items costs.

  a. 10 oz. of ham at $2.10 per lb. Cost of 10 oz.:   _____

  b. 8 oz. of cheese at $1.95 per lb. Cost of 8 oz.:   _____

  c. $\frac{3}{4}$ yd. of material at $5.75 per yd. Cost of $\frac{3}{4}$ yd.:   _____

  d. 5 pairs of socks at $17 per doz. Cost of 5 pr.:   _____

  e. $\frac{3}{4}$ lb. of steak at $2.10 per lb. Cost of $\frac{3}{4}$ lb.:   _____

5. Find the unit cost for each of the following if:

  a. $\frac{3}{4}$ lb. of chuck sells for $1.10. Price per lb.:   _____

  b. 12 oz. of cheese sells for 80¢. Price per lb.:   _____

  c. 5 shirts sell for $18. Price per doz.:   _____

  d. 3 pencils sell for 20¢. Price per doz.:   _____

  e. 5 pr. of stockings sell for $9. Price per doz.:   _____

6. Mrs. Wilson bought a refrigerator. The list price of $389.75 was reduced by a 30% discount. How much did Mrs. Wilson pay, if the sales tax was 7%?

             _____

Part XXI. Handling Money

Unit 98. Borrowing Money

Words to know

When you borrow money, you must pay back the amount you borrowed (the **principal**) and you must also pay a fee (the **interest**) for the use of the money. Interest is based on a percent of the amount. This percent is known as the **rate of interest**, or simply the **rate**.

When you borrow money from a credit union, a bank, or a loan company, you sign an agreement that states the amount of the loan, the rate of interest, and the time of the loan. As it is usual to repay loans in monthly installments, the agreement states the amount of each payment and when it is due every month.

To calculate interest, multiply three items: the **principal**, which is the amount of the loan; the **rate** of annual interest; the **time** of the loan, in years. This rule is usually stated as the **simple-interest formula**:

$$I = P \times R \times T$$

In this formula, I = interest, P = principal, R = rate, and T = time. Unless you are told otherwise, "interest" means "simple interest."

EXAMPLE 1. Calculate the simple interest on a loan of $1,000 at 6% for 1 year.

Solution: From the given information, $P = 1,000$; $R = 6\% = .06$; $T = 1$.

$$I = P \times R \times T$$
$$I = 1,000 \times .06 \times 1$$
$$I = 60 \times 1 = 60$$

$$\begin{array}{r} 1,000 \\ \times .06 \\ \hline 60.00 \end{array}$$

Answer: Interest is $60.00.

EXAMPLE 2. What is the interest on a loan of $475 at 6% for 2 years?

Solution: $P = 475$; $R = .06$; $T = 2$

$$I = P \times R \times T$$
$$I = 475 \times .06 \times 2$$
$$I = 28.50 \times 2 = 57.00$$

$$\begin{array}{r} 475 \\ \times .06 \\ \hline 28.50 \\ \times 2 \\ \hline 57.00 \end{array}$$

Answer: Interest is $57.00.

Many lending institutions **discount** the interest charges ahead of time. That is, the interest is subtracted from the principal and the borrower receives the **net amount**. In Example 2, if the loan were discounted, the borrower would receive the principal, $475.00, less the interest, $57.00.

$$\begin{array}{r} 475.00 \\ -57.00 \\ \hline 418.00 \end{array}$$

The borrower would actually receive only $418, not the full principal of $475. However, he must repay the full principal of $475.

EXAMPLE 3. To pay his income tax, Mr. Wilson borrows $1,500 at 8% for 1 year. If the loan is discounted, what is the net amount?

Solution: $P = 1,500$; $R = .08$; $T = 1$

$$I = P \times R \times T$$
$$I = 1,500 \times .08 \times 1$$
$$I = 120 \times 1 = 120$$

$$\begin{array}{r} 1500 \\ \times\ .08 \\ \hline 120.00 \end{array}$$

Find the net amount by subtracting the interest, $120, from the principal, $1,500.

$$\begin{array}{r} 1,500 \\ -120 \\ \hline 1,380 \end{array}$$

Answer: Net amount is $1,380.

"TRUTH IN LENDING" LAW

Because the rates, discount practices, and finance charges of different lending institutions vary greatly, it is often difficult for the borrower to figure out the percent of interest he actually pays. Therefore, a Federal law requires that all lending institutions tell what the simple interest is on an annual basis. This rate (simple interest for 1 year) is known as **true simple interest.**

Suppose you borrow $100 at 8% for 1 year. You receive a check from the bank for $100, and you agree to pay back $108 in 12 monthly payments of $9 each.

Here is how the bank explains it to you: The principal is $100 (this loan is not discounted), and the interest is $8 because $I = P \times R \times T = 100 \times .08 \times 1 = 8$. The amount that you must repay is the principal, $100, plus the interest, $8, a total of $108.

Dividing the $108 into 12 equal payments, you see that the monthly payments are $9 each.

$$\begin{array}{r} 9 \\ 12\overline{)108} \\ \underline{108} \end{array}$$

So far, so good. But when the bank tells you the rate of the true simple interest, you may be surprised

to learn that it is 13.7%, not 8%.

If the bank were lending you $100 at 8% for one year at true simple interest, they would let you keep the entire $100 for a whole year. At the end of the year, you would repay the full $108.

But the bank requires you to pay back $9 after the first month. Thus, you have borrowed $100 for only one month. After the month is over, you have only $91. Further, the month after that, you must pay back another $9, leaving you only $82. And so on.

The fact that you must pay back the loan in monthly installments makes the true simple interest rate higher than if you could keep the principal for the entire year.

CALCULATING TRUE SIMPLE INTEREST (OPTIONAL)

Consumer magazines give the following formula for figuring out the rate of true simple annual interest when you make purchases or borrow money on the installment plan.

$$R = \frac{2mI}{B(n+1)}$$

To understand how to use this formula, let us calculate the rate of true simple interest on $100 at 8% for 1 year, if the loan is to be repaid in 12 monthly installments of $9 each.

R = the rate of true simple interest. This is what we will find.

m = the number of payments per year. In our example, $m = 12$.

I = the amount of interest. In our example, $I = \$100 \times .08 \times 1 = \$8$.

B = the balance due. Here, the balance due is the principal, $100, plus the interest, $8, a total of $108.

n = the total number of payments. Here, $n = 12$.

In the formula, replace m with 12, I with 8, B with 108, and n with 12:

$$R = \frac{2 \times 12 \times 8}{108 \times 13} = \frac{192}{1,404}$$
$$= .137 = 13.7\%$$

EXERCISES

From the given information, find the amount of interest and the net amount for each of the following loans. As a sample solution, this information has been computed for the first loan.

	Amount Borrowed	Interest Rate	Length of Time	Amount of Interest	Net Amount
1.	$875	6%	3 yr.	157.50	717.50
2.	$1,500	8%	4 yr.		
3.	$3,500	6%	2 yr.		
4.	$5,500	$6\frac{1}{2}\%$	5 yr.		
5.	$2,800	7%	1 yr.		
6.	$4,500	6%	3 yr.		
7.	$1,750	7%	4 yr.		
8.	$3,900	8%	2 yr.		

1.
$$I = P \times R \times T$$
$$= 875$$
$$\times .06$$
$$\overline{52.50}$$
$$\times 3$$
$$\overline{157.50}$$

875.00
−157.50
717.50

APPLICATION PROBLEMS

1. Mel borrowed $2,500 from his bank to pay for a car. If the interest rate is 6%, how much will the interest be over 3 years?

2. Mr. Mantee needs to borrow $1,500 to pay a hospital bill. What will be the net amount of the loan if the interest rate is $6\frac{1}{2}\%$ and the loan will be paid back over 2 years?

3. If you borrow $1,000 at 10% for two years, how much will each of your monthly payments be? (*Hint:* Figure the interest and add it to the principal to find the total amount you must repay. Then divide the total amount by the number of months in two years.)

4. The Star Sales Company borrowed $5,000 for one year at a certain rate of interest. The loan was discounted. How much will the Star Sales Company have to repay? (*Hint:* You don't need to know the rate of interest; you should be able to answer without doing any calculating.)

5. Which loan will have the greater monthly payments?
   Loan No. 1: $2,000 at 8% for 2 years, discounted
   Loan No. 2: $2,000 at 5% for 2 years, not discounted

Unit 99. Interest for Periods of Time in Days or Months

For short-term loans, the time may be for days or months. To simplify the calculation of interest, it is common practice to use a 360-day year. The 360-day year, known as the **commercial year**, consists of *12 months of 30 days each.*

EXAMPLE 1. Find the interest on $1,000 at 6% for 90 days.

Solution: $P = 1,000$; $R = .06$; $T = \frac{90}{360} = \frac{1}{4}$. Recall that time must be expressed in terms of years.

$$I = P \times R \times T$$

$$I = 1,000 \times .06 \times \frac{1}{4}$$

$$I = 60 \times \frac{1}{4} = 15$$

Answer: Interest is $15.00.

EXAMPLE 2. Find the interest on $1,000 at 10% for 1 month.

Solution: $P = 1,000$; $R = .10$; $T = \frac{1}{12}$

$$I = P \times R \times T$$

$$I = 1,000 \times .10 \times \frac{1}{12}$$

$$I = 100 \times \frac{1}{12} = \frac{100}{12} = 8.33$$

Answer: Interest is $8.33.

EXERCISES

From the given information, find the amount of interest for the indicated periods of time for each loan.

	Amount of Loan	Interest Rate	Period of Loan	Amount of Interest
1.	$1,200	6%	60 da.	
2.	$2,575	7%	5 mo.	
3.	$3,875	$6\frac{1}{2}\%$	30 da.	
4.	$4,650	6%	90 da.	
5.	$2,850	$5\frac{1}{2}\%$	120 da.	
6.	$4,550	8%	8 mo.	
7.	$5,750	7%	20 da.	
8.	$6,500	6%	45 da.	

APPLICATION PROBLEMS

1. Mr. Andrews borrowed $2,500 from a bank at 6% interest, for 45 days. What are the interest charges he must pay back to the bank at the end of the 45 days?

_____

2. Mr. Swenson borrowed $3,500 from a finance company at 7% interest for 2 months. What is the **total amount** he must pay back to the finance company after 2 months?

_____

3. If the loan in Problem 2 were discounted, what would be the net amount?

_____

4. A finance company offers Mr. Davis the choice of two loans:
   Loan No. 1: $1,000 at 8% for 6 months, discounted
   Loan No. 2: $950 at 10% for 6 months, not discounted
Which loan should he choose in order to receive the greater amount of cash?

_____

5. In Problem 4, which loan will require Mr. Davis to pay the greater amount at the end of six months? (Mr. Davis does not make monthly payments; he repays the full amount he owes at the end of the loan period of six months.)

_____

Unit 100. Installment Buying

The **list price**, or _selling price_, of an expensive item such as a refrigerator or an automobile is usually greater than most people can pay all at once. Hence, such expensive items are often sold on the **installment plan**.

In an installment-plan purchase, the buyer agrees to pay a small part of the list price as a **down payment**. Subtracting this down payment from the list price gives the **balance due** on the purchase. The balance due is then divided into equal installments that are paid monthly over a specified period of time.

In allowing the buyer to pay off his purchase over a period of time, the retailer is actually lending the buyer money. Just as a bank charges interest for the use of money, the retailer adds **carrying charges** to the monthly installments.

The carrying charges for installment buying are usually higher than the interest for a comparable bank loan. The higher rates are charged because, in addition to the interest, the retailer adds the clerical costs of maintaining the installment plan. Many buyers, however, are willing to pay the higher rates for the convenience of "buying now and paying later."

EXAMPLE 1. A television set whose list price is $122.50 may be purchased on the installment plan for $25 down and 12 monthly payments of $10.50 each. Find the carrying charges.

Solution: Multiply the amount of each payment by the number of payments to find the balance due.

$$
\begin{array}{r}
10.50 \\
\times 12 \\
\hline
21\ 00 \\
105\ 0 \\
\hline
126.00
\end{array}
$$

Add to the balance due, $126.00, the down payment of $25.00.

$$
\begin{array}{r}
126.00 \\
+25.00 \\
\hline
151.00
\end{array}
$$

The total cost of the television set on the installment plan is $151.00.

To find the carrying charges, subtract the list price, $122.50, from the installment-plan price, $151.00.

$$\begin{array}{r} 151.00 \\ -122.50 \\ \hline 28.50 \end{array}$$

Answer: Carrying charges are $28.50.

Note: Using the formula on page 304, the true simple interest charged for this purchase is 41.7%. We get this percent by applying the facts of Example 1 to the true simple interest formula: $m = 12$; $I = 28.50$; $B = 126.00$; $n = 12$.

$$R = \frac{2mI}{B(n+1)}$$

$$R = \frac{2 \times 12 \times 28.50}{126(13)}$$

$$R = \frac{684}{1,638} = .417 = 41.7\%$$

In some instances, the retailer may permit the amount of the down payment to vary from one customer to another. The retailer then figures out the monthly installments on the basis of the balance due. In a case like this, the price of the item includes all carrying charges. This price is sometimes called the *installment price*.

EXAMPLE 2. You buy a ring for $317, making a down payment of $65. The balance due is to be paid in 12 monthly payments. How much do you pay each month?

Solution: To find the balance due, subtract the down payment, $65, from the price, $317.

$$\begin{array}{r} 317 \\ -65 \\ \hline 252 \end{array}$$

Divide the balance due, $252, by the number of payments, 12.

$$\begin{array}{r} 21 \\ 12\overline{)252} \\ \underline{24} \\ 12 \\ \underline{12} \end{array}$$

Answer: You pay $21 each month.

Note: Since you have no way of knowing what the carrying charges are, you cannot calculate the true simple interest. You would have to rely on the *Truth in Lending* law to give you this information.

EXERCISES

From the given information, find the amount of each monthly payment for the following items. As a sample solution, this information has been computed for the first item.

	Item	Installment Price	Down Payment	Number of Monthly Payments	Amount of Each Monthly Payment
1.	television	$473.80	$85	18	21.60
2.	washer	$362	$50	24	
3.	dryer	$297	$45	12	
4.	furniture	$867	$75	36	
5.	refrigerator	$389	$65	18	
6.	stereo	$991	$115	24	
7.	jewelry	$617	$95	36	
8.	camera	$324.80	$50	12	

1.
$$\begin{array}{r} 473.80 \\ -85.00 \\ \hline 388.80 \end{array}$$

$$\begin{array}{r} 21.60 \\ 18\overline{)388.80} \\ \underline{36} \\ 28 \\ \underline{18} \\ 108 \\ \underline{108} \end{array}$$

APPLICATION PROBLEMS

1. Jeff bought a car for $3,875, to be paid for over 36 months. If his down payment is $500, how much will each monthly payment be?

2. Mrs. Bustamante bought a dining room set for $875. She made a down payment of $85, and the balance will be paid for over 2 years. How much will each monthly payment be?

3. In buying a television set, which of the following installment purchase plans will cost you less?
Plan 1: No down payment and $9 a month for three years.
Plan 2: $60 down payment and $10 a month for two years.

4. Stu is planning to buy a motorcycle whose list price is $650. The store will sell him the motorcycle for nothing down and monthly payments of $35 for two years. Stu's bank will lend him the $650 at 8% interest, to be repaid over two years. How much will Stu save by borrowing the money from the bank and then buying the motorcycle at its list price, compared to using the installment plan?

5. In Problem 4, suppose that Stu has already saved the $650. How much will he save, compared to the bank loan? _____

How much will he save, compared to the installment plan? _____

Unit 101. Savings Accounts

When you open a savings account, you deposit money in the bank and receive interest on that money. In effect, you are lending money to the bank.

Why is a savings bank willing to pay interest to its depositors? The bank is able to invest the depositors' money in business enterprises that pay a higher percent of profit than the interest paid for the use of the money.

Of course, there is always the possibility that the bank might go out of business because of poor investments. To protect depositors against this risk, the Federal Deposit Insurance Corporation insures and guarantees deposits of up to $20,000. Should the bank fail, the depositor would receive his money and interest in full.

COMPOUND INTEREST

The interest is added to the depositor's account at regular intervals, usually four times a year, which is every three months. The interest is said to be **compounded quarterly**. The usual interest rate paid by a savings bank varies from 4% to 6%, compounded quarterly. This **compound interest** is greater than **simple interest** because the bank pays interest on the interest that was added to the deposit in the previous quarter.

Suppose you deposit $400 in a savings bank and the bank pays 4% interest, compounded quarterly. You have already studied how to calculate interest for short periods of time. Since a quarter is 3 months, the interest for the first quarter is:

$$\$400 \times .04 \times \frac{3}{12} = \$16 \times \frac{1}{4} = \$4$$

Thus, the interest for the first quarter is $4.00.

However, for the second quarter, the bank calculates 4% interest for 3 months on $404.00, which is the original deposit of $400 plus the first-quarter interest of $4.00. By the end of this second quarter, the amount of money in your savings account will

be $408.04.

This process of adding the interest to the principal at the end of each quarter, which is quite tedious to figure by hand, is usually done with the aid of tables or with electronic computers. By the end of one full year, your $400.00 would have grown to $416.24. And by the end of ten years, assuming that you did not withdraw or deposit any money, your original $400.00 would be $595.49.

COMPOUND INTEREST TABLES

Following are examples of how compound interest may be calculated using Table XVII: Compound Amounts, page 312. In compound interest tables, the **amount** is always the sum of the interest added to the original principal.

EXAMPLE 1. Find the compound interest on $1,000 at 4%, compounded quarterly, for 5 years. Use Table XVII.

Solution: Divide the annual rate, 4%, by the number of times the interest is to be compounded in one year, 4.

$$4\% \div 4 = 1\%$$

This rate, 1%, is the rate paid per interval, the interval in this example being a 3-month period. Since there are 4 intervals per year, the total number of intervals in 5 years is $4 \times 5 = 20$ intervals.

In Table XVII, go down the *Intervals* column until you come to "20." Then read across to the column headed "1%." This amount, 1.220190, is the total amount you would have in a bank if you deposited $1 at 4%, compounded quarterly, for 5 years.

To find what amount $1,000 will bring, multiply 1.220190 by 1,000.

$$1.220,190$$

$$1220.19 = \$1,220.19$$

Table XVII: *Compound Amounts (Principal is $1.00)*

Inter-vals	1%	1½%	2%	2½%	3%
1	1.010000	1.015000	1.020000	1.025000	1.030000
2	1.020100	1.030225	1.040400	1.050625	1.060900
3	1.030301	1.045678	1.061208	1.076891	1.092727
4	1.040604	1.061364	1.082432	1.103813	1.125509
5	1.051010	1.077284	1.104081	1.131408	1.159274
6	1.061520	1.093443	1.126162	1.159693	1.194052
7	1.072135	1.109845	1.148686	1.188686	1.229874
8	1.082857	1.126493	1.171659	1.218403	1.266770
9	1.093685	1.143390	1.195093	1.248863	1.304773
10	1.104622	1.160541	1.218994	1.280085	1.343916
11	1.115668	1.177949	1.243374	1.312087	1.384234
12	1.126825	1.195618	1.268242	1.344889	1.425761
13	1.138093	1.213552	1.293607	1.378511	1.468534
14	1.149474	1.231756	1.319479	1.412974	1.512590
15	1.160969	1.250232	1.345868	1.448298	1.557967
16	1.172579	1.268986	1.372786	1.484506	1.604706
17	1.184304	1.288020	1.400241	1.521618	1.652848
18	1.196148	1.307341	1.428246	1.559659	1.702433
19	1.208109	1.326951	1.456811	1.597650	1.753506
20	1.220190	1.346855	1.485947	1.638616	1.806111
21	1.232392	1.367058	1.515666	1.679582	1.860295
22	1.244716	1.387564	1.545980	1.721571	1.916103
23	1.257163	1.408377	1.576899	1.764611	1.973587
24	1.269735	1.429503	1.608437	1.808726	2.032794
25	1.282432	1.450945	1.640606	1.853944	2.093778

Since this amount is the interest *plus* the original principal, subtract the principal.

$$
\begin{array}{r}
1220.19 \\
-1000.00 \\
\hline
220.19
\end{array}
$$

Answer: The interest is $220.19.

EXAMPLE 2. Find the compound interest on $500 at 6%, compounded twice a year for 6 years. Use Table XVII.

Solution: 6% ÷ 2 = 3%, the interest per 6-month interval. The number of 6-month intervals in 6 years is 6 × 2 = 12. In Table XVII, go down the *Intervals* column to "12" and read across to the column headed "3%." Multiply this amount, 1.425761, by 500.

$$
\begin{array}{r}
1.425761 \\
\times 500 \\
\hline
712.880500 = \$712.88
\end{array}
$$

Subtract the original principal.

$$
\begin{array}{r}
712.88 \\
-500.00 \\
\hline
212.88
\end{array}
$$

Answer: Interest is $212.88.

EXAMPLE 3. In the text, we discussed the compound interest on $400 at 4%, compounded quarterly, for 1 year. We said that the amount was $416.24. Check this amount by using Table XVII.

Solution: 4% ÷ 4 = 1% per 3-month interval. There are 4 intervals in 1 year. In Table XVII, go down the *Intervals* column to "4" and read across to the column headed "1%." Multiply this amount, 1.040604, by 400.

$$
\begin{array}{r}
1.040604 \\
\times 400 \\
\hline
416.24(1600) = \$416.24
\end{array}
$$

Answer: The amount of $416.24 agrees with the amount in the text.

EXERCISES

Use Table XVII to find the compound amount (principal plus interest) on:

1. $1,000 at 4%, compounded quarterly, for 2 years. _____

2. $5,000 at 6%, compounded quarterly, for 1 year. _____

3. $2,000 at 4%, compounded quarterly, for 9 months. _____

4. $100 at 5%, compounded twice a year, for 10 years. _____

5. $500 at 12%, compounded quarterly, for 5 years. _____

6. $10 at 3%, compounded annually, for 25 years. _____

APPLICATION PROBLEMS

Use Table XVII to solve the following problems.

1. Tom deposited $200 in a savings account that pays 6% interest, compounded quarterly. At the same time, Jack deposited $200 in a savings account that pays 7% simple interest.
At the end of 1 year, who has the larger amount in his savings account?

How much larger?

2. In Problem 1, suppose that both Tom and Jack let their savings accounts alone for 6 years.
Now, who has the larger amount?

How much larger?

3. Mr. Parks, the banker, claims that you will double your money if you put it into a savings account at 6%, compounded semi-annually, for 12 years. According to Table XVII, is he right? (*Hint:* Look down the appropriate column until the compound amount is " 2.000000 " or larger. This is where $1 has doubled and has become $2. Then, from the number of intervals, figure out how many years it took for $1 to become $2.)

4. Which amount is larger: $100 at 6%, compounded twice a year, for 5 years; or $100 at 12%, compounded 4 times a year, for $2\frac{1}{2}$ years?

5. Arnie needs $500 to pay for moving to another town. Six years ago, he invested $250 in a certain stock that paid 12%, compounded quarterly. Does he have enough to pay for the move?

   What is the amount of the stock?

Review of Part XXI (Units 98 to 101)

1. Tom needs to borrow $950 to pay for college expenses. If the interest rate is 7% per year, find the net amount of the 1-year loan.

2. Harry borrowed $3,650 to buy a car, and will repay the loan over 3 years. If the interest rate is $6\frac{3}{4}$%, find the net amount of the loan.

3. Find the interest on a loan of $4,675 at 5% for 60 days.

4. What will the interest charges be on a loan of $6,850 at $7\frac{1}{2}$% for 120 days.

5. John bought a car for $3,754 to be paid off in 36 equal payments over 3 years. If his down payment was $550, how much is each monthly payment?

6. A television set can be bought for $295 cash. The same set can be bought on the installment plan with a $50 down payment and 12 monthly payments of $24.75 each. How much would a buyer save by paying cash?

7. Mrs. Shillitoe bought a refrigerator for $387 to be paid off in 2 years. If she made a down payment of $75, how much will each of her monthly payments be?

In 8 and 9, use Table XVII (page 312).

8. John deposited $3,750 in a savings account that pays 6% interest, compounded quarterly. If he does not withdraw any money, how much will he have in the bank at the end of the year?

9. A certain savings bank pays 6% interest, compounded twice a year. How much interest will $2,500 earn in ten years?

10. What is the net amount of a discounted loan of $2,450 at $7\frac{1}{2}$% for 3 years?

Part XXII. Graphs

Graphs are used to present numerical facts visually. When a reader can see a picture that represents a number or an amount, it is easy for him to understand these facts. Instead of reading paragraphs of information or puzzling over columns of figures, the reader can see the facts in the graph and can make comparisons between them, almost at a glance.

Unit 102. The Pictorial Graph

A **pictorial graph** uses pictures to represent numerical facts. To make a pictorial graph, do the following:

Step 1: Gather the data.

Step 2: Round off the figures.

Step 3: Decide on an appropriate picture to represent the items in the graph. (Use a picture of a pile of money for dollars, or the picture of a man in overalls to represent wage-earners, etc.) Also, decide how many units each picture will represent.

Step 4: Find out how many pictures are needed to represent each rounded-off number in Step 2.

Step 5: Draw the required number of pictures.

Step 6: Label the graph, including a description of what each picture represents.

Let us construct a pictorial graph showing the average number of students attending public school in the United States in the decades from 1930 to 1970.

Step 1: Gather the data. (The figures in Table XVIII are from the 1972 *World Almanac*.)

Table XVIII: *Average Daily United States Public School Attendance, Ages 5 to 17*

Year	Number of Students	Rounded Off (To Nearest Million)
1930	21,264,886	21,000,000
1940	22,042,151	22,000,000
1950	22,283,845	22,000,000
1960	32,477,440	32,000,000
1970	42,495,346	42,000,000

Step 2: Round off the numbers to the nearest million.

Step 3: Decide on this symbol to represent 5,000,000 students:

Step 4: To find how many pictures are needed to represent each rounded-off number in Step 2, divide the rounded-off number by 5 million (the number of students that every picture represents).

Year	Rounded-Off Number (in millions)	Number ÷ 5 (millions)	Number of Pictures
1930	21	$\frac{21}{5} = 4\frac{1}{5}$	$4\frac{1}{5}$
1940	22	$\frac{22}{5} = 4\frac{2}{5}$	$4\frac{2}{5}$
1950	22	$\frac{22}{5} = 4\frac{2}{5}$	$4\frac{2}{5}$
1960	32	$\frac{32}{5} = 6\frac{2}{5}$	$6\frac{2}{5}$
1970	42	$\frac{42}{5} = 8\frac{2}{5}$	$8\frac{2}{5}$

Steps 5 and 6: Draw the graph and label it. The completed graph may look like this:

Average Daily United States Public School Attendance, Ages 5 to 17

EXERCISES

Use the above graph to answer these exercises. Do *not* use the data in Table XVIII.

1. To the nearest million, how many more students attended public school each day in 1970 than in 1930?

2. In what two years was attendance the same?

3. In which 10-year period was the biggest increase in the *percent* of attendance?

4. To the nearest 10%, what was the percent of increase in Exercise 3?

5. From the data for 1950, 1960, and 1970, what do you think the daily school attendance will be in 1980?

APPLICATION PROBLEMS

In 1 and 2, draw a pictorial graph for the given data.

1. Apple harvesting in New York State for the years 1966-1970.

1966: 98,320 bushels   1969: 175,340 bushels
1967: 112,740 bushels   1970: 238,270 bushels
1968: 137,690 bushels

Round off each number to the nearest thousand bushels. Let one picture of an apple represent 25,000 bushels of apples.

2. Consumption of hot dogs in the school cafeteria for February to June.

Feb., 353; Mar., 412; Apr., 548; May, 763; June, 810

Round off each number to the nearest ten. Let one picture of a hot dog represent 100 hot dogs.

Unit 103. The Line Graph

A **line graph** is often used to show how a measured quantity *changes* with respect to time or distance. For example, line graphs may be used to show how the population of a country changes from year to year, or how the average income of a certain group changed during the past decade.

A line graph will show at a glance the trends followed by the quantity being considered. When the line in the graph *rises*, the quantity *increases*. When the line *falls*, the quantity *decreases*. When the line is *horizontal*, the quantity is *not changing*.

A line graph uses two **scales**, which are lines drawn from the same point at right angles to each other. The vertical scale usually indicates the amount of the measured quantity, such as temperature, dollars, or population. The horizontal scale usually indicates a uniform change, such as hours, years, or feet.

To make a line graph, do the following:

Step 1: Gather the data.

Step 2: Round off the figures.

Step 3: Decide on appropriate lengths for both the vertical scale and the horizontal scale. Label the scales in uniform units.

Step 4: Using the two scales, draw a dot on the graph for each set of rounded-off figures in Step 2. (See the *note* just before the exercises.)

Step 5: Connect the dots, using straight lines.

Step 6: Label the graph.

Let us construct a line graph showing the population of the United States from 1900 to 1970, for every 10-year period.

Steps 1 and 2: The following information was obtained from the United States Census Bureau:

Table XIX: *Population of the U.S.*

Year	Population	Population to Nearest Ten-million
1900	75,994,575	80
1910	91,972,266	90
1920	105,710,620	110
1930	122,775,046	120
1940	131,669,275	130
1950	150,697,361	150
1960	179,323,175	180
1970	204,765,770	200

Steps 3 to 6: Here is the completed line graph:

U.S. Population, 1900 to 1970

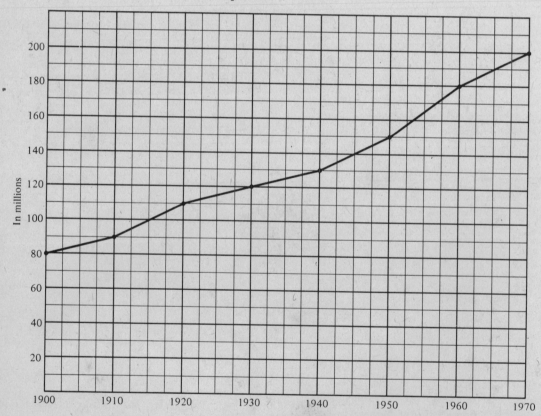

Note: To draw a dot on the graph for each set of figures in Table XIX, proceed as follows:

In 1900, the population was 80 million. Find the line labeled "1900" and move up it until you reach the line labeled "80." Make a dot where the "1900" line and the "80" line meet.

In 1910, the population was 90 million. Find the line labeled "1910" and move up it. Note that there is no "90" on the graph's scale. Since the number 90 is halfway between 80 and 100, move halfway between the line labeled "80" and the line labeled "100." Make a dot on the "1910" line, where "90" should be.

Continue this process for the rest of the years.

EXERCISES

Use the preceding graph to answer these exercises. Do *not* use the data in Table XIX.

1. In which three 10-year intervals was the population increase the smallest? _____

2. In which 10-year interval was the population increase the greatest? _____

3. Since 1900, the U.S. population has _____
(Answer *increased 50%*, *doubled*, or *more than doubled*.)

4. What do you think the population of the United States will be in 1980? (Answer to the nearest ten-million.) _____

APPLICATION PROBLEMS

In 1 and 2, draw a line graph for the given data.

1. The monthly sales of John Wilson in 1970 were as follows:

Jan., $8,570; Feb., $11,690; Mar., $10,400; Apr., $13,600; May, $15,800; June, $16,500; July, $14,300; Aug., $13,500; Sept., $15,900; Oct., $17,500; Nov., $18,300; Dec., $16,500

Let the horizontal scale represent the twelve months. Let the vertical scale represent the amounts of sales. Mark this scale in intervals of $5,000. Round off the given amounts to the nearest thousand.

2. The monthly sales for the first six months of this year for Brown's Clothing Store were as follows:

Jan., $9,500; Feb., $11,700; Mar., $10,500; Apr., $13,500; May, $15,500; June, $12,500

Let the horizontal scale represent the six months. Let the vertical scale represent the amounts of sales. Mark this scale in multiples of $5,000. Round off the given amounts to the nearest thousand.

Unit 104. The Bar Graph

The **bar graph** is used to show comparisons between numerical facts. In a bar graph, the length of each bar stands for a quantity. By comparing the lengths of the bars, the reader compares the quantities being represented.

A bar graph is constructed in the same way as a line graph. However, instead of connecting the points as in a line graph, bars are drawn from one of the scales to each point.

If the bars are drawn vertically (straight up from the horizontal scale), the graph is called a **vertical bar graph**. If the bars are drawn horizontally (sideways from the vertical scale), the graph is called a **horizontal bar graph**.

To make a bar graph, do the following:

Step 1: Gather the data.

Step 2: Round off the figures.

Step 3: Decide on the horizontal scale and the vertical scale.

Step 4: Decide on a vertical bar graph or a horizontal bar graph.

Step 5: Draw dots that represent the rounded-off figures in Step 2.

Step 6: Draw bars of equal width from the 0 of the vertical or horizontal scale to the dots.

Leave the same amount of space between bars.

Step 7: Label the graph.

Note: By using graph paper, which is ruled into squares, it is easy to draw the bars accurately and to

leave equal spaces between the bars.

Let us construct a vertical bar graph showing the population of the United States from 1900 to 1970. Using the data from Table XIX in the preceding unit, the completed graph may look like this:

U.S. Population, 1900 to 1970

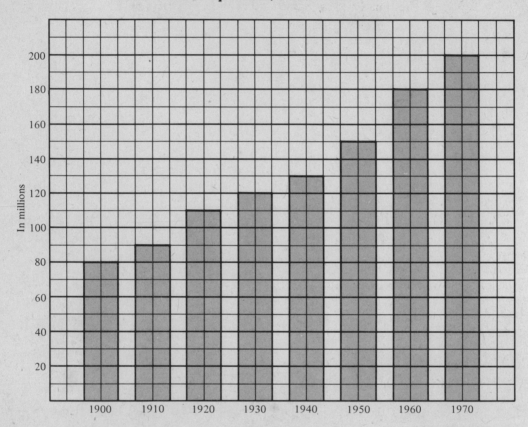

APPLICATION PROBLEMS

In 1 and 2, draw a bar graph for the given data. (*Note:* The bars in a bar graph can be shown vertically or horizontally.)

1. The quarterly sales of John Wilson for last year were as follows:

1st Quarter, $9,500; 2nd Quarter, $14,000; 3rd Quarter, $11,500; 4th Quarter, $17,000

Arrange the four quarters on either the horizontal scale or the vertical scale. Bar graphs are most easily drawn on graph paper. Use the squares on the graph paper to make a convenient width for the bars and to leave equal space between the bars. Round off the given amounts to the nearest thousand, and mark the scale that represents these amounts in intervals of $5,000.

2. The sales of the Brown Appliance Co. for last month were as follows:

TV sets & Radios, $4,600; Dryers, $1,500; Ranges, $2,300; Freezers, $1,200; Washers, $3,700; Other appliances, $1,800

On the scale that represents sales, let each square of the graph paper represent $100. Mark this scale in intervals of $1,000.

3. Study the graph in Problem 2 and complete the following statements:

   a. The _____ department sold the most appliances.

   b. The Washers department sold _____ than the Ranges department. (Answer *more* or *less*.)

   c. The sales for the Freezers department were $_____ (estimated to the nearest $100).

   d. The sales of the TV & Radios department were _____ more than the sales of the Dryers department (estimated to the nearest $100).

Unit 105. The Circle Graph

The **circle graph** is used to show how something is divided into smaller parts. For example, a circle graph labeled "How Your Tax Dollar Is Spent" would show what percent of your tax dollar was spent for defense, what percent was spent on education, etc.

To construct a circle graph, you let the entire circle represent 100% of the quantity being studied. Then, with your data expressed as percents, you determine how many degrees of the circle must be used to represent a given percent. A whole circle contains 360°.

EXAMPLE 1. How many degrees of a circle will represent (*a*) 25% (*b*) 60% (*c*) 1.1%?

Solutions:

a. 25% of a circle is 25% of 360°.

$$
\begin{array}{r}
360 \\
\times\ .25 \\
\hline
18\ 00 \\
72\ 0 \\
\hline
90.00 = 90° \\
\end{array}
$$

b. 60% of a circle is 60% of 360°.

$$
\begin{array}{r}
360 \\
\times\ .6 \\
\hline
216.0 = 216° \\
\end{array}
$$

c. 1.1% of a circle is 1.1% of 360°.

$$
\begin{array}{r}
360 \\
\times\ .011 \\
\hline
360 \\
3\ 60 \\
\hline
3.960 = 4.0° = 4°, \text{ to the} \\
\end{array}
$$
                                                 nearest degree

Answers: (*a*) 25% = 90°   (*b*) 60% = 216°
(*c*) 1.1% = 4°

To make a circle graph, do the following:

Step 1: Gather the data.

Step 2: If necessary, change the data to percents.

Step 3: Determine how many degrees of a circle each percent represents.

Step 4: Draw a circle to represent 100% of the quantity being graphed. Then, using the degrees in Step 3, divide the circle into **sectors** ("slices of pie") by drawing a line from the center to the outer edge of the circle. Measure the angles with a **protractor**.

EXAMPLE 2. Using a protractor, mark off a 60-degree sector in a circle.

Solution: Place the center of the protractor on center of the circle. Then make a dot at the "0" mark and make another dot at the "60" mark:

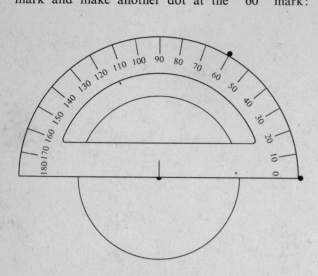

Remove the protractor. Draw a straight line from the "0" dot to the center of the circle; draw a straight line from the "60" dot to the center of the circle. The shaded area in the following figure is the required sector:

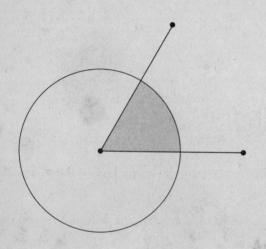

Step 5: Label the graph. Include the percents in each sector.

EXAMPLE 3. Mr. Allen's take-home pay last year was $8,200. During that year, the Allen family used their income as follows:

Savings: $820   Shelter: $1,640
Clothing: $984   Food: $2,050
Car: $820   Other: $1,886

Make a circle graph showing the Allen family budget.

Solution:

Steps 1 and 2: Change each expenditure to a percent of Mr. Allen's pay, $8,200.

$$\text{Savings} = \frac{820}{8200} = \frac{1}{10} = .1 = 10\%$$

$$\text{Clothing} = \frac{984}{8200} = .12 = 12\%$$

$$\text{Car} = \frac{820}{8200} = \frac{1}{10} = .1 = 10\%$$

$$\text{Shelter} = \frac{1640}{8200} = .2 = 20\%$$

$$\text{Food} = \frac{2050}{8200} = .25 = 25\%$$

$$\text{Other} = \frac{1886}{8200} = .23 = 23\%$$

Step 3: Change each percent to degrees of a circle.

$$\text{Savings} = 360 \times .10 = 36°$$

$$\text{Clothing} = 360 \times .12 = 43.2 = 43°$$

$$\text{Car} = 360 \times .10 = 36°$$

$$\text{Shelter} = 360 \times .20 = 72°$$

$$\text{Food} = 360 \times .25 = 90°$$

$$\text{Other} = 360 \times .23 = 82.8 = 83°$$

Step 4: Using a protractor, mark off the sectors using the number of degrees in Step 3.

Step 5: Label the graph.

Solution: The completed graph may look like this:

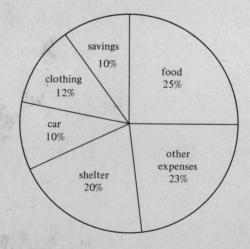

Note that the percents in the circle graph must total 100%: $25 + 23 + 20 + 10 + 12 + 10 = 100$

EXERCISE

1. Next year, the Allen family's total income will be $9,850. Find the amounts spent for each of the items in the preceding graph. (Assume that the percents remain the same.)

APPLICATION PROBLEMS

1. Draw a circle graph to represent the Wilson family's vacation expenses for last year. Use the following data:

Transportation, 25%; Lodging, 30%; Food, 35%; Amusement, 10%

2. Using the information in the graph for Problem 1, find the amounts of money that the Wilsons spent on each item. The total amount spent was $875.

Unit 106. Scale Drawings

When an architect draws the floor plan of a house he has designed, it is impossible for him to make the drawing the same size as the actual house. Instead, he makes a **scale drawing** that shows the exact shape of the house, but with greatly reduced dimensions. He may let $\frac{1}{4}$ inch on the plan represent 1 foot of the actual size of the house. He then reduces all actual dimensions by this ratio, called the **scale**. A scale is usually shown with an equals sign:

$$\text{Scale: } \frac{1}{4} \text{ in.} = 1 \text{ ft.}$$

The first term in the scale always represents a measurement on the drawing. The second term represents the actual distance represented by the first term. The second term is often called the "equivalent measurement."

When the first term is smaller than the second term, you know that the drawing is smaller than the actual object being represented.

There are times when the actual object is extremely small, as with certain machine parts. In this case, the scale drawing will be larger than the object being represented. The engineer who is making the scale drawing may let 1 inch on the plans represent $\frac{1}{10}$ of an inch of the actual size of the machine part. He then enlarges all the dimensions by this ratio. The scale would appear on the plans as:

$$\text{Scale: } 1 \text{ in.} = \frac{1}{10} \text{ in.}$$

Since the first term (which always represents a measurement on the drawing) is larger than the second term, you know that the drawing is larger than the actual object.

EXAMPLE 1. On a floor plan, a rectangular living room measures 3 in. × 4 in. If the scale is $\frac{1}{4}$ in. = 1 ft., what is the actual size of the room?

Solution: Since $\frac{1}{4}$ in. on the drawing equals 1 ft. of actual size, you must find how many times $\frac{1}{4}$ in. is contained in the length of 3 in. and in the length of 4 in. You find how many times a number is contained in another number by division:

$$3 \div \frac{1}{4} = \frac{3}{1} \times \frac{4}{1} = 12$$

There are 12 $\frac{1}{4}$'s in 3.

$$4 \div \frac{1}{4} = \frac{4}{1} \times \frac{4}{1} = 16$$

There are 16 $\frac{1}{4}$'s in 4.

Multiply the 12 and the 16 by the equivalent measurement in the scale, in this case 1 ft.:

$$12 \times 1 \text{ ft.} = 12 \text{ ft.}$$
$$16 \times 1 \text{ ft.} = 16 \text{ ft.}$$

Answer: The actual size of the room is 12 ft. × 16 ft.

EXAMPLE 2. A schoolyard measures 96 feet by 168 feet. Find the scale-drawing size of the yard on a set of plans whose scale appears as:

$$\text{Scale: } \frac{1}{4} \text{ in.} = 3 \text{ ft.}$$

Solution: Find the number of times that 3 is contained in 96 and in 168:

$$
\begin{array}{cc}
\phantom{3\overline{)}}32 & \phantom{3\overline{)}}56 \\
3\overline{)96} & 3\overline{)168} \\
\phantom{3\overline{)}}9 & \phantom{3\overline{)}}15 \\
\hline
\phantom{3\overline{)}}6 & \phantom{3\overline{)}}18 \\
\phantom{3\overline{)}}6 & \phantom{3\overline{)}}18 \\
\hline
\end{array}
$$

There are 32 3's in 96 and there are 56 3's in 168. Since 3 feet of actual length are represented by $\frac{1}{4}$ inch on the plans, multiply 32 and 56 by $\frac{1}{4}$ inch:

$$\frac{\overset{8}{\cancel{32}}}{1} \times \frac{1}{\cancel{4}} \text{ in.} = 8 \text{ in.} \qquad \frac{\overset{14}{\cancel{56}}}{1} \times \frac{1}{\cancel{4}} \text{ in.} = 14 \text{ in.}$$

Answer: On the plans, the scale-drawing size of the yard is 8 inches × 14 inches.

EXAMPLE 3. On the blueprint of a machine, the diameter of a certain bolt measures $1\frac{1}{2}$ in. If the scale is $\frac{1}{2}$ in. = 3 mm, what is the actual diameter of the bolt?

Solution: Find the number of times $\frac{1}{2}$ is contained in $1\frac{1}{2}$ by dividing $1\frac{1}{2}$ by $\frac{1}{2}$:

$$1\frac{1}{2} \div \frac{1}{2} = \frac{3}{2} \div \frac{1}{2} = \frac{3}{\underset{1}{\cancel{2}}} \times \frac{\overset{1}{\cancel{2}}}{1} = 3$$

There are 3 $\frac{1}{2}$'s in $1\frac{1}{2}$. Thus, multiply the 3 by the equivalent measurement in the scale, 3 mm:

$$3 \times 3 \text{ mm} = 9 \text{ mm}$$

Answer: The diameter is 9 mm.

EXERCISES

1. From the given information, find the actual measurements or distances.

Scale	Measurement on Scale Drawing	Actual Measurement or Distance
$\frac{1}{4}$ in. $= 25$ mi.	$3\frac{1}{2}$ in.	
$\frac{1}{8}$ in. $= 4$ ft.	$1\frac{3}{4}$ in.	
1 in. $= 20$ mi.	$4\frac{5}{8}$ in.	
$\frac{1}{8}$ in. $= 1$ ft.	$6\frac{1}{2}$ in.	
1 in. $= \frac{1}{8}$ in.	6 in.	
1 in. $= 40$ mi.	$6\frac{3}{4}$ in.	
1 in. $= 1$ in.	5 in.	
$\frac{1}{16}$ in. $= 5$ ft.	$3\frac{1}{4}$ in.	

2. What are the distances represented by line segments a, b, and c (below) if the scale is $\frac{1}{4}$ in. = 15 mi. ?

_____   _____   _____
       a.   b.   c.

3. A garage measures 22 ft. × 18 ft. Give the dimensions of the scale

drawing of the garage using the scale: $\frac{1}{4}$ in. = 2 ft.

_____

Review of Part XXII (Units 102 to 106)

1. Use the graph paper below to make a line graph showing the quarterly sales of the Franklin Manufacturing Company for last year.

    1st Quarter: $21,568
    2nd Quarter: $21,320
    3rd Quarter: $20,390
    4th Quarter: $24,685

Round off each amount to the nearest $1,000. On the vertical scale, choose a convenient number of squares to represent $1,000; the vertical scale need only be labeled from $20,000 to $25,000.

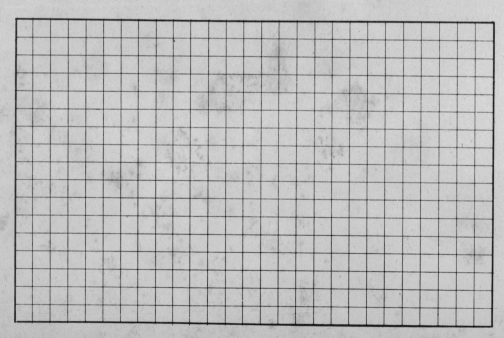

2. Use the graph paper below to make a vertical bar graph showing the sales by department of the Ajax Department Store for last year.

Clothing: $38,895; Furniture: $36,380; Appliances: $26,595; Toys: $8,419; Shoes: $13,485.

Round off each amount to the nearest $1,000. On the vertical scale, let each square represent $1,000 and mark this scale in intervals of $5,000.

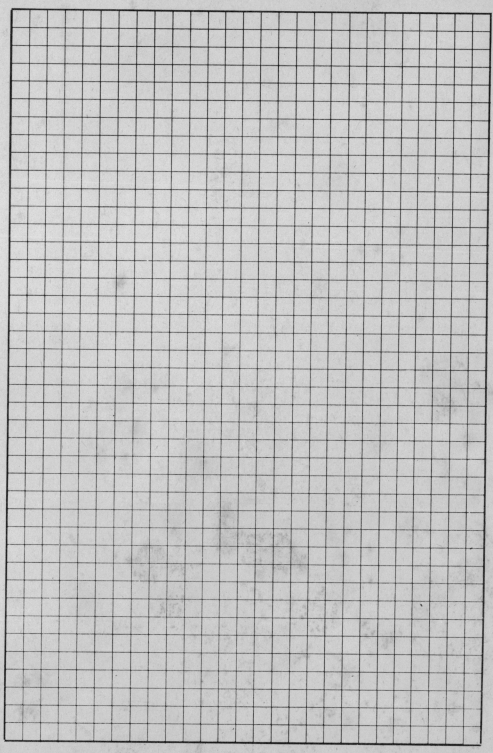

3. In a certain office, 8% of the employees are classified as executives, 28% are in the sales department, 22% are in the billing department, 10% are file clerks, and 32% are typists. Find, to the nearest whole degree, how many degrees of a circle should be used to represent each of these jobs on a circle graph. (Do not actually draw the circle graph.)

        executives: _____ °

        sales dept.: _____ °

        billing dept.: _____ °

        file clerks: _____ °

        typists: _____ °

4. Given the following scale:

$$\text{Scale:} \frac{1}{2} \text{ in.} = 10 \text{ ft.}$$

What is the actual size of a rectangular lot that measures $1\frac{3}{4}$ in. × 3 in. on a map?

5. Given the following scale:

$$\text{Scale: } 1 \text{ in.} = \frac{1}{10} \text{ in.}$$

On a set of plans, a machine part measures 2.5 inches. What is the actual size of the part?

Part XXIII. Algebra

Unit 107. Algebraic Expressions

Algebra is a form of mathematics that uses number symbols and letter symbols to solve problems.

A **number symbol** is any word, numeral, combination of numerals, or picture that stands for a certain specific number. For example, all of the following number symbols stand for the number we know as "12":

XII 3×4 $15 - 3$ dozen

$24 \div 2$ $8 + 4$ $\dfrac{12}{1}$ $\dfrac{6 \times 6}{3}$

twelve   卅卅 || number of months in a year

A **letter symbol** is a letter that stands for a number to be found or for the value of an unknown number. The letters x, y, and z in the following mathematical sentences are examples of letter symbols:

$$x = 5 + 14 \quad y = 27 \div 3 \quad z = 9 \times 7$$

By using number symbols, letter symbols, and the symbols of arithmetic that we already know ($+$, $-$, $\times$, $\div$, $=$), we can write statements about numbers much more briefly than we can with words. The mathematical sentence, "When five is added to some unknown number, the sum is fourteen," may be written as follows:

$$5 + n = 14$$

Just as we can change around the words in a sentence, so we can change around the symbols in a mathematical sentence. Here are three possible ways of rearranging the previous mathematical sentence, both in words and in symbols:

"When some unknown number is added to five, we get a total of fourteen." In symbols: $\square + 5 = 14$ (Here, we used a "box" instead of a letter. In algebra, you can use any convenient symbol to stand for an unknown number.)

"Fourteen is the sum of five and some other number we want to find." In symbols: $14 = 5 + x$

"Fourteen is what you get when you add an unknown number to five." In symbols: $14 = ? + 5$

Mathematical sentences that contain letters or other symbols in place of numbers are called **open sentences**.

In algebra, a letter is used to represent a number until the value of this number is discovered. In an algebra problem, we write an open sentence from the given facts and then find the value of the unknown number. Just as word sentences are made up of groups of words, so open sentences are made up of **algebraic expressions**. Therefore, in order to write an open sentence, we must learn to take a word statement and to rewrite it as an algebraic expression.

Here are some examples: (In each case, the letter n stands for the value of the unknown number.)

Word Statement	Algebraic Expression
the number plus five	$n + 5$
the number minus 8	$n - 8$
the number increased by 6	$n + 6$
the number decreased by 9	$n - 9$
the number divided by 7	$n \div 7$ or $\dfrac{n}{7}$ or $\dfrac{1}{7}n$
the number multiplied by 3	$n \times 3$ or $3n$
the product of 8 times the number	$8 \times n$ or $8n$

Note: In algebra, the symbol × is not usually used to show the product of a number and a letter symbol. Thus, $3 \times n$ and $8 \times n$ should be shown as $3n$ and $8n$. Also, the division sign, ÷, is seldom used in algebra. $n \div 7$ should be shown as $\dfrac{n}{7}$ or $\dfrac{1}{7}n$.

Here are some more examples. For practice, cover the right-hand column and try to guess what the algebraic expression should be. Then see if you guessed correctly.

Word Statement	*Algebraic Expression*
1. 8 more than x	**1.** $x + 8$ or $8 + x$
2. r multiplied by 5	**2.** $5r$
3. 5 more than the product of y times 6	**3.** $5 + 6y$
4. d times 3, decreased by 7	**4.** $3d - 7$
5. a boy's age 12 years from now (Use a for his age.)	**5.** $a + 12$
6. one-half a given number n	**6.** $\dfrac{1}{2}n$ or $\dfrac{n}{2}$
7. s divided by 4 (Don't use the ÷ sign.)	**7.** $\dfrac{s}{4}$ or $\dfrac{1}{4}s$
8. ten more nickels than dimes (Use d for the number of dimes.)	**8.** $d + 10$
In examples 9 and 10, write a complete number sentence.	
9. Jane is twice as old as Mary. (Use J for Jane's age and M for Mary's age.)	**9.** $J = 2M$
10. The express train travels 25 miles per hour faster than the local train. (Use E for the speed of the express and L for the speed of the local.)	**10.** $E = L + 25$

EXERCISES

In 1 to 10, write an algebraic expression for each word statement. Do not use the symbols × or ÷. Use n or any convenient letter for the unknown number.

1. a number increased by 23

2. 16 less than a number

3. ten times a number

4. one-tenth of a number

5. the sum of a number and 13

6. 52 divided by some number

7. one-half the product of 7 and a number

8. one-third of the quotient you get when a number is divided by 17

9. twice the quotient of a number divided by 5

10. a number multiplied by three

In 11 to 20, write an algebraic expression for each word statement. Use the letter symbol that is given.

11. x times y

12. x divided by y

13. the sum of n and m

14. p times 3, minus 5

15. 18 divided by x, plus 12

16. 5 times n, divided by 4

17. 3 times n, decreased by 15

18. 26 divided by x, decreased by 7

19. 5 more than the product of n and 7

20. 2 times y, divided by a plus 6

In 21 to 25, write a complete number sentence.

21. The area A equals the length L multiplied by the width W.

22. The distance D is the product of the time T and the rate R.

23. x is one-half of n, plus 10 more.

24. z is 15 more than 5 times n.

25. 6 times r, divided by 7, is the same as two-thirds of s.

APPLICATION PROBLEMS

1. Tom is x years old. Write John's age if he is twice as old as Tom.

2. The length of a room is 4 ft. longer than the width. Using w for the width, express algebraically the length of the room.

3. Jane is x years old. Mary is twice her age, and Sue is 5 years younger than Mary. Express Sue's age algebraically.

4. Bill has n dimes, half as many nickels, and 5 more quarters than nickels. Express algebraically the number of quarters Bill has.

5. Bill weighs x pounds and Jim weighs y pounds. If Jim gains 10 pounds and Bill loses 18 pounds, represent their total weight algebraically.

Unit 108. Equations

When we have a mathematical sentence such as $6 + 11 = 17$ or an open sentence such as $2n = 12$, we say that the *quantity* to the left of the equals sign is equal to the *quantity* to the right of the equals sign. This expression of equality is called an **equation**. The quantity to the left of the equals sign is called the **left member** of the equation; the quantity to the right of the equals sign is called the **right member**.

An equation may be a mathematical sentence, such as $3 \times 3 = \dfrac{18}{2}$; or it may be an open sentence that has one or more letter symbols, such as $3x = 18$ or $4S = P$.

When we find the value of the unknown number that is represented by the letter symbol in an open sentence, we say we **solve the equation**. To solve the equation $n + 15 = 20$, we must find some number that we can add to 15 to get 20. By counting ("sixteen, seventeen, eighteen, nineteen, twenty"), we see that the missing number is 5. In algebra, the solution would look like this:

$$n + 15 = 20$$
$$n = 5$$

We always *check* the found value of a letter symbol by putting its value back in the original equation.

Check:
$$n + 15 = 20$$
$$5 + 15 = 20$$
$$20 = 20 \checkmark$$

The left member equals the right member, so we know that $n = 5$ is the correct value. The value of the letter that makes an equation true is called the **root** of the equation.

One of the most important uses of algebra is to solve word problems. There are two basic steps to follow in solving most word problems:

1. Express the facts of the problem as an equation.
2. Solve the equation by finding the root of the equation.

The first step is often the more difficult of the two. By reading the problem carefully and by using a letter symbol in place of the unknown number, you will soon be able to rewrite most word statements as equations.

EXAMPLE 1. Write each of the following sentences as an equation:

a. Three times a certain number equals 36.
b. A number increased by 12 equals 25.
c. A number times 3, increased by 5, is equal to 38.

Solutions:

a. $3n = 36$
b. $x + 12 = 25$
c. $3n + 5 = 38$

Often, you will have to read the problem carefully, rewrite the facts as *one complete sentence*, and then rewrite this sentence as the equation.

EXAMPLE 2. Jeri bought four cheeseburgers and paid for them with $2.00. If she got 20¢ in change, how much did *each* cheeseburger cost? Write an equation that can be used to solve this problem.

Solution: First, rewrite the above facts as one complete sentence. "The cost of 4 cheeseburgers plus $.20 change totals $2.00." Now, write this sentence as an equation, using C as the unknown cost.

Answer: $4C + .20 = 2.00$

EXAMPLE 3. When Tom started college, he was half his present age. When he graduated four years later, he was 22 years old. What is his present age? Write an equation that can be used to find the unknown age.

Solution: Rewrite the facts as one complete sentence. "Half of Tom's present age plus 4 years is

22." Use *a* for the unknown age and write an equation.

Answer: $\frac{1}{2}a + 4 = 22$

EXAMPLE 4. Henry is paid every two weeks, receiving a paycheck that is twice his weekly salary. Every payday, Henry puts $30 in the bank, which is $\frac{1}{8}$ of his paycheck. Write an equation that will enable you to find his *weekly* salary.

Solution: Rewrite the facts as one complete sentence. "When Henry's weekly salary is doubled, and then divided by 8, it is equal to $30." Write this sentence as an equation, using s as the unknown salary.

Answer: $\frac{2s}{8} = 30$

EXERCISES

In 1 to 12 write an equation for each word statement.

1. 8 taken from 4 times a number equals 64.

2. A number reduced by 15 is 36.

3. When 24 is subtracted from a number, the result is 15.

4. A number divided by 8, increased by 15, is equal to 47.

5. When 18 is added to a number, the result is another number.

6. One-quarter of a number added to 6 times the number is 53.

7. 8 added to 5 times a number results in 32.

8. If 3 times a given number is divided by 5, the result is 58.

9. When a number is decreased by 12, the result is 84.

10. The product of 8 and a number is 96.

11. A number multiplied by 5, increased by 10, results in 75.

12. When 10 is subtracted from 3 times a number, the result is 58.

In 13 to 20, answer each question by writing an equation.

13. Tom had x amount of money. If he spent \$12, which is $\frac{1}{3}$ of the amount, write an equation to find how much money Tom had.

14. Jim weighs 8 pounds more than twice as much as Harry. If Harry weighs x pounds, write an equation to find Jim's weight.

15. Harry had x dollars. If he spent $\frac{1}{6}$ of his money, write an equation to find how much money Harry has left.

16. The price of a TV set is reduced by \$30. If this is $\frac{1}{3}$ of the original price, write an equation to find the original price.

17. 25% of an amount is equal to \$38. Write an equation to find the amount.

18. If 5 typewriters cost \$1,200, write an equation to find the cost of one typewriter.

19. A coat selling for \$68 was reduced to \$54. Write an equation to find the amount of the reduction.

20. Mary paid x dollars for a dress. If Jane bought a dress for twice as much, write an equation to find how much Jane paid for the dress.

Unit 109. Solving Equations by Using Addition and Subtraction

In the preceding unit, we solved the equation

$$n + 15 = 20$$

We found the root to be $n = 5$. We started with an equation where the solution was not known; we ended up with an equation where the letter symbol was all alone in the left member.

To solve an equation, we change it around so that *the letter symbol is in one member of the equation and all the number symbols are in the other member.*

In solving equations, we use addition, subtraction, multiplication, and division.

Consider the equation $n + 15 = 20$. We solved this equation by "common sense" in the preceding unit. Now, let's solve it by using algebra. The left member is $n + 15$. Since we want to get the n alone, we must separate the n from the 15. To do this, we use the following fact:

The opposite of addition is subtraction.

The letter symbol n is *added* to 15. Therefore, we must *subtract* 15 from the left member. When we subtract 15, however, we must follow this basic rule of solving equations:

Rule: Whatever you do to one member of an equation (add, subtract, multiply, or divide), you must do to the other member.

Here's how we solve the equation:

Subtract 15 from both members.
$$\begin{array}{r} n + 15 = 20 \\ -15 \quad -15 \\ \hline n \quad = \quad 5 \end{array}$$

(When you subtract 15 from 15, you get 0; but since $n + 0$ is the same as n, it is not necessary to write the 0 in the left member.)

The root of $n + 15 = 20$ is $n = 5$.

Here are some more examples of solving equations by using subtraction. In every case, the unknown number has some other number added to it.

EXAMPLES. Solve each of the following equations for the unknown value of the letter symbol. Check each root in the original equation.

a. $5 + n = 18$
b. $20 = x + 9$
c. $s + 20 = 9 \times 3$

Solutions:

a. Subtract 5 from both members.
$$\begin{array}{r} 5 + n = 18 \\ -5 \quad -5 \\ \hline n = 13 \end{array}$$

Check: $5 + n = 18$
$5 + 13 = 18$
$18 = 18$ ✓

Answer: $n = 13$

b. Subtract 9 from both members.
$$\begin{array}{r} 20 = x + 9 \\ -9 \quad -9 \\ \hline 11 = x \end{array}$$

Check: $20 = x + 9$
$20 = 11 + 9$
$20 = 20$ ✓

Answer: $x = 11$

c. $$s + 20 = 9 \times 3$$

To simplify the equation, perform the indicated multiplication in the right member.

Subtract 20 from both members.
$$\begin{array}{r} s + 20 = 27 \\ -20 \quad -20 \\ \hline s \quad = \quad 7 \end{array}$$

Check: $s + 20 = 9 \times 3$
$7 + 20 = 9 \times 3$
$27 = 27$ ✓

Answer: $s = 7$

Remember: When you subtract any number from one member of an equation, you must subtract the same number from the other member.

You may think of an equation as a balanced scale, a scale with equal weights on both sides. Whenever you remove a weight from one side, you must remove the same weight from the other side in order to keep the scales balanced.

Consider the equation

$$x - 15 = 64$$

Here, the letter symbol has 15 subtracted from it. Since we want to get the x alone, we must separate it from the 15. To do this, we use the following fact:

The opposite of subtraction is addition.

The 15 is *subtracted* from the x. Therefore, we must *add* 15 to both members.

Add 15 to
both members.
$$x - 15 = 64$$
$$\underline{+15 \quad +15}$$
$$x \quad = 79$$

The root of $x - 15 = 64$ is $x = 79$.

EXAMPLES. Solve each of the following equations for the unknown value of the letter symbol. Check each root in the original equation.

d. $x - 23 = 64$
e. $27 = n - 13$
f. $s - 4 = 12 - 2$

Solutions:

d.   Add 23 to
both members.
$$x - 23 = 64$$
$$\underline{+23 \quad +23}$$
$$x \quad = 87$$

Check: $x - 23 = 64$
$87 - 23 = 64$
$64 = 64$ ✓

Answer: $x = 87$

e.   Add 13 to
both members.
$$27 = n - 13$$
$$\underline{+13 \quad +13}$$
$$40 = n$$

Check: $27 = n - 13$
$27 = 40 - 13$
$27 = 27$ ✓

Answer: $n = 40$

f. $$s - 4 = 12 - 2$$

First, do the indicated subtraction in the right member.

Add 4 to
both members.
$$s - 4 = 10$$
$$\underline{+4 \quad +4}$$
$$s \quad = 14$$

Check: $s - 4 = 12 - 2$
$14 - 4 = 12 - 2$
$10 = 10$ ✓

Answer: $s = 14$

Remember: When you add any number to one member of an equation, you must add this same number to the other member.

EXERCISES

In 1 to 9, solve each equation for the value of the letter symbol.

1. $n + 3 = 42$

2. $x + 13 = 27$

3. $y - 5 = 17$

4. $t - 3\frac{1}{2} = 15$

5. $n + 35 = 112$

6. $28 - x = 18$

7. $35 + y = 47$ **8.** $p - 15 = 120$ **9.** $t + 28 = 57$

In 10 to 20, write an equation and then solve it for the unknown number.

10. A number, decreased by 15, equals 52.

11. What number, increased by 28, is equal to 75?

12. When 13 is added to a number, the result is 85.

13. A number, reduced by 27, is equal to 85.

14. A number, added to 15, results in 33.

15. What number, less 24, is equal to 51?

16. When 27 is taken from a number, the result is 83.

17. What number, decreased by 35, results in 47?

18. A number, increased by 17, is equal to 39.

19. A number, plus 32, equals 51.

20. If 13 is subtracted from a number, the result is 57.

In 21 to 25, write and solve an equation to answer the question.

21. Tom earns $35 more than Jim. If Tom earns $185 a week, find Jim's salary.

22. Harry sold his car for $565 less than he paid for it. If he paid $3,250 for the car, how much did he sell it for?

23. A class has 8 more girls than boys. If there are 28 students in the class, how many girls are there?

24. Jim bought a television set and made a down payment of $58. If he still owes $215, on the set, what was the full price of the television set?

25. Jane is 5 years younger than Mary. How old is Jane if Mary is 23 years old?

Unit 110. Solving Equations by Using Division and Multiplication

The word statement, "Five times a certain number is equal to 60," can be rewritten as the equation:

$$5x = 60$$

In this equation, the left member is $5x$, which means that the letter symbol is *multiplied* by 5. Since we want to get the x alone, we must separate the x from the 5. To do this, we use the following fact:

The opposite of multiplication is division.

The letter symbol x is *multiplied* by 5. Therefore, we must *divide* the left member by 5. Since whatever we do to one member of an equation we must do to the other member, we must divide the right member by 5, also.

Divide both members by 5.

$$5x = 60$$
$$\frac{5x}{5} = \frac{60}{5}$$
$$x = 12$$

Algebraic division	*Arithmetic division*
$$\begin{array}{r} x \\ 5\overline{)5x} \\ 5x \\ \hline \end{array}$$	$$\begin{array}{r} 12 \\ 5\overline{)60} \\ 5 \\ \hline 10 \\ 10 \\ \hline \end{array}$$

We check to see if $x = 12$ is the root of the equation.

$$5x = 60$$
$$5 \times 12 = 60$$
$$60 = 60 \checkmark$$

The root of $5x = 60$ is $x = 12$.

Here are some examples of solving equations by using division. Notice that "algebraic division" is very similar to the arithmetic division that you have studied. In every case, the unknown number (the letter symbol) is multiplied by some other number.

EXAMPLES. Solve each of the following equations for the unknown value of the letter symbol. Check each root in the original equation.

a. $9n = 36$
b. $49 = 7x$
c. $3x = 6 \times 4$

Solutions:

a. Divide both members by 9.

$$9n = 36$$
$$\frac{9n}{9} = \frac{36}{9}$$
$$n = 4$$

Algebraic division	*Arithmetic division*
$$\begin{array}{r} n \\ 9\overline{)9n} \\ 9n \\ \hline \end{array}$$	$$\begin{array}{r} 4 \\ 9\overline{)36} \\ 36 \\ \hline \end{array}$$

Check: $9n = 36$
$9 \times 4 = 36$
$36 = 36 \checkmark$

Answer: $n = 4$

b. Divide both members by 7.

$$49 = 7x$$
$$\frac{49}{7} = \frac{7x}{7}$$
$$7 = x$$

Arithmetic division	*Algebraic division*
$$\begin{array}{r} 7 \\ 7\overline{)49} \\ 49 \\ \hline \end{array}$$	$$\begin{array}{r} x \\ 7\overline{)7x} \\ 7x \\ \hline \end{array}$$

Check: $49 = 7x$
$49 = 7 \times 7$
$49 = 49 \checkmark$

Answer: $x = 7$

c.

$$3x = 6 \times 4$$

To simplify the equation, perform the indicated multiplication in the right member.

Divide both members by 3.

$$3x = 24$$
$$\frac{3x}{3} = \frac{24}{3}$$
$$x = 8$$

Algebraic division   *Arithmetic division*

$$3\overline{)3x}^{\,x}$$
$$\underline{3x}$$

$$3\overline{)24}^{\,8}$$
$$\underline{24}$$

Check: $3x = 6 \times 4$

$3 \times 8 = 6 \times 4$

$24 = 24$ ✓

Answer: $x = 8$

The word statement, "A certain number, divided by 5, is equal to 80," can be rewritten as the equation:

$$\frac{n}{5} = 80$$

In this equation, the left member is $\frac{n}{5}$, which means that the letter symbol is *divided* by 5. Since we want to get the n alone, we must separate the n from the 5. We do this by using the following fact:

The opposite of division is multiplication.

The letter symbol n is divided by 5. Therefore, we *multiply* both members by 5.

$$\frac{n}{5} = 80$$

Multiply both members by 5.

$$5 \times \frac{n}{5} = 5 \times 80$$
$$n = 400$$

Algebraic multiplication

$$5 \times \frac{n}{5} = \frac{\overset{1}{\cancel{5}}}{1} \times \frac{n}{\cancel{5}} = \frac{n}{1} = n$$

We check to see if $n = 400$ is the root of the equation.

$$\frac{n}{5} = 80$$
$$\frac{400}{5} = 80$$
$$80 = 80$$ ✓

The root of $\frac{n}{5} = 80$ is $n = 400$.

Here are some examples of solving equations by using multiplication. In every case, the letter symbol is divided by some other number.

EXAMPLES. Solve each of the following equations for the unknown value of the letter symbol. Check each root in the original equation.

d. $\frac{x}{8} = 6$

e. $19 = \frac{n}{2}$

f. $\frac{1}{4}x = 1\frac{3}{4}$

Solutions:

d.

$$\frac{x}{8} = 6$$

Multiply both members by 8.

$$8 \times \frac{x}{8} = 8 \times 6$$
$$x = 48$$

Algebraic multiplication

$$8 \times \frac{x}{8} = \frac{\overset{1}{\cancel{8}}}{1} \times \frac{x}{\cancel{8}} = \frac{x}{1} = x$$

Check; $\frac{x}{8} = 6$

$$\frac{48}{8} = 6$$
$$6 = 6$$ ✓

Answer: $x = 48$

e.

$$19 = \frac{n}{2}$$

Multiply both members by 2.

$$2 \times 19 = 2 \times \frac{n}{2}$$
$$38 = n$$

Algebraic multiplication

$$2 \times \frac{n}{2} = \frac{\cancel{2}}{1} \times \frac{n}{\cancel{2}} = \frac{n}{1} = n$$

Check:

$$19 = \frac{n}{2}$$

$$19 = \frac{38}{2}$$

$$19 = 19 \quad \checkmark$$

Answer: n = 38

f. $$\frac{1}{4}x = 1\frac{3}{4}$$

In dealing with mixed numbers, in algebra as well as in arithmetic, it is usual to change them to improper fractions when dividing or multiplying. Since $\frac{1}{4}x$ is the same as $\frac{x}{4}$ and since $1\frac{3}{4} = \frac{7}{4}$, we rewrite the

original equation as follows:

$$\frac{1}{4}x = 1\frac{3}{4}$$

$$\frac{x}{4} = \frac{7}{4}$$

Now, we solve by getting the x alone in one member.

Multiply both members by 4. $$4 \times \frac{x}{4} = 4 \times \frac{7}{4}$$

$$x = 7$$

Check; $$\frac{1}{4}x = 1\frac{3}{4}$$

$$\frac{1}{4} \times 7 = 1\frac{3}{4}$$

$$\frac{7}{4} = 1\frac{3}{4}$$

$$1\frac{3}{4} = 1\frac{3}{4} \quad \checkmark$$

Answer: x = 7

EXERCISES

In 1 to 10, solve and check each equation.

1. $\dfrac{n}{12} = 2$ 2. $\dfrac{1}{5}t = 25$ 3. $9x = 27$ 4. $46 = 23y$ 5. $3x = 4\dfrac{1}{2}$

6. $11n = 110$ 7. $15 = \dfrac{y}{4}$ 8. $\dfrac{t}{3} = 3$ 9. $\dfrac{x}{5} = 3.2$ 10. $24 = \dfrac{1}{3}t$

ALGEBRA

In 11 to 25, write an equation from the facts given in each problem. Then solve for the unknown number.

11. Three times a number is 54. Find the number.

12. A number multiplied by .4 is 8. Find the number.

13. Two-fifths of a number is 65. What is the number?

14. Thirteen is equal to $\frac{1}{3}$ of a number. What is the number?

15. 5% of a number is equal to 25. Find the number.

16. A number divided by 8 equals 6. What is the number?

17. Three-quarters of a number is 150. Find the number.

18. When 120 is divided by a number, the result is 40. Find the number.

19. If 15 is equal to a number divided by 9, find the number.

20. A number divided by 50 is equal to $\frac{1}{2}$. Find the number.

21. John got a 15% increase in salary. If the increase was $25, what is his new salary?

22. Henry has a savings account that pays 6% interest per year. If he earned $75 in interest one year, how much money does he have in the bank?

23. Mary bought a coat at $\frac{1}{3}$ off the original price. If she saved $36, find the original price.

24. A salesman sold a new car for $3,490 and earned $174.50 in commissions. Find his rate of commission.

25. Jim saved $\frac{1}{5}$ of his weekly income. If he saved $45, find his weekly income.

Unit 111. Solving Two-Step Equations

The equation $3x + 6 = 30$ states that, "When 3 times a certain number is increased by 6, the result will be 30."

Since this equation indicates *two* mathematical operations (the number symbol is both multiplied by 3 and has 6 added to it), we must use *two* steps to solve it.

We must get the x alone in one member, so the first step is to eliminate the " $+6$ " by subtracting 6 from both sides of the equation.

$$\begin{array}{r} 3x + 6 = 30 \\ -6 \quad -6 \\ \hline 3x \quad = 24 \end{array}$$

The left member of this new equation is $3x$. Therefore, the second step is to divide both members by 3.

$$3x = 24$$
$$\frac{3x}{3} = \frac{24}{3}$$
$$x = 8$$

Algebraic division	Arithmetic division
$3\overline{)3x}$ gives x	$3\overline{)24}$ gives 8
$\underline{3x}$	$\underline{24}$

We check to see if $x = 8$ is the root of the original equation.

$$\begin{array}{r} 3x + 6 = 30 \\ 3 \times 8 + 6 = 30 \\ 24 + 6 = 30 \\ 30 = 30 \quad \checkmark \end{array}$$

The root of $3x + 6 = 30$ is $x = 8$.

In algebra, so as not to confuse the multiplication sign $\times$ with the letter x, it is usual to indicate multiplication by using parentheses (). The above check would appear like this:

$$\begin{array}{r} 3x + 6 = 30 \\ 3(8) + 6 = 30 \\ 24 + 6 = 30 \\ 30 = 30 \quad \checkmark \end{array}$$

Rule: When solving two-step equations, do the addition or subtraction first. Then do the multiplication or division.

Here are some examples of solving two-step equations.

EXAMPLES. Solve each of the following equations for the unknown value of the letter symbol. Check each root in the original equation.

a. $4n - 20 = 4$

b. $\dfrac{x}{3} + 9 = 13$

c. $45 = 24 + 3s$

Solutions:

a.

Add 20 to both members.
$$\begin{array}{r} 4n - 20 = \quad 4 \\ +20 \quad +20 \\ \hline 4n \quad = 24 \end{array}$$

Divide both members by 4.
$$\frac{4n}{4} = \frac{24}{4}$$
$$n = 6$$

Check:
$$\begin{array}{r} 4n - 20 = 4 \\ 4(6) - 20 = 4 \\ 24 - 20 = 4 \\ 4 = 4 \quad \checkmark \end{array}$$

Answer: $n = 6$

b.

$$\dfrac{x}{3} + 9 = 13$$

Subtract 9 from both members
$$\begin{array}{r} -9 \quad -9 \\ \hline \dfrac{x}{3} \quad = \quad 4 \end{array}$$

Multiply both members by 3.
$$3\left(\dfrac{x}{3}\right) = 3(4)$$
$$x = 12$$

Check:
$$\dfrac{x}{3} + 9 = 13$$
$$\dfrac{12}{3} + 9 = 13$$
$$4 + 9 = 13$$
$$13 = 13 \quad \checkmark$$

Answer: $x = 12$

c.

$$45 = 24 + 3s \qquad 7 = s$$

Subtract 24 from both members.

$$\begin{array}{rcl} 45 &=& 24 + 3s \\ -24 && -24 \\ \hline 21 &=& 3s \end{array}$$

Check: $45 = 24 + 3s$
$45 = 24 + 3(7)$
$45 = 24 + 21$
$45 = 45$ ✓

Divide both members by 3.

$$\frac{21}{3} = \frac{3s}{3}$$

Answer: $s = 7$

EXERCISES

In 1 to 10, solve each equation for the value of the letter symbol.

1. $8x + 15 = 63$

2. $3n - 11 = 19$

3. $\dfrac{z}{5} + 5 = 12$

4. $\dfrac{1}{5}x - 3 = 6$

$\left(Hint: \dfrac{1}{5}x \text{ is the same as } \dfrac{x}{5}.\right)$

5. $40 = 25 + \dfrac{n}{6}$

6. $\dfrac{1}{4}x + 5 = 33$

7. $36 = 5x + 6$

8. $10 = \dfrac{x}{2} - 6$

9. $8 + 5x = 35 + 8$

10. $3n = 10\dfrac{1}{2}$

In 11 to 25, write an equation from the given facts. Then solve it for the unknown number.

11. Two times a certain number, decreased by 8, equals 64. Find the number.

12. When a number is multiplied by 5, and then increased by 21, the result is 56. Find the number.

13. If 13 is subtracted from 8 times a certain number, the result is 83. Find the number.

14. When you triple a number and add 31, the result is 76. Find the number.

15. When a number is divided by 5 and the quotient is increased by 8, the result is 16. Find the number.

16. When 18 is added to a number that has been multiplied by 3, the result is 30. Find the number.

17. One-third of a number, increased by 10, is equal to 40. Find the number. $\left(Hint: \dfrac{1}{3} x \text{ is the same as } \dfrac{x}{3}.\right)$

18. If 63 is equal to 6 times a certain number, increased by 15, find the number.

19. George saved $25 more than three times the amount Harry saved. If Harry saved $95, how much did George save?

20. Jane spent $12 for two tickets to a concert, tax included. If the tax was 80¢, how much did *each* ticket cost?

21. Jack is 25 years old. He is 5 years less than three times the age of his sister. How old is his sister?

22. One-third the number of boys in a class equals the number of girls. If there are 7 girls in the class, how many boys are there?

23. Jim earns $15 less than twice the amount earned by Pete. If Jim earns $95 a week, how much does Pete earn a week?

24. Mary spends one-third of her salary on clothes. If she spent $28, how much is her salary?

25. The perimeter of a rectangle is 86 inches. If the width is 10 inches, find the length. (*Hint:* Draw a figure, using the facts of the exercise and your knowledge of rectangles. Then write an equation for the perimeter using a letter symbol for the length, and the given values for the width and the perimeter.)

Review of Part XXIII (Units 107 to 111)

In 1 to 5, write an algebraic expression for each word statement. (Use *n* or any convenient letter for the unknown number.)

1. A number multiplied by 8.

2. 48 decreased by a number.

3. A number divided by 15.

4. $\frac{3}{5}$ of 35 times a number.

5. 8 times a number, divided by 4.

In 6 to 10, write an algebraic expression for each word statement. Use the given letter symbol.

6. 38 divided by *x*, plus 15.

7. The product of *y* and 13, minus 12.

8. *a* more than the product of *n* and 7.

9. The product of *x* and *y*, divided by 3.

10. The quotient of *m* divided by 8, minus 11.

In 11 to 15, write an equation for each word statement.

11. A number multiplied by 6 and increased by 9 equals 66.

12. If 13 is added to 8 times a given number, the result is 63.

13. When 18 is added to 5 times a number, the result is 94.

14. One-half the product of 15 times *x*, increased by 23, is equal to 132.

15. When 5 is added to a number that is multiplied by 8, the result is 53.

In 16 to 20, do not actually solve the problems.

16. Mary is 3 years more than twice as old as Jane. If Jane is 15 years old, write an equation to find Mary's age.

17. A coat was reduced by 25%. If the amount of reduction was $32, write an equation to find the original price.

18. John has $5 less than twice as much as Harry. If John has $63, write an equation to find how much money Harry has.

19. Mary spends $\frac{1}{5}$ of her income on rent. If her rent each month is $135, write an equation to find Mary's monthly income.

20. A television set costs $365. If this represents 75% of the original price, write an equation to find the original price.

In 21 to 34, write an equation from the given facts. Then solve for the unknown number.

21. John is 8 years younger than Harry. If Harry is 31 years old, how old is John?

22. Jane had $563 in the bank after withdrawing $85. How much did Jane have in the bank before making the withdrawal?

23. Harry's take-home pay was $173.40. If his deductions amounted to $47.50, find his gross pay (his pay before deductions).

24. Eight years from now, Mary will be 27 years old. How old is she now?

25. A coat selling for $127 was reduced by $29.50. Find the new price.

26. John deposited a sum of money in a savings account that paid 5% simple interest. One year later, his deposit had earned $93. What was the amount of the deposit?

27. A car traveled at the average speed of 55 miles per hour. How many hours will it take to travel 875 miles?

28. A lamp selling for $65 was placed on a "$\frac{2}{3}$ off" sale. Find the new price of the lamp.

29. The length of a rectangle is $2\frac{1}{2}$ times the width. If the width is 8 feet, find the length of the rectangle.

30. Mary is 3 times as old as Jane. If Jane is 12 years old, how old is Mary?

31. The length of a rectangle is 5 feet more than twice the width. If the width is 11 feet, find the length.

32. The number of girls in a class is 5 less than one-half the total number of students. If there are 36 students in the class, how many girls are there in the class?

33. Twice a number plus 26 is equal to 110. Find the number.

34. One-half a number, decreased by 7, is equal to 83. Find the number.

Appendix. The Metric System

Table XX shows all six metric prefixes used with common metric equivalents. The abbreviations in the table are used by most scientists throughout the world. Note that the letter *k* is used in all abbreviations for *deca* to avoid confusion with *deci*. Thus, decameter is abbreviated dkm, while decimeter is abbreviated dm. Note, too, that the abbreviations in the metric system do not have periods after them.

Table XX: *The Metric System*

MEASURES OF LENGTH

	1 millimeter (mm)	$= \dfrac{1}{1,000}$ meter (m)
10 millimeters (mm)	= 1 centimeter (cm)	$= \dfrac{1}{100}$ meter (m)
10 centimeters (cm)	= 1 decimeter (dm)	$= \dfrac{1}{10}$ meter (m)
10 decimeters (dm)	= 1 meter (m)	
10 meters (m)	= 1 decameter (dkm)	= 10 meters (m)
10 decameters (dkm)	= 1 hectometer (hm)	= 100 meters (m)
10 hectometers (hm)	= 1 kilometer (km)	= 1,000 meters (m)

MEASURES OF CAPACITY

	1 milliliter (ml)	$= \dfrac{1}{1,000}$ liter (l)
10 milliliters (ml)	= 1 centiliter (cl)	$= \dfrac{1}{100}$ liter (l)
10 centiliters (cl)	= 1 deciliter (dl)	$= \dfrac{1}{10}$ liter (l)
10 deciliters (dl)	= 1 liter (l)	
10 liters (l)	= 1 decaliter (dkl)	= 10 liters (l)
10 decaliters (dkl)	= 1 hectoliter (hl)	= 100 liters (l)
10 hectoliters (hl)	= 1 kiloliter (kl)	= 1,000 liters (l)

MEASURES OF WEIGHT

	1 milligram (mg)	$= \dfrac{1}{1,000}$ gram (g)
10 milligrams (mg)	= 1 centigram (cg)	$= \dfrac{1}{100}$ gram (g)
10 centigrams (cg)	= 1 decigram (dg)	$= \dfrac{1}{10}$ gram (g)
10 decigrams (dg)	= 1 gram (g)	
10 grams (g)	= 1 decagram (dkg)	= 10 grams (g)
10 decagrams (dkg)	= 1 hectogram (hg)	= 100 grams (g)
10 hectograms (hg)	= 1 kilogram (kg)	= 1,000 grams (g)
1,000 kilograms (kg)	= 1 metric ton (t)	

Index